# POPULAR MECHANICS
# SHOP NOTES

## FOR 1916 VOL.12

*Algrove Publishing ~ Classic Reprint Series*

Algrove Publishing Limited
1090 Morrison Drive
Ottawa, Ontario
Canada  K2H 1C2

**Canadian Cataloguing in Publication Data**

Main entry under title:

    Popular mechanics shop notes for ...

(Classic reprint series)
Includes indexes.
Originally published: Chicago : Popular Mechanics Co., 1905-
"Compiled from the "Shop notes" department of Popular mechanics
    magazine, and "Written so you can understand it;" tells easy
    ways to do hard things" --Added t.p., v. 1.
Contents: v. 1. 1905 - v. 2. 1906 - v. 3. 1907 - v. 4. 1908 - v. 5. 1909 - v. 6. 1910 - v. 7. 1911 -
    v. 8. 1912 - v. 9. 1913 - v. 10. 1914 - v. 11. 1915 - v. 12. 1916 - v. 13. 1917 - v. 14. 1918 -
    v. 15. 1919 - v. 16. 1920 - v. 17. 1921 - v. 18. 1922 - v. 19. 1923.
ISBN 0-921335-87-3 (v. 11) - ISBN 0-921335-91-1 (v. 12) - ISBN 0-921335-94-6 (v. 13) -
ISBN 0-921335-96-2 (v. 14) - ISBN 0-921335-98-9 (v. 15) - ISBN 0-921335-93-8 (v. 16) -
ISBN 0-921335-95-4 (v. 17) - ISBN 0-921335-97-0 (v. 18) - ISBN 0-921335-99-7 (v. 19) -

    1. Do-it-yourself work.  2. Industrial arts.  I. Title: Shop notes for ...  II. Series: Classic
reprint series (Ottawa, Ont.)

TJ1160.P66 2000                     600                     C99-900763-7

Printed in Canada
#10800

# *Publisher's Note*

Virtually every woodworking magazine in the English-speaking world has a shop notes section and has published an accumulation of them in book form. This was all started in 1905 with the first annual issue of *Popular Mechanics Shop Notes*, a compilation of advice on jigs, fixtures, methods of work, processes and projects. The earlier issues focussed primarily on metalworking, but with tips for a variety of other trades liberally sprinkled throughout. As years went by, the contents shifted more and more to woodworking and handyman projects. Each book is profusely illustrated. The line drawings of the earlier issues were supplanted by superb engravings until photographs started to creep in during the 1920s. Each year has its charm but all issues share the attribute of being clear, concise and widely informative.

Leonard G. Lee, Publisher
Ottawa
September, 1999

# WARNING

This is a reprint of a book compiled in the early 1900s. The book describes what was recommended to be done in accordance with the knowledge of the day.

It would be advisable to treat all corrosive, explosive and toxic materials with much greater caution than is indicated here, particularly any materials that come in contact with the body.

Similarly, some of the recommended projects were dangerous then and remain so now. All of this material should be regarded with a judicious eye and necessary precautions taken.

# POPULAR MECHANICS

# SHOP NOTES

### FOR

# 1916

---

## EASY WAYS TO DO HARD THINGS

---

### OF DAILY USE
### TO EVERY MECHANIC

---

*Vol. XII—Table of Contents, Pages 2471-2479*

---

POPULAR MECHANICS, CHICAGO

This Volume is Reprinted from the

## Shop Notes Department

of

## Popular Mechanics

Edited by H. H. WINDSOR

## A Boat Dump

IN a park where a large number of boats were used, the manager constructed a device to remove the water

The Projections on the Lower End of the Frame Pick Up the Boat and Dump It as the Upper Part is Pulled Down

from the pleasure boats. It saves the labor of one helper, cuts the time required by the other helper to less than one hour a day, and a few dollars represents the entire investment for the pier and all.

The dump consists of a U-shaped frame with the free ends extending downward into the water. At the lower ends of the frame and extending away from the pier are nailed arms, about 3 ft. long, which are placed low enough to extend under the keel of any pleasure boat used in the park at any stage of the water. A short distance above the long arms are nailed shorter arms that extend over the bulwarks of the boat.

When a boat comes to the landing with water in it—and pleasure boats will ship water when in constant use even with the best of care—it is run alongside the pier and the dump frame is drawn back. The boat is thus turned on its side above the water level and the water within runs out in a very short time and with little effort on the part of the operator.

The sides of the frame are made of timbers, 4 in. square and 10 ft. long, while the top pieces are 6 ft. long and 2 by 4 in. in size. The short arms are about 1 ft. long and 4 in. wide. The long arms are made of 2-in. material, 6 in. wide and 3 ft. long. The frame is attached to the pier with two long-wing hinges, such as are used on heavy farm gates or doors.—Contributed by J. W. Tudor, Homer, Ill.

### Drawing-Board Attachment

In the illustration is shown a useful attachment for the drawing board, consisting of an adjustable frame, or

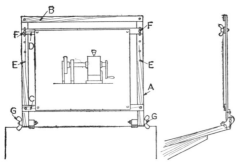

An Adjustable Drawing Holder Fastened to the Drawing Board in Front and Out of the Draftsman's Way

holder, fastened to the back of the board facing the draftsman. On it can be tacked such drawings or sketches as may be required for constant reference.

The holder may be simply a thin board with strips, A, fastened to the sides, or if desired to have a very light holder, it may consist of a frame of two pieces, A, rigidly fastened to the cross braces B and C. An adjustable cross-piece, D, must then be provided so that

the drawing may be attached to piece B or C, on one edge, and to D, on the opposite edge. It is, therefore, necessary to drill several sets of holes, E, for the thumb nuts and screws, F, which are used to hold the piece D in position. If the sidepieces A are made sufficiently strong, a slot may be cut in each to take the place of the holes E, and a wider range of adjustment is thus obtained.

The finished frame should be attached to the drawing board by means of hinges, G, having a bolt and thumb nut so as to fasten the attachment at any desired angle.

### Air-Hose Reel for a Garage

The owner of a large garage desired to have an air-hose outlet for filling tires of automobiles handily arranged with the least amount of piping and connections, as the one fault of an air outfit is that the numerous connections cause a continuous drop in pressure. A successful apparatus was constructed as follows: A hose reel was attached to the ceiling in the center of the room, with enough hose to reach any part within and out in front to the street. The inner end of the hose was connected to a revolving joint on the end of a pipe line run from the air tank in the rear.

The reel has two drums, one for the hose, and the other for a rope provided with a counterweight so that the hose is reeled up by the weight when released from the tire. The end of the

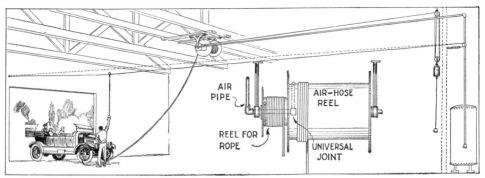

An Automobile Located in Any Part of the Room can be Reached with the End of the Air Hose, and the Tires Filled from a Pressure Tank at the Rear of the Building

hose, having the tire-valve connection, is protected so that it can be drawn back over the floor without injury.

The valve is operated by an ingenious arrangement. A small rope is fastened to the valve lever and drawn taut across the room the long way. On this is run a pulley having a rope drop. The drop can be taken along with the hose end to where it is used, and when connections are made, a pull on the drop opens the valve at the tank. The slight sag in the rope will run the drop back to the center near the reel.

## Cleaning Stick for Machine Spindles

The usual method of cleaning hollow spindles for centers or drills is to use waste, frequently wound around some handy article such as a file. A better and safer method would be to use a

*The Notches Catch the Dirt as It is Loosened from the Center Bore*

tapered stick, notched as shown, and covered with a layer of felt. As this fits the spindle hole closely, a thorough job of cleaning is done, and the accumulated dirt is brushed off into the notches, thereby preventing any scratching or grinding as often results with waste and a file.—Contributed by John Harger, Honolulu, H. I.

## Valve for a Drinking Fountain

To reduce the waste of cooled and filtered drinking water in a large shop, a valve attachment, as shown, was made for each fountain. The nicked disk A of the valve keeps the overflow bowl cleansed at all times without an extravagant waste of water and, besides, keeps the water in circulation through the cooling coils. The threads were turned off from the stem B, out of the bonnet, to allow the insertion of a coiled spring, C, made of No. 14 gauge brass wire. The long lever with the ring at its end will be found valuable by the workman passing through

the shop with his hands full of tools, as the valve can be raised by engaging the

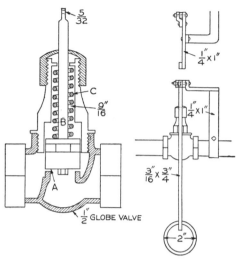

*A Valve Operated with a Spring and a Long Lever for Use on a Fountain*

ring in almost any manner without necessitating loss of time in dropping or placing the burden to grasp a valve or hand lever.—Contributed by F. W. Bently, Milwaukee, Wis.

## Combination Blacksmith Tongs for Round or Square Work

These tongs will hold securely round, square, tapered, and irregular-shaped stock, in sizes from a needle up to the full jaw opening. As shown in Fig. 1, the upper jaw is made with a V-shaped slot, while the lower jaw is shaped to fit into this slot, with the

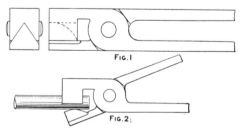

*Round Stock of Any Size within the Capacity of the Tongs is Held Rigidly in the Jaws*

inner end rounded off. Figure 2 shows the jaws gripping a large piece of round material.—Contributed by Wm. A. Robinson, Waynesboro, Pa.

## Fuel Gauge for Motorcycles

A fuel gauge for a motorcycle can be easily made from a piece of stiff wire and a cork. A small hole, large enough  for the wire to pass through, is drilled in the filler cap, and after putting the wire in the hole the cork is stuck on the lower end. The cap is put on the can with the cork float inside and the wire pushed down until the cork end touches the bottom. Cut the wire off just above the cap and bend the end over so that it will not drop out when the cap is removed. Fasten a small piece of brass on the cap to turn over the end of the wire to keep the float down when not in use.—Contributed by Abner B. Shaw, N. Dartmouth, Mass.

## To Duplicate the Contour of Molding

A simple tool for use in the building and interior-decorating trades for duplicating molding without removing it from the wall is shown in the illustration. It consists of fine steel strips held together with a yoke of brass, having a screw at one end to clamp the strips after the impression is taken. The strips are 3½ in. long, $\frac{3}{32}$ in. wide, and about $\frac{1}{64}$ in. thick. Enough of these 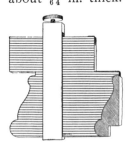 strips are put together to make the tool about 4 in. long.

To use, simply loosen the screw in the end, allowing the strips to slide free, then place the device against the molding and push each strip with a penknife or other keen-edged instrument until it touches the molding. After all the molding surface has been covered closely, tighten with the screw in the end, and an impression of the molding will be had, as accurate as could be desired.

If the screw is tightened sufficiently, the tool can be carried in the pocket for an indefinite length of time.—Contributed by Fred M. Griswold, New York City.

## Saving Time with a Greenhouse Watering System

In using a gasoline engine to pump water through a system of piping for a greenhouse, 15 gal. of water were discharged per minute. The gravity tank on the same system would deliver only 8 gal. per minute. I decided that a great deal of time could be saved, if water were taken directly from the pump and the tank entirely cut out.

To do this, the water must be taken care of in some way while changing the hose from one faucet to another. This was done by running a branch pipe line over the well and attaching an old 2-in. steam blow-off valve on the end of it. A pressure gauge was put in near the pump, and this registered 50 lb. while the pump drove the 15 gal. per minute directly through the hose in the greenhouses. Just enough weight was placed on the arm of the blow-off valve to keep it closed at 50-lb. pressure. As soon as the water in the greenhouses is shut off, the pressure rises, and the valve opens and takes care of the water.—Contributed by Bert H. Stanley, Portage, Wash.

## Graphite Used on Automobile Spark Plugs

A very annoying accident, and a difficult one to repair, is that of twisting off the base of a spark plug in trying to remove it from the cylinder head. A simple and sure preventive is to make it a rule to coat the threads of the spark plug and cylinder head with powdered graphite before screwing the two together. The graphite not only facilitates the removal of the plug, but also makes a better joint, permitting greater compression and holding it longer.—Contributed by D. C. Gaff, Knoxville, Tenn.

# Pattern and Core Boxes for Water-Jacketed Cylinder

By J. A. SHELLY

In the construction of complicated machine parts much needless work can frequently be prevented in the pattern shop, foundry, and machine shop if the draftsman is acquainted with the various processes necessary to build the machine, from the making of the pattern to the machining of the casting. The simplest machine parts are often drawn so that considerable core work is necessary, where, if a little forethought had been used, and the drawing but slightly changed, a simple coreless pattern might have answered just as well. The water-jacketed cylinder, Fig. 1, has been so designed that the patterns and foundry operations are as simple as could be hoped for in such a large casting. Had the designer—possibly for some unimportant reason—put the side bosses of the cylinder at an angle of 45° instead of on the center

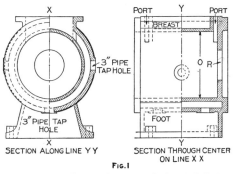

FIG. 1

End and Front Views of a Water-Jacketed Cylinder, with Sections Showing Water Space

line, considerable work would have been added in all departments having to do with its manufacture. Tap holes are frequently added which, though they do not increase the value of the completed machine, may materially reduce the cost of production.

The external appearance of the completed pattern and core prints, for the water-jacketed cylinder, is shown in Fig. 2. The parting line passes through the center of the cylinder, perpendicular to the base. In this way, the sim-

plest construction is made possible, as every part will draw. If the parting had been made through the cylinder center, but at right angles to the one

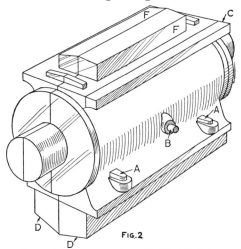

FIG. 2

External Appearance of the Finished Cylinder Pattern with All Core Prints Attached

shown, it would have been necessary to make at least two additional core boxes besides complicating the construction of the pattern. In large work, the smaller parts are usually made loose so they will remain in the sand when drawing the main parts. This is the best construction, as the small, irregular parts can then be drawn out carefully, without breaking the mold; such pieces are shown at A, B, and C, Fig. 2.

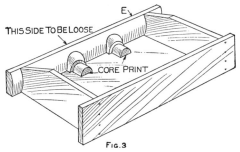

FIG. 3

Core-Box Form for the Cylinder-Base Extension with Loose Side to Separate Core from the Box

In small patterns, the draft can be very slight, sometimes even ignored entirely, due to the clearance between pattern and mold caused by the molder's rapping. In large pieces, such

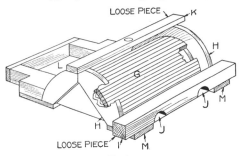

FIG. 4

Core Box for Forming Water Pocket and Cylinder Breast, with Loose Pieces Necessary for Molding Tap-Hole Cores

clearance cannot be produced. It is therefore necessary to check up this draft on long surfaces which are at right angles to the parting line. The pattern, Fig. 2, should have draft on the end faces of the footpiece, on the cylinder heads, on the top and bottom faces of the cylinder, and even on the ends of the main cylinder core, if this be of considerable diameter.

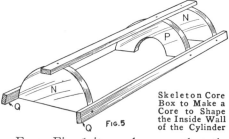

Skeleton Core Box to Make a Core to Shape the Inside Wall of the Cylinder

FIG. 5

From Fig. 1 it can be seen that the core necessary to form the interior of the cylinder footpiece connects to the water jacket at only two places. It is therefore necessary to provide a core print, D, Fig. 2, sufficiently long to balance the part extending into the foot. The core box for this is shown in Fig. 3, and consists of a four-sided box form. The side E, with the bosses and core prints attached to it, should be made loose; the box can then be withdrawn from the core without the necessity of turning it over. The core prints correspond to the cores forming the 3-in. pipe tap holes in the water jacket. The core box for the water jacket is

the most difficult to make and requires the greatest care, for should this core shift, the thickness of the cylinder wall would be changed. The main anchorage is provided by that part of the core which occupies the space formed by the prints F, Fig. 2. These should be of sufficient length so the core will balance that part of it which forms the cylinder breast, shown in Fig. 1. The core box itself, Fig. 4, consists of a built-up stave cylinder, G, corresponding in diameter and length to the outside surface of the inside cylinder wall. The flanges H form a circle corresponding to the inside diameter of the outer wall. The loose piece I, doweled in place, contains the round sections J,

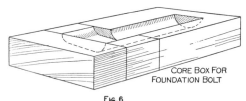

CORE BOX FOR FOUNDATION BOLT

FIG. 6

A Core Box to Form the Core to Make the Foundation Bolt Hole

which form the core holes for the bottom pipe taps. The loose piece K, also doweled in place, forms the core for the side taps. At the end L is formed that part of the core corresponding to the breast, and space shaped by prints F. The various parts of the box are held together by the two bottom crosspieces M.

The core forming the inside cylinder wall is made in halves and pasted to-

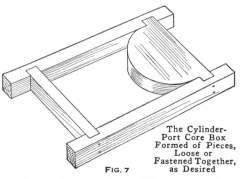

The Cylinder-Port Core Box Formed of Pieces, Loose or Fastened Together, as Desired

FIG. 7

gether. Its core box, Fig. 5, is a simple affair, consisting of two half-circle end pieces, N—corresponding to the cylinder diameter O, Fig. 1, with stock allowed for machining—and an intermediate section, P, Fig. 5, all fastened together by cross strips, Q. The opening in P corresponds to the cylinder-head opening R, Fig. 1, with stock allowed for machining. Sufficient length of core prints outside of the cylinder heads should be allowed for, so as to overcome the floating tendency of the core, due to the large extent of surface.

Figures 6 and 7 represent the core boxes for the foundation holes and port cores, and are of such simple construction that they require no special explanation.

---

## Emergency Repair for a Rifle Sight

Just when I needed my rifle most I found the bead broken off the front sight, and not having time to order a new one, I made a bead which has proven satisfactory in every respect.

The broken sight was removed and the edge filed smooth, whereupon the top was slotted with a sharp chisel and the sides turned out to form a Y-shaped piece. In the groove thus formed a piece of brass wire, slightly larger in diameter than the required bead, was soldered. The surplus ends of the wire and the solder were removed, and the bead ends polished. To check the height of the sight, fasten the gun securely and set up a target some known distance away. Fire the gun and adjust the rear sight until the sights target properly.

The brass bead proved to be better than the one it replaced, as it does not rust and will take a polish that makes it more visible in a weak light.—Contributed by C. F. Heizer, Falfurrias, Texas.

---

## Chart for a Life-Saving Station

A life-saving station on the coast carries a crew of 16 men, and these men in turn patrol the beach every night. Formerly there was a straight ordinary list of the men's names written and posted. With this list a man could

figure when it was his turn to patrol, but this caused some trouble.

One of the men originated the dial

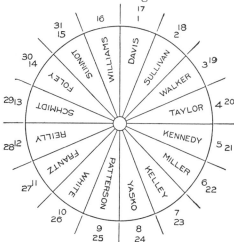

The Dial is Set the First of Each Month and Designates Each Man's Patrol Nights

shown in the illustration which has every man's name on it. This automatically indicates to a man when it is his turn to patrol the beach.—Contributed by Wm. J. Kelly, Jersey City, New Jersey.

---

## Slotting Tool for the Shaper

The intervening metal between two holes is difficult to remove without a slotting machine, but a very accurate job was accomplished on a few machine parts with the use of a shaper equipped with the tool illustrated. The body A was made of machine steel and casehardened, one end being drilled and slotted, and a clamping screw securely held the cutting tool B in place. The latter was turned in a lathe, using a good grade of tool steel, then it was tapered, as shown, to give it the proper clearance.—Contributed by A. Dane, Pottstown, Pa.

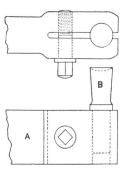

## Pumping Water from a Distance

Considerable time and labor can frequently be saved if, in supplying water from a well or spring, the pump is placed in a convenient spot near or at the place where it is to be used. It is necessary in figuring on such a lo-

A Check Valve is Placed at the Foot of the Line to Hold the Water in the Pipe

GROUND LEVEL

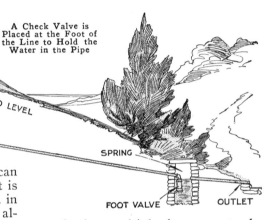

SPRING

FOOT VALVE　　　OUTLET

cation to determine the probable lift of the pump. In a perfect vacuum, a column of water can be lifted 34 ft. at sea level, but as it is impossible to create such a vacuum in a pump barrel, a smaller lift must always be figured on, a good lift being about 24 ft. In such a lift must be included the so-called friction head. This will cut down the actual height the water can be raised, depending on the size and length of the pipe, and the number of bends and fittings. A small pipe and numerous fittings can cause sufficient friction to cut down the available lift to practically nothing where, if a straight line of large pipe were substituted, a considerable lift might be obtained. It is necessary to have all connections tight, for if air enters, the vacuum of the pump will be spoiled, and its operation interfered with. Every pump suction line should be provided with a foot valve near the extreme end, to prevent the water from leaving the line when once drawn into it. For short, straight lengths, a foot valve may be dispensed with, but in longer lines, especially those over 20 ft., the pump cannot be operated without a foot valve close to the bottom of the suction line. —Contributed by Wm. J. Barkley, Chicago, Ill.

## Figuring Sizes of Reamer Drills

Reduce the reamer size to eighths and multiply the numerator by the denominator, which gives the numerator in sixty-fourths. Subtract one from the numerator, and it gives the reamer-drill size. A drill for a ¾-in. reamer would be figured as follows: $\frac{3}{4} = \frac{6}{8}$ and $6 \times 8 = \frac{48}{64}$; $\frac{48}{64} - \frac{1}{64} = \frac{47}{64}$ in., the reamer-drill size.

When the reamer size is in sixteenths, just multiply the numerator by 4, which gives the numerator in sixty-fourths, less $\frac{1}{64}$, which gives the reamer-drill size. Thus a $\frac{7}{16}$-in. reamer equals $7 \times 4 = \frac{28}{64} - \frac{1}{64}$ or $\frac{27}{64}$ in. the reamer-drill size. — Contributed by Wm. J. Kittle, Pearl River, N. Y.

---

## Safety Collar for Watch Stems

A simple manner to protect a watch from dropping out of the pocket where it is carried is shown in the sketch.

About a shop where a person is continuously stooping in the performance of work, the watch often drops out of the pocket and, if held with a chain, is liable to strike against something which may result in a damage that will be of considerable expense to the wearer.

A small rubber washer is slipped

over the stem just below the chain ring and prevents the watch, by its own weight, from slipping out of the pocket by engaging the surface of the cloth. The washer can be cut from rubber of almost any kind and drawn into the cupped shape by the application of heat to its center. The arrangement is a trifle unsightly, but as it is worn only about a shop, it is worth while in the saving of many crystals and other damage to a valuable watch.

## Weighing Insulated Wire to Determine Length

A storekeeper in an electrical concern was expected to supply the workmen with coils of wire approximately 100 ft. long. As there was no measuring machine, the following method was used to deal out 100-ft. lengths from the large coil. A large coil was first weighed, then 100 ft. of the wire was measured out with a tape and the coil again weighed. It was thus found that the 100-ft. piece weighed 4½ lb. By setting the large coil on the scale platform and placing the balance back 4½ lb. for each 100 ft., the balance would drop when the right amount in length was taken from the coil.—Contributed by R. E. Coram, Lynn, Mass.

## A Pasteboard for Labels

Gum tragacanth is extensively used for labeling, as it makes a clean paste, which also allows the labels to be easily removed if the object is placed in water for a short time. This is a decided advantage in establishments where bottles, etc., are frequently labeled.

The pasteboard shown is a very convenient article to use in connection with this paste. A piece of board is fitted with a square tray to hold the paste which is filled in level with the top. Then a piece of cheesecloth is spread over it and held by a frame fitting tightly around the outside of the tray.

The part on which the labels are kept is built up level with the tray top. The labels are drawn across the cheesecloth

with slight pressure, which causes enough paste to stick to them so that

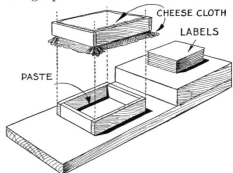

Applying Adhesive to Labels with the Use of a Pasteboard Prepared with Tragacanth

they can be applied to the surface as required.

## Individual Tap Holders

Where a number of taps of different sizes are used I found that changing the taps in the holder not only consumed considerable time but was very annoying besides. To overcome this difficulty I made a holder for each tap. A pattern was made of a piece of white pine, and from it I had a dozen castings made in gray iron at a slight cost. The ends were bored and tapped to admit a 4-in. bolt of small diameter—one at each end. The heads were cut off and the ends filed round. A hole was drilled into the body of the casting at right angles to the line of the bolts. This hole was of the same size as for

Individual Holders for Taps Where a Number of Them are in Use from Time to Time

the tap used. Each holder was drilled for its tap. The tap is held rigid by screwing the bolts up against the square end.—Contributed by Jas. A. Hart, Philadelphia, Pa.

❡Paint spruce siding, first coat, with white lead, thinned with raw linseed oil and a small portion of benzol, using very little driers.

## Coal Bin Provided with Inclined Chute

To make a coal bin so that the contents will not run out on the floor every time some of it is taken out, an in-

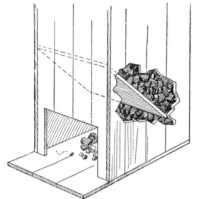

*The Slanting Board Provides an Easy Access to the Coal and Keeps It from Falling Out*

clined board should be fastened in the bin, as shown. This board must be so long that, when its upper end is fastened about 15 in. above the bottom of the box, the lower end will be about 6 in. from the back and above the bottom. This slant is just sufficient to allow the coal to drop down without having a tendency to roll out of the door at the front. The bottom of the bin is extended out in front of the door to permit easier shoveling of the coal. The cover may be just a plain hinged board, to keep the dust from passing out every time the coal pile settles slightly.—Contributed by L. E. Turner, New York City, N. Y.

## Holding a Loose Wrist Pin in Place

Having occasion to repair a gasoline motor on an automobile, it was found that a loose wrist pin had slipped end-

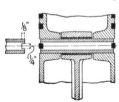

ways and scored the wall of the cylinder. To hold the pin in place a slot, ¼ in. wide and ⅛ in. deep, was milled on each end of the pin, a groove cut in the piston, and an ordinary piston ring in-

serted as shown. This not only prevented the pin from touching the cylinder walls, but it also gave better compression.

## An Automatic Siphon

A simple and interesting siphon which is entirely automatic in action and differs from the ordinary type only in that the shorter branch has a bell-like enlargement at the end, is shown in the illustration. To start the siphon the end of the longer arm is stopped with the finger, whereupon the other branch is immersed in the liquid until the enlarged part is below the surface. When the finger is removed from the end of the longer branch, the liquid, which could not enter the enlarged part on account of the air pressure in the siphon, suddenly rushes up in the siphon to seek its level, and a small quantity is by the momentum carried up into the smaller part and over the

bend, and the siphon begins to work.

It stands to reason that the bend of the siphon cannot be very high above the surface of the liquid, but in the laboratory the device can be used to advantage in a number of cases, especially when it is desired to draw off the clear part of a solution from a precipitate, because the wide mouth of the shorter branch can be brought very close to the precipitate without disturbing it, as the suction is very slight.

## Singletrees Kept Parallel with Evener by a Spring

Singletrees attached to eveners on double-span rigs have a tendency, when worn loose, to swing back into the wagon wheels, causing considerable annoyance. This may be prevented if an ordinary coiled screen-door spring is attached with screw eyes to the inner ends of each singletree. This not only tends to keep them parallel with the evener, but also prevents the reins from slipping under them while driving.—Contributed by G. H. Holter, Jasper, Minn.

## Casting Oil Grooves in Babbitted Bearing

One of the simplest means of casting oil grooves in a bearing when babbitting it, is to wind several turns of string around the mandrel or shaft. This will form small spiral grooves in which the oil can freely move, and, being well distributed, will tend to keep the bearing cool and provide a good lubrication.—Contributed by H. Walker, Corvallis, Ore.

## Tool for Cutting Long Keyways

The illustration shows a reliable and simple keyway cutter which overcame the troublesome chattering of an ordinary forged tool. The rod A may be made of cold-rolled steel, of a diameter sufficiently small to admit it and the projecting end of the tool B into the place to be keywayed. One end of the rod A is slotted to receive the cutting tool B, allowing for sufficient end clearance so it may freely swing back and forth around a pivot pin, C, thereby preventing injury to the cutting edge on the return stroke. The tool need extend out of the rod only far enough to allow it to cut to the required depth, without having the rod A scrape on the bottom of the shaft hole. The other

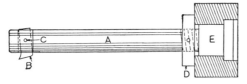

An Oscillating Cutter in a Bar to Provide Clearance for the Edge on the Back Stroke

end of the rod is threaded to fit a lock nut, D, and a tool-post nut, E, thus clamping it securely in position.

## Carrying Box for Oils on Delivery Wagon

To prevent the sugar and other groceries from being flavored with kerosene, a grocer has attached an addition

The Oilcans Placed in the Box Beneath cannot Contaminate Articles in the Upper Part

to the delivery wagon which might be adopted by grocers in general.

The sketch shows the simple box fixture, which is fastened permanently underneath the box of the wagon, and in which are carried the oils and gasoline, while ordinary articles are kept above, and therefore are not contaminated by contact or exposed to the disagreeable odors. While this may seem crude, it is a fine example of simplicity and effectiveness with a minimum of expense.—Contributed by T. B. Lambert, Chicago.

## Drawing Safe to Building with Elevator

In placing a heavy safe on the tenth floor of an office building, one elevator was used to haul it from the truck on the other elevator. A wire cable was wound around the safe and over a pulley at the base of the elevator shaft; and when the car was started, the safe was pulled in from the street and onto the other car. It was then slowly raised to the floor desired.—Contributed by L. T. Ward, Des Moines, Iowa.

## Automatic Valve Grinding for Automobiles

This device does away with the slow and tiresome grinding of valves by the use of screwdrivers. Procure a suitable-sized rod 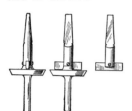 that will fit into the socket of an automatic hand drill. Slot this at the bottom for a rod, ¾ in. long, ½ in. wide, and $\frac{1}{16}$ in. thick. The reciprocating action of the handle gives the valve the necessary rotary motion to produce grinding.—Contributed by P. D. Merrill, Chicago, Ill.

## Handle for Starting Split Rivets

This very handy tool is made of sheet metal with two slots cut in one end, forming three tongues, the middle one  being as wide as the space between the rivet points. The tack is inserted in the tongues in the manner shown, and is then ready to be driven.—Contributed by Everett V. Hoar, Bowmanville, Massachusetts.

## Laying Out New Keyways

A simple method of accurately laying out a keyway on a shaft at some other place than it originally occupied is the following: Plug up the old keyway with wood or lead, and then face

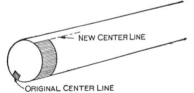

The Old Keyway Filled and Its Center Line Used to Locate the New Keyway

it down to correspond with the surface of the shaft. Get the exact length of the shaft circumference with a squared strip of paper, starting from

a center line marked on the plugged keyway. One end of the paper can then be cut off to a length having the same ratio to the entire strip that the angular distance between the centers of the old and new keyways has to 360. For example, since $\frac{180}{360} = \frac{1}{2}$, one-half of the length is used for a distance of 180 deg.; since $\frac{90}{360} = \frac{1}{4}$, one-fourth of the length, for 90 deg., etc. The new keyway can then be laid out with its center line corresponding to the end of the paper.—Contributed by J. B. Murphy, Plainfield, N. J.

## Tub Attachment for a Vacuum Clothes Washer

One of the best ways to wash heavy clothes or blankets is by pounding with an old-fashioned wood pounder, or with one of the vacuum washers. A barrel is best to use in connection with these washers, to prevent the spattering of the suds, but it is very unhandy while wringing the clothes. As the barrel I had leaked, it was sawed in two just below the second or third hoop from the bottom. A piece of old rubber belting was nailed around the barrel near the bottom to make it fit snugly inside the top of the tub, which prevented any water from getting out on the floor.

When the pounding was finished the barrel was removed from the tub and the wringer put on in the regular way. The tub should be set on a low bench to be handy. A barrel and tub of the right size should be selected for this combination.—Contributed by Monroe R. Jenkins, Red Creek, N. Y.

## Depth Determined by the Turns of a Bit

Carpenters using a full set of auger bits will find it very handy to mark them for depth gauges in this manner: Commence to count the turns when the bit begins to remove the stock, and not when the parting lip marks the outside, for boring just 1 in. deep. Mark this number on the shank with a steel stamp.

# An Electric Door Lock

## By ARTHUR MOORE

The door lock consists of an electromagnet that can be energized from one or more points by simply pressing an ordinary push button, connected in series with the winding of the electromagnet and the source of electrical energy, which may be a battery or bell-ringing transformer. When the armature is drawn up by the magnet it permits the latch of the lock to move back into the housing of the lock and away from in front of the latch on the door.

The housing, or case, of the lock is made from ⅛-in. sheet brass, as shown in Fig. 1. The dimensions given are all inside, and in bending the projections A and B back at right angles to the sides, care should be taken to make them exact for length. A cut, ⅛ in.

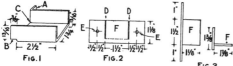

FIG.1    FIG.2    FIG.3

The Lock Housing for the Electromagnets and the Jamb Plate for the Door

deep, is made in each corner, as shown at C, so that the outer surface of the two projections A and B will be flush with the edge of the lower portion of the housing.

The dimensions of the jamb plate, also made of brass, are given in Fig. 2. Two slots, D, are sawed in this piece, as shown, and two holes, E, are drilled and countersunk for good-sized wood screws to fasten it to the jamb. Bend the portion F down at right angles to the remainder of the plate along the dotted line, to make it appear as shown in Fig. 3.

The piece shown in Fig. 1 is riveted to the jamb plate, as shown in Fig. 4. Two rivets are placed in each of the projections A and B, and two or more through the projection F, Fig. 3, and the bottom of the housing. The edge of this bottom is filed off, as shown at G.

Cut two pieces of sheet brass, ⅛ in. thick, in the shape shown by the shaded portion H, Fig. 5. Solder, or

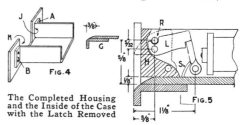

FIG.4    FIG.5

The Completed Housing and the Inside of the Case with the Latch Removed

rivet, these two pieces in the corners J and K, Fig. 4. Cut two pieces of brass to the shape shown by L, Fig. 5. These two pieces are filed down just a little, so that they will be thinner than the pieces H, and then fastened to the sides of the housing by means of small rivets, or screws, countersunk in the inside surface of the pieces. These triggers should be perfectly free to turn on the rivets, or screws, holding them. The latch M, Fig. 6, is made of a piece of cast brass. The back side of the completed latch is shown in Fig. 7. A notch, N, is cut in the back side to a depth represented by the dotted line in Fig. 6. Drill two holes, O, in the sides of the latch to be used in mounting it in the housing.

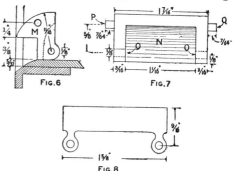

FIG.6    FIG.7

FIG.8

Dimensions and Position of the Latch in the Lock Together with Details of the Armature

Two lugs, P and Q, are provided on the ends so that they will fit into the depression R, Fig. 5, in the triggers L. Provide a coil spring to be mounted on the small steel shaft that is to support the latch, and coil it up so that it will tend to hold the latch in the position shown in Fig. 6, when one protruding end rests against the latch

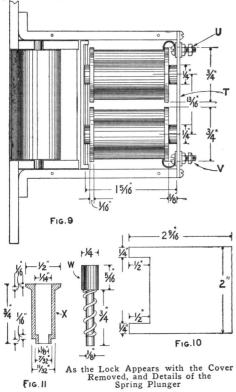

FIG. 9

FIG. 10

FIG. 11 — As the Lock Appears with the Cover Removed, and Details of the Spring Plunger

and the other against the bottom of the housing.

A small soft-iron armature is made, as shown in Fig. 8, and mounted as shown in Fig. 5. A light coil spring is mounted on the shaft supporting this armature so that it will be held away from the cores of the magnets and against the stop S, Fig. 5.

A top view of the completed lock is shown in Fig. 9, in which the dimensions of the electromagnets are given. The piece T, which is made of soft iron, forms the end of the case for the lock, and is fastened in place with screws, as shown. The soft-iron cores of the electromagnet are riveted to the piece T. The spools are wound full of No. 24 gauge insulated wire, and the ends are brought out to two insulated terminals, U and V. The

dimensions for the top of the lock are given in Fig. 10. This part is fastened in place with four small screws.

A spring plunger is made as shown in Fig. 11. The object of this plunger is to force the door open when the lock is operated. The plunger W fits into the tube X. A spiral spring tends to force the plunger out of the tube, but as the lower end of the plunger is riveted down around the edge, after being put in place in the tube, it cannot come out entirely. This plunger is mounted in the edge of the door jamb so that the door pushes the plunger W into the tube X when it closes. The electric lock, of course, holds the door closed, but upon touching a button the door will be forced partly open by the spring.

## Molding-Cutting Attachment for Lathe

It sometimes occurs that a special shape of wood molding is desired, which is either hard to get or can be had only after a long wait. To avoid such trouble, an ordinary high-speed lathe may be fitted up with a simple attachment to do the work satisfactorily. A special cutter is shown in Fig. 1, driven by the lathe headstock and the guide frame attached to the lathe bed. The cutter head, Fig. 2, consists of a body, A, to which are attached two tool-steel cutters, B, one on each side, by means of two cap screws, which have been machined to the desired shape and slotted for adjustment and wear. The body A consists of a rectangular piece of machine steel, turned at one end to fit the tapered center hole in the headstock shaft. The other end is drilled and countersunk for the tailstock center. The frame, forming the bed of the attachment, consists of a rectangular box of the proper height, so that the stock will be cut to the required depth when guided along the top board C, Fig. 1. The two guide strips D are spaced a distance apart corresponding to the width of the molding stock. The cross strips, or tension pieces, E are attached to the strips F, which, in turn, are fastened—at one end only—to the guides D. This arrangement permits the strips to spring up when forced from underneath. It should be made so it will exert a slight tension or downward pressure on the molding stock at all times, thereby preventing chattering which would result—due to variations in thickness of the stock—if the strips were rigidly attached, corresponding to one set height. The three-sided box, shown in Fig. 3, is the guard for the cutter head. It is screwed to the bed frame, as shown by the dotted outline in Fig. 1, by four braces, G. When ready for operation, the box frame is securely attached to the lathe bed, then the cutter head is put in place, and the tailstock brought up, so its center will guide the outer end of the cutter head. If at any time it is necessary to regrind the cutters or examine them while on the lathe, the tailstock can be drawn back, and the entire cutter head taken out—without first removing the frame. The direction of rotation being as indicated in Fig. 1, the stock should be fed in from the near side of the lathe, so the cutters will have a tendency to

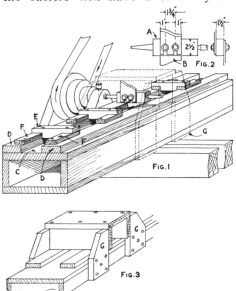

Cutter Attachment for a Speed Lathe to Make Duplicate Pieces of Molding for Matching Work

push the stock out instead of drawing it in.—Contributed by D. D. Gurnee, Hempstead, N. Y.

## A Varying Counterbalance Weight

It is almost impossible to raise a heavy cellar door, or the top of a table similar to the one shown in the sketch, without having some form of counterbalance. In the majority of cases the action

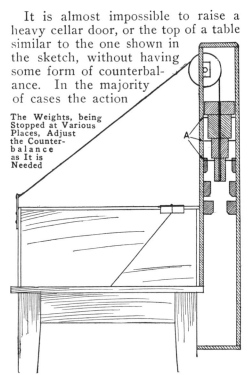

The Weights, being Stopped at Various Places, Adjust the Counterbalance as It is Needed

of this weight is very different for various positions of the object being lifted, and the results are far from satisfactory. It can be easily seen from the sketch that an unchanged weight will produce a greater and greater effect upon the table top as the top moves toward its vertical position. If the weight is adjusted so that it balances the weight of the table top when the top is horizontal, it will be a great deal too heavy for a balance when the top nears its vertical position. The arrangement shown overcomes this difficulty to a great extent by dividing the counterweight into sections and allowing the different sections in turn, from the top down, to rest upon the projections in the housing for the weights as the cord carrying them moves downward. The total weight, as shown, is divided into four parts, and the three upper parts come to rest at different positions. Each of the three lower weights should be provided with projecting pins, shown at A, two on each of the opposite sides and near the corners so that the weights will always travel in the center of the housing. The projections upon which the weights are to rest do not extend entirely across the sides of the housing, and sufficient space is allowed at each end for the guiding pins to pass. The position of the various supports are determined experimentally, and the weights may be so adjusted that the object being lifted will come to rest at almost any point in its complete travel.

### Jig for Forming Gear-Pattern Teeth

In making wooden teeth for gear patterns, the method frequently used is to mark out the required shape on

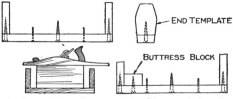

The Ends of the Jig Guide the Plane and Are the Exact Shape of the Tooth

blank blocks of suitable size, which are then gripped in a vise and planed down to the outline. Unless great care is taken, the teeth will not all be the same shape. By means of the simple jig illustrated, the teeth can be cut exactly to the correct form, with a great saving of time and requiring less skill.

Two blocks of hard wood, about 1 in. thick, are squared up and marked for the tooth outline, after which they should be cut out, filed, and sandpapered to the exact size. A base is provided, consisting of a board sufficiently long to allow several inches of clearance between each end of the tooth blanks and the jig templates, when these are fastened in position as shown. The plane to be used and the size of the jig should be such that neither end of the plane will leave the templates in finishing the gear tooth. The templates are fastened to the ends of the base block; the teeth blanks are secured to the base by means of a screw and nails. The jig can be held in a vise

when ready for use. In using the plane, the protruding cutting edge should be gradually withdrawn, so that, when the plane bottom runs on the jig templates, no cut can be taken. The accuracy of the work can be determined by placing a thin steel straightedge across the templates.

This jig can be used for bevel-gear teeth as well as for spur gears. In this case it would be necessary to have the templates correspondingly larger or smaller, as determined from a drawing layout of the gear. In cutting the teeth, they should all be set and held in place against a buttress block to make them uniform.—Contributed by Joe V. Romig.

### To Prevent Headaches Resulting from Handling Dynamite

In handling dynamite, if one wears a pair of canvas gloves, he will escape the otherwise resultant headache. It is not the fumes nor the concussion that causes the headache, but the penetration of the dynamite into the system. In using the explosive, one should always wear gloves and refrain from putting the hands to the face.—Contributed by Alvah H. Pulver, Sodus, N. Y.

### Double-Lipped Pouring Ladle

It quite frequently occurs that, in order to produce the best work in pouring molds or babbitting shafts, it is necessary to have two ladles operating at the same time. With the two-lipped ladle shown in the illustration, one man can do the work alone. It is only necessary to have the two pouring

Two-Lipped Ladle to Pour Metal into Two Gates at the Same Time

holes the same distance apart as the ladle lips.—Contributed by J. W. Ladlow, Globe, Ariz.

## Making Reamer Cut Oversize

The size of hole that a reamer will cut may be increased by placing a piece of small round rod in one of the reamer flutes. The size cut will depend on the diameter of the rod, which should fit securely in the flute, at the

**Small Rod in the Flute of a Reamer to Make it Cut Oversize**

same time preventing the teeth on the rod side from cutting.—Contributed by J. J. Kolar, Maywood, Ill.

## Aid to Light a Heating Stove

Finding it difficult to light a fire in my heating stove, which has a circular front draft near the bottom, I made a supporting iron for the solid fuel, as shown in the sketch. This holds up the larger sticks of wood, allowing the paper to burn until it ignites the fuel, and gives a quicker fire with less

**A Support to Keep the Weight of the Fuel from the Paper While Starting a Fire**

bother than any other arrangement I have tried.—Contributed by Geo. B. Weaver, Sandpoint, Idaho.

## To Prevent Wall Showing between Butted Wall Paper

In hanging oatmeal or any plain paper where it is necessary to butt the edges of the paper, the white wall is liable to show a little in places. To overcome this, procure a colored crayon the same tint as the paper, and line the wall. Neither the edges of the paper nor the wall will show where this method is used.—Contributed by A. E. Johnson, Frankfort, Ind.

ⓒTo bleach out a stain in wood, sandpaper the work, and apply a mixture of 7 parts fresh lime and 1 part caustic soda.

## Fitting a Handle or Plug

To make an accurately fitting plug, or a properly tapered handle end, proceed as follows: Take the bit that fits the hole into which the plug, or handle, is to be inserted, and bore into the end of the plug, or handle, for a distance sufficient to mark it with

the lips of the bit. The wood can then be cut, or rasped, off evenly down to the edge of the drill hole without danger of a lopsided handle resulting.

## Fitting a Barrel Cover Tightly

An ordinary barrel head is greatly improved by having a groove gouged out of its under surface to fit the stave ends. The groove prevents the cover or head from being pushed off as well as helps to keep out dust and insects.

## Nonskid Casing for a Motorcycle Wheel

Having considerable trouble with my motorcycle skidding on the wet pavement, I tried the following method with good results: A long piece of sail canvas was procured, a little longer than the wheel circumference and wide enough for the face of the tire, with about 1 in. surplus on each side, which was turned over, whereupon grommets were placed at intervals of 2 in. An old belt was cut into V-shaped narrow strips, which were riveted to the canvas about 1 in. apart. The canvas was laced over the tire with rawhide thongs.

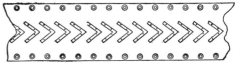

**Canvas Strip, with V-Shaped Pieces of Leather Attached, to Make a Nonskid Casing**

This will not only prevent the skidding, but it will protect a ripped or cut casing.—Contributed by Joseph C. Laackman, Philadelphia, Pa.

## To Prevent Noisy Gears on a Drill Press

The sketch illustrates a drill-press arm with an attachment to stop the noise of rattling gears caused by raising the spindle too high. The locknut A comes in contact with the lower end of the large gear B and pushes it up against the small gear C. A small pin, D, made of cold-rolled steel, is shaped with a file at one end as shown. This is fastened with a screw to the upper end of the rack, so that its end will strike the frame before the locknut comes in contact with the gear. —Contributed by Walter Butz, Pearl River, N. Y.

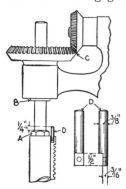

## Drill Jig for Drilling Slanting Holes in Studs

Where it is necessary to drill a hole at an angle in the end of a stud for an oil passage to the grooves in the bearing, the drilling is quite difficult, unless some sort of jig is used. The illustration shows a very simple jig for this work, it being made of a piece of metal of sufficient strength for the work, bent in the shape shown. The

The Stud is Held in the Proper Position to Drill the Hole on an Angle

jig can be fastened to the platen of the drill in the desired position for drilling the hole.—Contributed by Russell E. Hollis, Chicago.

⟪Gasoline feed pipes should not be allowed to vibrate; tie them with rawhide thongs.

## Stopping Nail Holes in Shingles Made with Staging

In putting on shingles with the use of staging there will be holes left where the staging nails were driven. If the shingle directly below that which has the holes is driven slightly upward, it will close the holes and save plugging them.—Contributed by Otto B. Vaughn, Belfast, Me.

## Adjustable Ladder Supports for Paper Hangers

A workman using a plank between stepladders for a stage usually finds it either too high or too low to be comfortable for working, owing to the distance between the steps. Adjustments for height can be had by means of the simple arrangement shown in the sketch. Two pieces, A, and the rung B constitute the adjusting device. Each piece, A, is 4 in. wide and 7/8 in.

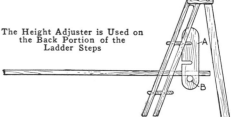

The Height Adjuster is Used on the Back Portion of the Ladder Steps

thick. Two notches are cut in one edge to fit over the steps of the ladder. The rung B holds the two pieces spaced at the proper distance for the ladder width. With this arrangement, two adjustments for height are possible between each step of the ladder.

## Gas-Stove Burner Used as Lawn Sprinkler

A gas-stove burner can be easily converted into a lawn sprinkler without any machine work being necessary. All the holes in it should first be cleaned out, and a hose wired to the spout of the burner. If a better connection is desired, a regular hose coupling may be soldered to the burner spout.—Contributed by I. E. Carpenter, South Bend, Ind.

# Lathe Attachment for Turning Circular Work

By J. H. RODGERS

In turning circular work, considerable difficulty may be experienced in obtaining a true circular arc unless some special fixture is used. A simple device of this kind is shown in Fig. 1. A suitable tool post, A, and rest, B, may be selected from a scrapped lathe, or, if such is not at hand, the necessary parts from an idle lathe can be used temporarily. Some suitable worm gear and worm must be provided to furnish the necessary circular feed.

The worm gear should be securely fastened to the bottom of the tool rest B, as shown in Fig. 2. A base, C, must be made, consisting of a cast-iron plate provided with two brackets, D, Fig. 1, at one side, which are to serve as bearings for the worm shaft. In order that the tool rest may revolve on the base C, when bolted to it, the worm gear should be drilled and counterbored in its exact center, to fit the bearing pin E, Fig. 2.

There should be sufficient length between the head of the pin and the lower shoulder to allow the gear, when fastened in place, to have a slight clearance permitting it to revolve freely, without producing unnecessary looseness. The base C should be provided with a tongue to fit in the groove of the rest F, Fig. 1, and may be fastened in place by means of a bolt and T-shaped nut. If there is only one groove in the rest F, the base plate C should be sufficiently wide so it may be provided with a projection to fit this groove and fastened, as before, with bolts and T-shaped nuts. Two lines should be marked on the rest B, one GH, on the side, and the other, IJ, on the end, each corresponding to the center line of the pin E, Fig. 2. The device should be located by these lines with respect to the work in two ways: first, it is necessary to have the line GH at a distance, K, Fig. 3, from the center of the work equal to that of the arc center from the work axis; second, the line IJ must be in an imaginary plane passing, perpendicular to the

work axis, through the center of the curved surface.

With the setting thus done, no further adjustments should be made which

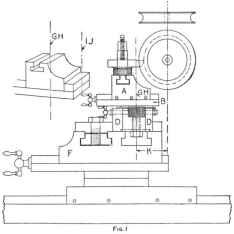

Fig. 1
General Arrangement of the Parts as They are Attached to the Tool Post of a Lathe

will in any way alter the location of the rest B, Fig. 1, with regard to the work. The tool post A can still be moved back or forth as desired, without in any way spoiling the setting of the attachment, and may be drawn a convenient distance away from the work to permit better adjustment. The tool should be set centrally on the tool post with its length approximately perpendicular to the work axis. The cutting edge should line up with the lathe centers and ex-

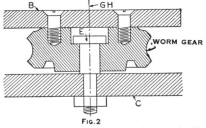

Fig. 2
Method of Fastening the Worm Gear to the Tool Rest with Its Cast-Iron Base

tend beyond the line GH of the rest B a distance equal to the radius of the required arc. If the work is concaved or a groove, the cutting edge must lie between the line GH and the work axis; if convex or spherical, then it must be outside of these two positions, as shown

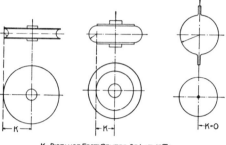

K=DISTANCE FROM CENTER OF LATHE TO CENTER OF TURRET
Fig.3
Tool and Tool Rest Set to Turn Concave, Convex, and Ball-Turning Work

in Fig. 3. With the tool held as thus described, the required radius would be cut. For the roughing cut, the tool post A should be drawn away from the work; in circular grooves this will produce a smaller arc; in convex work, a larger radius. In both cases, the cuts will all be parallel or concentric, as is necessary in all circular-cutting devices.

## Throttle Governor for Marine Gasoline Engine

Speed governors are frequently omitted on marine gasoline engines, so, when it is desirable to use them for sta-

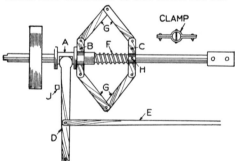

The Toggle Arms Tend to Close as the Speed Increases and Controls the Carburetor Lever

tionary purposes, some governor is usually required. An easily constructed throttle type can be made as here described. The parts necessary are: a shaft sleeve, A; one set of sleeve clamps, B; one set of shaft clamps, C; a swinging lever, D; a throttle-connect-

ing lever, E; a spiral spring, F; toggle levers, G; bolts, nuts, and rivets. The shaft sleeve A should be bored for a sliding fit on the shaft and provided with two collars at one end which are spaced to engage the forked end of the lever D, thereby transmitting to it any movement the sleeve A may have in a direction parallel with the shaft. The lever D is fastened at its lower end so it can swing back and forth with the sleeve A. The carburetor connecting lever E is attached to the throttle valve, at one end, and to the swinging lever D, at the other. The sleeve clamps B are made to fit the extension of the sleeve A, and, when in place, should be separated sufficiently to admit one end of the toggle levers G, which can be made of strong wood to any convenient length. These are held in place at one end by the clamp bolts; at the other end they can be held together by a loose-fitting rivet, thereby avoiding the danger of flying bolts and nuts. The shaft clamps C should not only have a tight fit on the shaft, but should be riveted to it as well by a center rivet, H. The spiral spring F should fit the shaft loosely, and have sufficient tension to balance the centrifugal force of the revolving toggle levers, this being most accurately determined through repeated trials.

In starting the engine, the throttle may be opened wide or only to a desired amount, if a stop, J, be provided, preventing the lever D from moving any farther. As the engine speeds up, the centrifugal force in the levers G becomes sufficient to compress the spring, thereby allowing the sleeve to slide toward the right. This movement is imparted to the forked lever D, and through it and the lever E to the throttle. The throttle gradually closes, reducing the power of the engine and thereby the speed, until this drops to a point where a greater throttle opening again increases the power and speed.—Contributed by H. A. Betts, Wallace Bridge, Nova Scotia.

❡ A newly tapped hole should be oiled before turning a bolt into it.

## A Chute for Fish to Pass over a Dam

TO provide a means for fish to pass upstream over a dam, a long, gradually sloping box is made, inside of which a series of pockets, or obstructions, are fixed to hold a sufficient quantity of water to allow the fish to pass from one to the other until it finally gains the summit and can swim into the stream above.

The chute consists of timbers, 2 in. thick and 10 in. wide, nailed together in box fashion. The length of the pieces will depend on the height of the dam, which governs the length of the box, or chute. A good size is one made five planks in width and one plank high. The planks should be surfaced on three sides so that the edges will make a good joint; then they are placed together and fastened securely to battens across the under side. The sides should be nailed with one edge set on the upper surface of the outer bottom boards.

The Chute Provides a Means for Fish to Pass over a Dam Where a Large Volume of Water is Not Flowing at Any One Place

If the dam is so high that it demands a longer chute than the stock sizes of the plank, it is best to stagger the board ends so that no two boards, lying side by side, will have the end joint at the same location. This will make a solid and continuous box, save for the top, which is left partly open for cleaning out the pockets.

It will be seen by the diagram that a part of the chute runs horizontally, or on a level with the top of the dam. A careful joint should be made at the bend A, and it should be securely fastened with straps of iron overlapping the parts.

The bottom and sides are built up and placed in position on the dam. The crib at the head, which is built on the bottom boards of the horizontal part, is located about 6 or 8 in. ahead of the opening in the box and is triangular in shape. The crib is well weighted with stone to prevent the structure from being washed away.

Within the box, which is now in a trough form, a series of staggered obstructions are placed so that the water spilling from one is caught in the one next below, and so on, until the bottom is reached. These are well nailed in place, whereupon the top planks are nailed on and nails driven through them into the pieces forming the pockets. These pieces are made of the same width planks, thus filling the space from top to bottom. As mentioned before, spaces are left between the top planks so that a stick or paddle can be used in cleaning out the pockets.

If it is necessary to build the chute

very long, a brace or support can be set under it at the center, to keep it from sagging under the weight. This

is approximately 100 lb.—to be exact, 100.2 lb.

Thus, if it is desired to know the re-

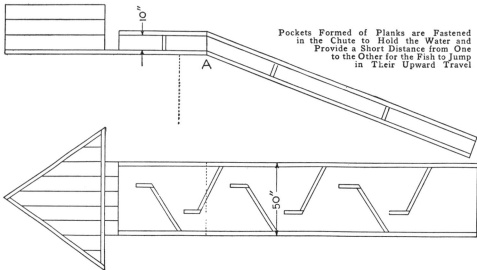

Pockets Formed of Planks are Fastened in the Chute to Hold the Water and Provide a Short Distance from One to the Other for the Fish to Jump in Their Upward Travel

can be made up in the form of a trestle and should be well anchored to keep it in place.

## A Reminder for the Wire Table

Although the following simple relations in connection with the Brown & Sharpe gauge wire table are not new, they will be of great service to anyone who has occasion to make frequent calculations involving certain data given in the wire table where no great degree of accuracy is required.

A wire which is three sizes larger than another wire has one-half the resistance, twice the weight for a given length, and twice the area.

A wire which is 10 sizes larger than another wire has one-tenth the resistance, 10 times the weight for a given length, and 10 times the area.

A No. 10 gauge wire is approximately 0.1 in. in diameter—to be exact, .1019 in., or 101.9 mils; it has an area of approximately 10,000 circular mils —to be exact, 10,380 circular mils; it has a resistance of 1 ohm per 1,000 ft., at 20° C., or 68° F., and it weighs approximately 32 lb. per 1,000 ft.—to be exact, 31.43 lb.

The weight of 1,000 ft. of No. 5 wire

sistance and weight, say, of a No. 4 wire per 1,000 ft., it can be determined with sufficient accuracy for all practical purposes from the foregoing relations as follows: Since a wire three sizes larger than another has one-half the resistance, it follows that a No. 7 wire will have a resistance equal to one-half of a No. 10, and a No. 4 will have one-half the resistance of a No. 7, or one-fourth of a No. 10; hence the resistance of a No. 4 wire will be one-fourth ohm per 1,000 ft., and it will weigh four times 32, or 128 lb. per 1,000 ft.

The procedure in calculating the resistance of a wire that differs in number from a No. 10 by an amount that is not a multiple of three is a little different from the above. For example, if the resistance and weight of a No. 8 is desired to be known, proceed as follows: First find the resistance of a No. 20, which is ten times a No. 10, or 10 ohms per 1,000 ft.; then find the resistance of a No. 17, No. 14, No. 11 and a No. 8. The resistance of a No. 17 is one-half of a No. 20; of a No. 14, one-fourth of a No. 20; of a No. 11, one-eighth of a No. 20, and of a No. 8, one-sixteenth of a No. 20, or .62 ohm per 1,000 ft. The weight of a No. 8

would be 16 times that of a No. 20, but a No. 20 weighs one-tenth of a No. 10 or 3.2 lb. per 1,000 ft.; hence a No. 8 would weigh 16x3.2 or 51 lb.

If the area in circular mils is known, the approximate number of feet per ohm can be obtained by dropping one cipher.

The approximate weight for a given length may be found by dropping four ciphers from the area in circular mils, and then multiplying by the weight of a No. 10 wire.

The values, as calculated above, are not exact and do not correspond with those given in a wire table, but they are sufficiently accurate for almost all ordinary purposes.

## Protecting Polished Steel Surfaces

A coating that will protect hardware and machinists' tools from rusting may be made as follows: Mix well 4 oz. of demar varnish with ½ gal. turpentine and dip the articles into it or apply it as a wash. A thin coat of this colorless varnish will not show on the polished surfaces of tools, but will protect the surfaces indefinitely, unless scratched.

## A Gardener's Weeding Cart

With the use of the weeding cart shown it is not necessary for the gardener to get on his knees to pull weeds out of the growing plant rows. The plan shows its construction. It is also useful in picking green beans. For weeding I use wheels 12 in. in diameter, and for picking 18 in., on the rear axle. A canopy or umbrella can be

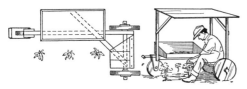

A Weeding and Picking Cart That will Greatly Assist the Gardener Having a Large Acreage

attached for use in the sunshine.—Contributed by A. S. Thomas, Amherstburg, Ont.

## Installation of Water-Heating Plant

The general layout and pipe connections for a water-heating plant in large apartment buildings and hotels is il-

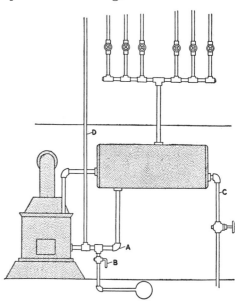

The Arrangement of Pipe Connections to a Hot-Water Boiler and the Heater for a Large Building

lustrated in the drawing. It is first necessary to locate the boiler and heater and make pipe connections between them with 2-in. pipe as shown. The sediment pipe A introduces the cold water to the heater and it should have a blow-off valve, B, with connections to the sewer. The boiler supply C feeds into the lower part, thus forcing the hot water to the top and into the system. The return pipe D affords free circulation and provides a means of drawing hot water at any tap.

Each of the pipes leading from the top of the boiler to the different departments has a valve so that it is not necessary to shut down the whole plant if repairs are to be made on one system.—Contributed by Geo. M. Crawley, Newark, N. J.

❡An emergency screwdriver for use in tightening a screw in eyeglasses can be had by turning a steel pen end for end in its holder.

### Starting Hardy Plants

A reliable way to obtain best results in starting plants of the laurel and oleander group is as follows: A branch, which through the evenness

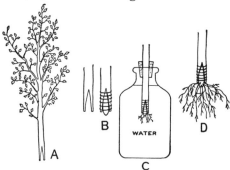

The Oat Kernel Assists the Growing of Slips before Setting the Branch into the Earth

of its shoots promises to become a perfect plant, is selected from a plant that has proven to be healthy in growth and rich in flowers. The best size for a branch is 8 or 9 in., with a stem end about the size of an ordinary pencil. This end is cut with a sharp knife, as shown at A, and an oat grain is inserted, head upward, in the split, where it is secured by winding a bit of thread around the branch, as shown at B.

The end of the branch with the oat kernel is placed in a bottle of water, C, and adjusted to the center of the neck by means of cork wedges, as shown. This will prevent the branch from dropping to the bottom of the bottle. The branch should be as nearly vertical as possible to obtain a perfectly straight growth.

The bottle is kept in a warm place, and in a few days the oat grain will sprout and through its close connection with the stem will draw and feed water to the branch. In four or five weeks the roots started on the stem D are strong enough to permit the branch to be planted in very soft and loose earth in a pot. The pot should have a hole in the bottom and should be placed in a deep dish, which should be kept filled with water.

It is important to have plenty of room for the plant to spread its roots, and when necessary it should be transplanted to a larger pot, but without disturbing the mass of earth that adheres to the roots.—Contributed by Pierre Wagner, Indianapolis, Ind.

### Automatic Dish Washer

Solder together two small pie tins, as shown, and cut a ½-in. hole in the center of the one used for the top; also make a ½-in. hole in the center of the bottom of a large dish or bread pan. The ½-in. tube used in these holes should be supplied with a valve, A, and a removable sheet, B, which distributes the hot water through numerous small holes drilled in it. The tube is soldered in the holes of the pie tin and pan to make a water-tight joint.

The tray C is a piece of wire screen, with ½-in. square mesh, having the edges bent down. This tray keeps the dishes out of the water. The valve is a simple check valve, the seat D being made of a piece of thick brass with a center hole to fit on the tube where it is soldered, and six smaller holes drilled around the central one. The disk E is a thinner piece of brass with only one hole in the center. This disk works loosely in the space made for it. This space consists of a larger tube with a covering which is soldered to the upper tube.

The washer acts in the same manner as a percolator. The water is heated in the pie tins and the expansion forces it up through the pipe, where it falls over the dishes through the holes in

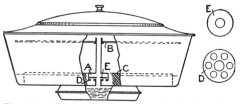

The Principle of the Percolator is Used in This Dish Washer to Throw Hot Water over the Dishes

the sheet B, then returns to be heated again. After 10 or 15 minutes the pan is taken from the heat and the cover removed. No drying cloth is necessary, as the heated pieces will evaporate what little moisture remains.—Contributed by H W. Hahn, Chicago, Ill.

## Fly-Cutter Holder for Milling Machines

The amount of work required for cutting one gear to replace a broken one does not warrant the outlay for a special circular milling cutter. For this reason the tool illustrated was devised for use in a milling machine to cut the teeth. The tool is simple and easy to make. A piece of carbon steel, ½ in. square, was procured and one end shaped to fit the space between the teeth of the broken gear. In shaping the steel it was carefully ground to give clearance, then properly hardened. This steel was held in a taper shank with a setscrew in the end.

The gear blank was first roughed out with a stock cutter. If such a cut-

A Fly Cutter for Use in Shaping Teeth in a Special Gear Quickly

ter is not at hand, a slitting saw may be used. The holder and fly cutter were next placed in position and the work set to make the cut to the proper depth.

It is well to remember that a tool of this kind has only one cutting edge and will not remove the metal as fast as the circular cutter, therefore it necessitates a finer cut. However, with this tool it is possible to do this and similar work quickly.—Contributed by A. Dane, Pottstown, Pa.

## Adjustable Stand to Hold Blacksmith's Tongs

In forging small hoops it is a great help to have a stand to support the handle of the tongs as they hold the work upright. A very handy stand for this purpose is constructed as shown in the sketch. It consists of a vertical

piece fastened to a base, the upright part having several holes drilled for receiving an adjusting pin. The pin

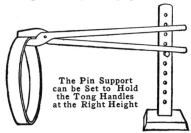

The Pin Support can be Set to Hold the Tong Handles at the Right Height

can be placed in a hole at the right height for the work.—Contributed by D. C. Goff, Knoxville, Tenn.

## Protection for Chisel Edges

A means to protect the cutting edge of a chisel when not in use is to wrap a piece of medium-heavy paper around the chisel body to form a paper ferrule. The paper is cut into a strip, about 1½ in. wide and 6 in. long. One side is glued and it is then wrapped around the chisel. The protector is slipped up on the body when it is in use, but when placed in a chest the ferrule is brought down over the edge.

## Faucet Stem Used as a Ring Stand

The laboratory faucet makes an excellent ring stand. All the utensils necessary are kept on hand and near the water, which in many instances is one of the ingredients used in mixing chemicals. The rings are fastened to the faucet shank with clamps so that

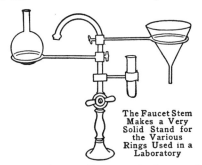

The Faucet Stem Makes a Very Solid Stand for the Various Rings Used in a Laboratory

they can be easily attached or taken off, as desired.—Contributed by R. C. Kyle, McMinnville, Ore.

### A Homemade Hand-Lever Punch

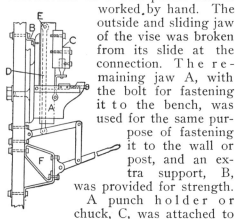

A broken and discarded vise provided the main working parts in the construction of a wall punch that is worked by hand. The outside and sliding jaw of the vise was broken from its slide at the connection. The remaining jaw A, with the bolt for fastening it to the bench, was used for the same purpose of fastening it to the wall or post, and an extra support, B, was provided for strength. A punch holder or chuck, C, was attached to the slide in place of the broken jaw. Instead of using the screw, the threads were bored out of the stationary jaw part, and a rod, D, made to slip in the hole snugly. The rod was attached to the sliding part at E. A bracket, F, was made of stake iron, and a double lever arrangement attached to it as shown. With this device it is easy to punch a ⅜-in. hole through ⅛-in. stock.—Contributed by G. E. Koener, Springfield, Ill.

### To Stop Dripping Noise in a Flush Box

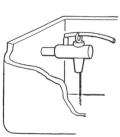

The sound caused by the continual dripping of water in the flush box, due to the small leakage and imperfect seating of the valve, is very annoying and as a remedy I hit upon the following idea. A piece of wire was soldered to the mouth of the inlet valve, as shown, and it entirely eliminated the troublesome noise.
—Contributed by Henry G. Manley, Brooklyn, N. Y.

### Green-Sand Cores for Molds

Having need of two cores, one 1¼ in. in diameter by 3 in. long, and the other 2 in. in diameter and 5 in. long, and no core box for these sizes being at hand, I hastily made substitute cores as follows: Two pieces of cold-rolled steel, having the right diameter, were procured, and heavy paper was wrapped around them, allowing the paper to extend over the end of the steel for a length equal to the length of the core. The paper was tied to the steel. Ordinary molding sand was rammed into the paper and ventilated, and retaining wires were run in lengthwise. These made good cores in place of the baked ones.—Contributed by Carl Snyder, Richmond, Ind.

### Emery-Wheel Diamond-Dresser Holder

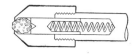

The usual method of setting a diamond in the end of a steel rod for dressing emery wheels is greatly improved by the use of a holder as shown in the sketch. The parts are constructed similar to a draw chuck, except that a strong coiled spring keeps the diamond in the taper hole at the end. The spring absorbs the shock and the diamond is not so apt to be cracked. The size depends on the size and shape of the diamond used.

### Operating Typewriter-Carriage Shift with Foot Lever

A stenographer doing a great deal of typewriting made an attachment whereby the carriage shift was worked by the right foot. A piece of cord was tied to the thumb lever of the carriage, then run over a pulley and down to the floor where it was attached to a treadle. Pressure on the treadle draws the carriage to any desired position and at the same time turns the roller when a new line is to be written.—Contributed by Harold Goff, Salt Lake City, Utah.

## To Clean a Water Column on a Steam Boiler

When connecting the water column to a steam boiler, instead of making the turns with elbows use ordinary crosses and close the two openings not used with plugs. In this way the pipes can be easily cleaned out when the boiler is cooled off to wash out. The plugs are taken out and a scraper run through the pipes. It is only necessary to use the crosses on the lower or water connections, as the steam connections are not so likely to become plugged with sediment. If gate valves are used, they leave a straight opening, and the pipes can be easily cleaned.—Contributed by P. W. Tooth, Leastalk, California.

## Holding Gas in Pipe While Making Repairs

Desiring to make an extension of the shop gas pipe with as little disturbance as possible, I carefully unscrewed the cap at the pipe end and quickly plugged the pipe with warmed paraffin wax, thus sealing the pipe and preventing the escape of gas. The new pipe line was then connected and the wax plug melted away by heating the pipe at the joint.—Contributed by Dexter W. Allis, Boston, Mass.

## Varnish-Brush Cleaner

It is absolutely essential that the varnish brush be kept free from dust and grit. The device shown affords a 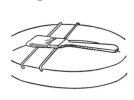 clean method of wiping a varnish brush, and also provides a good support for it at intervals while some article is being varnished. A clean pudding pan with a double wire, drawn taut across the top, is all that is necessary. The dirty varnish falling into the pan may be thinned with turpentine and added to old paint which is to be strained.

## Method of Removing a Stuck Cylinder Bushing

The sticking of large cylinder bushings which are shrunk or forced into the cylinder is by no means an uncom-

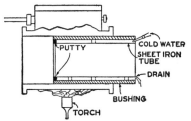

Heat Applied to the Outside and Cold Water Within Cause the Metals to Separate by Expansion

mon occurrence. Irregularities in the shape of the cylinder or in the size of the bushing are causes which at times make this fault almost unavoidable. However, the task of getting them out is the greatest difficulty, and in many cases it is only accomplished by ruining a new bushing.

The sketch shows a method that has been used in removing stuck cylinder bushings of various sizes and kinds, without in any instance having failed to effect a removal or caused damage to the bushing or cylinder. A piece of metal, the length of the bushing, is rolled to a diameter of about 1 in. less than the inside diameter of the stuck bushing. Pieces of wood are fastened to its outer surface at several points, to keep the tube in place when it is shoved into the cylinder bushing. The opening between the metal shell and the bushing is puttied up at the ends except at two points, one at the upper side and one at the bottom. This forms a jacket through which cold water is run to keep the bushing cool. Heat is then applied to the outside of the cylinder body. The cylinder alone expands by this method, allowing the bushing to be readily pulled or forced out.

⫷An automobile can be driven a considerable distance by repeated fillings of the carburetor float chamber when a feed pipe breaks.

## A Gauge-Hand Puller

Gauge-hand pullers are tools easily lost and somewhat expensive at best. The sketch illustrates one that can be

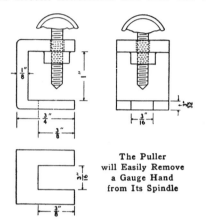

The Puller will Easily Remove a Gauge Hand from Its Spindle

readily made very cheaply from a stove bolt and a small piece of sheet steel. The nut of the stove bolt is soldered to the inside of the U-strip, and its head is flattened out to form a small thumbscrew head.

Stove bolts are cheap and standard in size, and it is consequently possible to have any number of stem points ground for different-size hand stems. For the mechanic on this class of work who must supply his own tools, this homemade device is a money saver.

---

## Preserving Oil Colors on a Palette

Occasionally I find time to start a sketch in oil, but other matters often interrupt the art work. Not wishing to

The Mixed Paints, Covered with Water, Keep Several Days and are Ready to Work Any Time

remix colors after having secured what I think is just right, I mix on a small piece of glass, and when stopping, the glass is placed in a shallow earthen dish and covered with water. In this way the colors keep workable for days. The glass can be secured to an ordinary wood palette with rubber bands.
—Contributed by James M. Kane.

## Remedying Loose Automobile Fenders

A number of automobiles, more especially the lower-priced ones, have fenders that will become loose and rattle after a little service. Some of the noise is due to loosened bolts and may be remedied by tightening up the nuts. Another cause for the rattling is that the rivet holes are worn large. This is usually found on the lower rear braces supporting the fenders over the rear wheels. The action of the chains and mud slinging is very apt to loosen the thin sheet metal from its fastening, and once started the hole enlarges rapidly. Sometimes a larger size of rivet will suffice. When the hole becomes too large for these repairs, a new fender will be required or the old one must be patched. The patching is usually unsightly. Frequently a large washer with a hole for a $\frac{1}{4}$ or $\frac{5}{16}$-in. rivet can be used over the tear and, if riveted down tightly, it will last quite well. If the edge of the washer is well tapered, this repair will not be noticeable after the entire fender has been painted over.

---

## Applying a Bright Finish to Screw Threads

In working tool steel, it is always difficult to produce a good finish in any other manner than grinding, and this cannot be applied to screw threads. Where a thread is used in tool making a good smooth finish is desirable, not only as a matter of appearance, but to maintain the accuracy and lengthen the life of the thread.

The best method to finish threads is to turn them to size, then procure a piece of soft wood and hold it against the threads, which forms a hand chaser. Dip it in oil, then in No. 0 or 00 emery, and chase over the threads. It will be impossible to remove over .001 in. of the material in this way, and a fine, ground finish is obtained quickly and in an inexpensive manner.—Contributed by J. B. Murphy, Plainfield, N. J.

## Draining Dished Porch Steps

In passing a house having a wood porch with steps at the entrance, I noticed that each step had three grooves or channels cut in its upper surface. On closer inspection I discovered each step was slightly warped and sagged in the center. When it rained, the water remained in the sunken part and the owner cut the grooves from the outer edge deep enough to drain the water off quickly.—Contributed by Fred Schumacher, Brooklyn, N. Y.

## Radius Templates for Mechanics

Usually a drawing calls for a radius on shafts and the workman must make

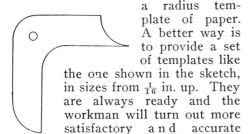

a radius template of paper. A better way is to provide a set of templates like the one shown in the sketch, in sizes from $\frac{1}{16}$ in. up. They are always ready and the workman will turn out more satisfactory and accurate work.—Contributed by John A. Kagerhuler, E. Dowingtown, Pa.

## Combination Chamfering and Facing Lathe Tool

In facing a large number of nuts on a single mandrel considerable time is lost either in shifting the tool to cham-

fer the top face of the nut, or in placing the nuts again on the mandrel if the tool is kept stationary.

The sketch illustrates a tool by means of which the chamfering and facing of the nuts can be done without shifting the tool and with only a slight forward movement of the lathe carriage. In a shop where a great number of nuts are faced off for different purposes, this tool is certainly a time and money saver.

## An Insulator Remover

The remover is made of a piece of spring steel, 10 in. long, $\frac{3}{4}$ in. wide and $\frac{1}{16}$ in. thick, bent as shown. The

The Notched Ends of the Steel Cut and Remove the Insulation as the Wire is Drawn through Them

ends are filed sharp and a notch is cut in the center of each. The edges of these notches are filed sharp and the wire to be cleaned is placed between them. The jaws are then closed by pressure of the hand and the wire is drawn through, which removes the insulation.—Contributed by Patterson Merrill, Chicago, Ill.

## Heating Range Boiler with Return Steam

In most boilers of the tubular or firebox type there are no provisions made for placing a coil in the firebox if a range boiler is to be heated and it necessitates the drilling of the boiler shell and placing a coil in the boiler. This is an expensive piece of work and requires skill, but just as good a job and one that will be entirely satisfactory is as follows:

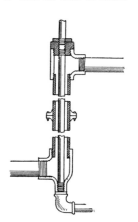

Disconnect the flange union on the steam return, remove the ells at the top and bottom and replace them with tees and connect the return in the usual manner. Cut a piece of $\frac{3}{4}$-in. galvanized pipe 2 in. longer than the vertical piece, including the tees, of the return pipe and cut long threads on each end. Place this within the return pipe and use reducers in the tees, as shown. The protruding ends of the pipe provide a means to make connections to the range boiler. It may be necessary to use a thin locknut and a gasket on the pipe ends to prevent a leak.

This method is much better than placing a coil in the firebox, as it will continue to heat long after the fire has gone out or as long as steam surrounds the ¾-in. pipe in the return steam pipe.—Contributed by John F. Vidler, Portland, Ore.

### A Handy Jack

A useful and handy jack for many purposes can be made of a piece of 2  by 4-in. material about 4½ ft. long, to which is attached a block with a hinged arm. The long piece has its upper end shaped into a handle. The hinged part should be just long enough to be easily placed under the object to be raised when the jack is in the position shown. It is obvious how the jack works.

### Signal Lamp on Chauffeur's Glove

The signal used by the driver of an automobile to notify following drivers that a turn is to be made is to extend the arm with the hand up. This signal serves the purpose in daylight, but cannot be seen at night. The device shown in  the illustration will permit the same signal at night. A small electric globe, inclosed in a transparent cover, is attached to the back of the glove. The connections are made to a pocket battery, and a small switch, or contact points on the leather of the thumb and finger, control the light. By pressing these two points together the light is flashed as the hand is waved.—Contributed by C. H. Thomas, Norristown, Pennsylvania.

### Removing Rusty Screws from Wood

In trying to remove a rusty screw which held two pieces of oak together, I was unable to do so with the ordinary screwdriver. Some soldering work being pressing, I turned to it, and after finishing the job, looked around for a place to lay the soldering iron. As the pieces with the rusty screw in them happened to be handy, I set the point of the soldering iron on the head of the screw and leaned the handle end against the wall. I did this simply to avoid burning anything with the iron. A short time afterward the iron was taken back to the stove. When I returned to the bench I thought I would have just one more try at the screw, and I discovered it came out quite easily. For a moment I was puzzled, but upon picking the screw up in my fingers I found it to be hot. Then I remembered having set the soldering iron on it. The next time I had a rusty screw to remove I applied heat to it, and the screw was easily taken out.—Contributed by W. S. Lockwood, Chicago.

### Suction Pump for Draining Crank Cases

An ordinary bicycle pump with the plunger valve reversed on the rod makes an excellent suction pump for draining automobile-engine crank cases. The closed upper end of the pump cylinder is cut off so that the oil may be poured out quickly. After the first charge the plunger is pushed down as far as it will go, displacing the oil into the upper part. This action is repeated until the pump is half full each time, and it takes only a short time to drain any case.—Contributed by Albert J. Hynd, Lakewood, O.

# Patterns for Cylinder Barrels

By JOSEPH A. SHELLY

There is no difficulty experienced in preparing the stock for turning small-cylinder barrels in halves when the stock is of sufficient thickness, but when the radius of the circle is in excess of the thickness of the lumber on hand, it becomes necessary to build up the halves. There are three ways of doing this, namely, by gluing up a solid block, stepping, and lagging.

In gluing up a solid block there are two methods in general use; one is to glue the pieces together parallel with the center line of separation, and the other, in strips. These are illustrated in Fig. 1. The strip method is generally considered the better of the two, as there is less liability of shrinking and warping.

The stepped form of construction is shown in Fig. 2. The filling-in pieces to close the ends are fitted in place and

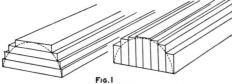

FIG. I
Two Ways of Making a Solid Piece by Gluing Several Boards or Planks Together

glued after the steps have been put together, the grain of all the pieces running lengthwise.

The staved barrel, Fig. 3, is used for small cylinders with thick walls. It is built on heads long enough for turning prints, but there must be considerable difference in the diameter between the two, otherwise the staves at the joint would be too thin to stand much hard usage. The opposite condition exists in Fig. 4. In this case there must not be too much difference in the diameters or it would leave very little thickness at the joint where the part is turned down for the prints, except where very thick stock is used. To obviate this, reinforcing pieces are sometimes glued to the inside ends of the joint staves, as shown in Fig. 5, or the barrel is built as shown in Fig. 6.

The joint staves in this case are made much thicker than the others. An excellent form of construction for large

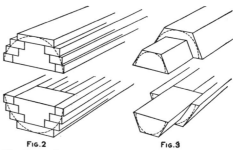

FIG. 2                    FIG. 3
The Stepped and Staved Forms of Construction Save the Material in the Center

cylinders is shown in Fig. 7. The prints are built up of staves first and these form the foundation for the barrel staves.

The first step in preparing to build a cylinder is to lay out a semicircle representing the print and barrel, as shown in Fig. 8. To the barrel diameter should be added enough to turn the pattern, say, $\frac{3}{32}$ in. all around. The outer circle should then be spaced off to suit the number of staves to be used. From two of the points stepped off on the outer circle, lines are drawn to the center. These lines should be drawn through and somewhat beyond the circle. A line tangent to the outside circle and connecting the two

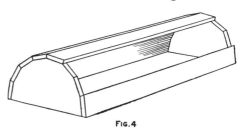

FIG. 4
A Larger-Size Barrel Where There is Not Much Difference in Diameters of Pattern and Print

radial lines is drawn to represent the outside of the stave. This line should intersect the radial lines at points equidistant from the center. The inside of the stave is drawn parallel with the outside and the points where this inside line intersects the radial lines fix the diameter of the circle for laying out the heads.

It is only necessary to lay out one

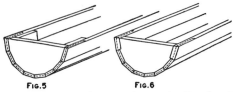

FIG.5　　　FIG.6

Where There is a Great Difference in Barrel and Print Diameters One of These Methods is Used

head for each diameter. Each one is planed up true on the surfaces and used as a template in marking the others. The staves should be made as close to size as possible on machine tools, the circular saw being used to cut them to the correct angle on the edges, but an allowance in width should be made for finishing them on the surface planer. With a good planer there should not be much necessity for fitting with a hand plane.

The molder always experiences more or less trouble in rapping and drawing patterns of this kind, unless some provision is made by the patternmaker for

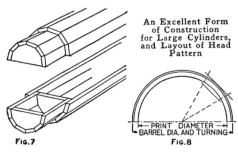

An Excellent Form of Construction for Large Cylinders, and Layout of Head Pattern

|←— PRINT　DIAMETER —→|
|←BARREL DIA. AND TURNING→|

FIG.7　　　FIG.8

doing so, as shown in Fig. 9. The bar fitted into the heads and flush with the joint runs the full length of the pattern, adding strength and making it unnecessary to have a straight board on which to build the first half, also providing the means for rapping and lifting.

One half of the pattern, starting at the top and working to the joint at each side, should be built up, then the joint should be planed up and dowel pins attached. The second half is built

up in the same manner, starting at the joint on each side and working to the top, but the bar in the second half should not be fitted until the pattern is taken apart; then it can be done easily.

It is a good plan to glue corner blocks inside of all staved work, particularly at the joint staves, where the glue is not apt to hold well on the end wood of the heads.

Heads are sometimes built up of segments, or framed, but for the general run of work the head sawn from a

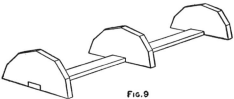

FIG.9

A Bar Mortised in the Heads for Rigidity and for Rapping the Pattern in the Mold

solid piece of plank answers the requirements and is easily and cheaply made.

---

## Surplus Oil Used in a Splash System

Certain models of automobiles had engines equipped with a splash-feed oiling system working in the manner shown in the sketch. A stamped metal plate, set in the case, formed the bottom of the oil reservoir. In this the connecting rods dipped at each downward stroke. At the sides were holes through which the oil overflowed into the space beneath when the level became normal or higher. A pump below returned the oil. It was found in some parts of the country that there was not depth enough of oil

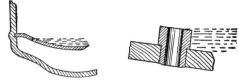

Raising the Oil Level in a Crank Case to Aid the Splash System on Hilly Roads

for the rough and severe usage which the cars received. To raise the oil level without procuring special parts was the problem that presented itself.

The difficulty was overcome in the following manner: The overflow holes were punched out larger, then pieces of brass were drilled out and turned to a shoulder. These were riveted and soldered in the holes. They projected above the plate ½ in., and consequently the oil had to rise that much higher before overflowing, so that the connecting rods picked up a greater quantity of oil at each dip; and their oiling was thus assured when the car was climbing a hill or passing over bumps.—Contributed by Donald A. Hampson, Middletown, New York.

## Homemade Clipper for Pruning Trees

Having some high branches to prune and being without a clipper used for such work, a pair of ordinary hand clip-

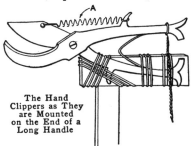

The Hand Clippers as They are Mounted on the End of a Long Handle

pers was rigged up on a wood arm that was mounted on a long handle. One handle of the clippers was lashed to the arm and a heavy cord attached to the other. An auxiliary spring, A, kept the lower jaw from sticking. The device worked well.—Contributed by James M. Kane, Doylestown, Pa.

## Making Loops on Wire Ends

Having to make loops on both ends of a large number of wires and the use for the wires requiring them to be of equal length and to have uniform-size eyes, I found the device illustrated to give very good satisfaction. The material used was piano wire, which, on account of its stiffness, is difficult to handle.

A piece of flat iron, ⅜ in. thick and 2 in. wide, was procured for the frame, as indicated by A. About 4 in. of each end was bent up at right

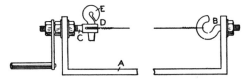

Making Loops of Uniform Size and of Equal Length on Very Stiff Piano Wire

angles, the length between the uprights being governed by the required distance between the loops on the wire, with allowance made for the swivel B and the head C. The head C was made from a piece of ½-in. rod, on one end of which a square blank nut was brazed, while the other was threaded for a sufficient length to allow for nuts and a handle, or crank. A slot was then sawed in the nut D along the axis of the body and at right angles to the hole in the nut. The pin E is tapered at the end for easy removal. When a loop has been formed, remove the pin E to release the wire, then place the loop on the swivel and proceed as before. A little practice will enable the operator to make uniform loops on very stiff wire. —Contributed by R. C. Price, Rapid City, S. D.

## Two Keys in One

Having use for two keys several times a day, I cut them in two about the middle and filed the ends of each, as shown at A. The two keys were then placed together, as shown at B, and riveted and soldered. The keys were thus easily found in the pocket,

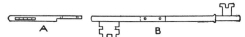

The Stems of Two Much-Used Door Keys Fastened Together for Convenience

and, in use, one was inserted in the lock while the other provided a means for turning it.—Contributed by J. J. Kolar, Maywood, Ill.

## Roller Ends on Steady-Rest Jaws

The jaws of the ordinary steady rest, used on an engine lathe, will often score and sometimes cut grooves in 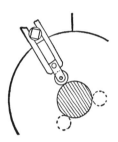 the shaft which is being machined. A very easy way to overcome this trouble is to attach a roller to each jaw end. This may be done by bolting or riveting sides, made of ¼-in. stock, to the jaws with projecting ends, between which a roller made of ¾-in. cold-rolled steel is pivoted. These will roll on the shaft and prevent the scoring.—Contributed by L. A. Bocksberger, Fort Wayne, Ind.

## Using Drills with Broken Shanks

Drills that have the small flattened end twisted off can be used successfully by making an extension socket  as shown. These sockets can be made from shanks of drills that have been broken. The broken drill shank is then ground to fit into the notch of the socket. One of these extensions for each size of drill socket makes a handy addition to the drill cabinet.—Contributed by V. S. Denison, Sandusky, Ohio.

## Ventilating a Cellar

In ventilating a basement or a cellar, the air admitted should be a little cooler than the air within. Warm air holds moisture and the cold air striking it causes a condensation of the moisture. If a cellar is opened on a warm day, the warm air entering and striking the colder air causes the moisture to settle on the walls in the form of a dew, which will be often seen running down in a stream. This makes the place damp, and consequently the contents will become moldy.

In airing a place of this kind, open the doors and windows at night when the air outside will be at the same or nearly the same temperature as that inclosed, and no dampness will be formed. Be sure to close the openings before the temperature begins to change in the early morning. The dampness in a cellar may be taken up with a little fresh lime placed in an open box.

## Machining Connecting-Rod Ends

Desiring to machine the large end of a small connecting rod, rather than file it into shape, I hit upon the following scheme of accomplishing the desired result on my lathe. The large end of the casting is represented by A in the sketch. It was desired to have it, when finished, as shown at B; that is, to have the split bearing in sleevelike form.

The casting was split, drilled and tapped from the bottom and the hole was bored to size. The sleevelike portions were roughed out with a hacksaw, leaving, in places, about ⅛ in. of metal oversize. The next step was to procure a piece of cold-rolled steel rod, C, of the same diameter as the hole in the bearing, which was centered in both ends and fitted with a rectangular block of steel. This block was provided with a hole, at D, to receive a small tool; the latter being located just far enough from the mandrel to cut the sleeve to the finished thickness. The face and inside edges of the tool were

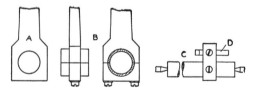

Shaping the Large End of a Connecting Rod into a Split Bearing with a Sleevelike Form

ground to a cutting angle, the holding block being tapped and fitted with set-screws, to engage the mandrel and the tool. The connecting rod was supported in the tool post, and the mandrel was run through the bearing while the work was fed against the cutter.

The cutting was rapid and perfectly smooth, and by using the take-up screws in the end, the bearing was made to run close to the mandrel, with just sufficient play to prevent chattering and yet to move freely.—Contributed by Harry F. Lowe, Washington, District of Columbia.

## Testing the Accuracy of Thermometer Readings

To determine the accuracy of the calibration on thermometers, or to ascertain whether the register marks along the side of the tube coincide with the height of the mercury column at the various temperatures, proceed as follows: Find the freezing point, zero on a centigrade or plus 32° on a Fahrenheit thermometer. This may be accomplished by filling a funnel, 5 in. in diameter at the top, with cracked ice and setting it in a milk bottle, or other receptacle, to catch the dripping water, then placing the thermometer in the ice, as shown, and allowing it to remain there about 12 minutes. The mercury level will then be at the freezing point, or the zero mark on a centigrade thermometer, and 32° for the Fahrenheit.

To find the boiling point, 100° C. or 212° F., procure a can which has a close-fitting cover and in the center of the latter make a hole to receive a cork of suitable size; then make a hole in the cork to fit the thermometer tube snugly. If the can cover fits so tightly that no steam will escape, make a small vent hole to release the excessive pressure and prevent a possible explosion. Fill the can about one-third full of water and place the cover and thermometer in position, making sure that the thermometer bulb does not touch the water. Set the can on a burner and when steam begins to escape, or in about 12 minutes, the mercury level will register 100° C. or 212° F., according to the thermometer being tested.

These two main points having been accurately marked, the remainder of

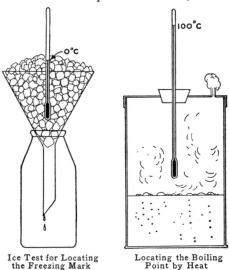

Ice Test for Locating the Freezing Mark    Locating the Boiling Point by Heat

the calibrations, or intermediate degrees, are tested by accurately spacing them off with a pair of dividers, to the necessary number of degrees between them, which should be 100 spaces on a centigrade and 180 on a Fahrenheit thermometer. All degrees above or below these points can be carried out by continuing with the same spacing.—Contributed by Russell E. Hollis, Chicago, Ill.

## Fastening an Anvil to a Block

The anvil is drilled through the central part of its stand, and the shanks of eyes are fitted in the hole from each side. Nuts are mortised in the anvil block and bolts placed in the eyes and

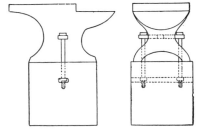

The Bolts, Passing through Eyes Attached to the Anvil, Hold It Securely to the Block

through the block to the nuts. If the anvil becomes loose a turn of the nuts will hold it rigidly.

## Cutting Holes for Ceiling Plates

The cutting of a hole in the ceiling plaster for the 3 or 4-in. ceiling plate is quite a task where the old method is employed. To overcome this difficulty I constructed a device for cutting these holes quickly. The ordinary ceiling plate was used as a cutter, the rim or edge being filed in saw-tooth fashion and then clamped on the end of a piece of 1-in. pipe, 10 in. long, by means of locknuts. A slot was cut in the side of the pipe at the point the square tapered end of a bit would reach while allowing the cutter end to project a trifle beyond the teeth filed in the plate edge. A screw was used in this slot to clamp the bit in place. The other end of the pipe was fitted with a reducer so that the square tapered end of a bit could be attached, as shown. This part was cut from a discarded bit. It only requires a few turns to remove the plaster to receive a ceiling plate.—Contributed by E. Hansen, Chicago.

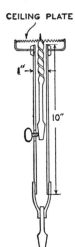

CEILING PLATE

1"

10"

## Spark-Plug Tester

A way to prevent getting a shock while testing out spark plugs is to provide an insulated handle to a device carrying two wires that will be made terminals by the contact plates A and B touching the spark plug and the engine head. The two wires are brought up through the insulation and the ends bent in close to each other, or the same as the terminal wires of the spark plug. Such a device is very handy to keep in the tool box or bag of an automobile or motorcycle.

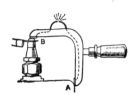

## Exterminating Water Bugs in Drains

In shops where dirty water is poured into sinks, or in kitchens, especially those of restaurants and lunch rooms, water bugs breed within the pipes. A way to kill all of these and at the same time kill all sewer-gas odors is to pour into the sinks small quantities of a solution of potassium permanganate. The chemical is secured from any druggist at a small price. Just a few grains for each 1 oz. of water will be sufficient. This weak solution is harmless, but should be kept from the hands, as it is liable to stain the skin. The solution should remain in the pipes for a little time before water is run in the sink.— Contributed by Loren Ward, Des Moines, Iowa.

## Outlet for a Range Boiler

The trouble and dirt caused by lifting the reservoir lining out of the kitchen range to empty it can be

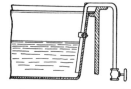

avoided by attaching a siphon outlet as shown. The permanent attachment will also make it unnecessary to raise the cover when water is taken out. The pipe is fastened to the reservoir with a clamp and a space for the pipe is cut out of the reservoir cover.— Contributed by J. V. Loeffler, Evansville, Ind.

## Irrigating with Drain Water from Kitchen Sink

Anyone living in the country or in a village can have the convenience of a drain from his kitchen by which all waste water may be carried out without the use of pails, and at the same time providing irrigation for the garden. The tank on our home place has a capacity of 3,000 gal. and supplies eight different faucets at convenient places on the grounds, and one in the kitchen. The drain from the kitchen sink consists of a ¾-in. pipe leading through the floor and into the earth to a depth of about 18 in., and from that end begins the irrigating device.

Old discarded tin fruit cans were procured, those of the 3-lb. size, and holes punched in the closed ends; the other ends, which had been cut out to remove the contents, were melted off. The cans were then placed end to end, as in laying drain tile. The water seeps through the holes in the cans and irrigates seven trees.—Contributed by Mrs. A. J. Cleveland, Slaton, Texas.

## A Steam Water Heater

A great many apartment buildings at the present time have no hot-water supply although they are steam-heated, making it necessary to heat all water by gas or other fuel, which is quite an expense to the occupant, to say nothing of the inconvenience. The following device, which is in use in an apartment, has proven very satisfactory, and its original cost has been saved almost every month in the gas bill.

The pipe leading from the main steam pipe to the radiator was taken apart and a tee inserted, with a side opening for a ¾-in. pipe. This tee was placed between the valve and the vertical pipe, so that steam could be obtained from the outlet with the radiator turned on or off. A ¾-in. iron pipe was run from the side outlet in the tee to within about 1 ft. of one end of the bathtub. A valve was placed in this pipe near the radiator and a piece of rubber hose, about 6 ft. long, was attached to the end nearest the tub. A balloon-shaped device, similar to the one shown, about 7 in. long and 3 in. in diameter, was made from some galvanized-iron wire and attached to the end of the hose. A cloth was wrapped around the outside of this wire device, so as to prevent the steam making an undesirable noise when it escaped into the water. The bathtub is first filled with water to the desired level, then the end of the hose is placed in the tub and the steam turned on.

A tub half full of water may be heated in from five to ten minutes under ordinary steam pressure.

At first some trouble was experi-

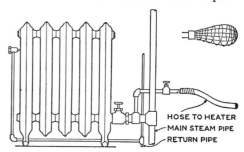

Connections for Attaching a Hose to the Radiator Steam Pipe for Heating Bath Water

enced in that the rubber hose broke near the end of the iron pipe, from repeated bending when its free end was put into and removed from the bathtub. This trouble was overcome by making a coil spring, with an inside diameter equal to the outside diameter of the hose and 6 or 7 in. long, and placing it outside the rubber hose where it was connected to the iron pipe, thus preventing an abrupt bend being made in the hose at this point.

A small box should be provided in which to place the end of the hose when not in use, so as to keep it clean.

## Homemade Trammels

An ordinary rule may be used for the bar with the trammel-point connections shown in the illustration. They are made of sheet steel of a size to correspond with the dimensions given. The holes are $\frac{5}{16}$ in. in diameter. An ordinary ¼-in. stove bolt is

The Bolt Clamps the Trammel to the Rule and Also Holds the Pencil in Place

used for the clamping device.—Contributed by J. A. Oesterle, Albany, New York.

❡When using a glass for a hot beverage, set it in another glass and it can be taken in the bare hand.

## Holding Conduit for Cutting

A very serviceable device for holding conduit or armored cable while cutting can be easily made by attach-

Two Pipe Straps Fastened to a Board over the Conduit Hold It Solidly While Cutting

ing two pipe straps of sufficient size over the part to be cut, as shown in the illustration, using a piece of wood for the base. The cut is made between the straps. The device is very handy, as it holds the cable solidly and can be carried anywhere work is to be done.—Contributed by R. G. Whipple, Chicago.

## Spigot for Use in a Barrel Side

Occasionally the closeness of metal hoops on a barrel near the ends prevents the insertion of a spigot as near the bottom as desired; and the barrel must be tilted to remove the contents remaining below the

spigot level. If the spigot shank projects some distance into the barrel the tilting will not remove all the contents. If, however, a fair-sized hole is drilled in the spigot shank at a point which will reach just inside the barrel, as shown, the operation of emptying the barrel will be greatly facilitated.

## Hardening Hacksaw Blade to Cut Tool Steel

Ordinary hacksaw blades are not intended for very hard steel and if it is desired to cut such steel, the blade should be hardened. In hardening these blades they would warp out of shape when brought to a cherry red, but by experimenting I find if a blade is bound flat on an old file and both heated together, the blade will be kept flat and the file will retain the heat while preparing to dip it.

The temper of the blade end should be drawn to prevent breaking. For extremely hard temper, heat to a cherry red and give the blade a mercury bath, but do not inhale the fumes, as they are poisonous. Saws or drills hardened in mercury will readily cut glass if moistened in turpentine. In using a hard blade do not press too hard, and run it slowly.

All steel instruments when heated to a red heat lose a portion of their carbon, which loss means a softening of the surface on the instrument. This loss is especially noticed in fine instruments, the more delicate ones being utterly ruined. To protect them from this loss, they should be covered with a layer of potash or other medium. This may be accomplished by heating slightly and rubbing them with soap. —Contributed by Dr. W. H. Albright, Bellevue, Ohio.

## Removing Stub End of a Broken Screw

Very often a screw is broken off in a piece of machinery. A common method of removing it is to drill a hole about $\frac{1}{8}$ in. smaller than the root diameter of the screw in the end, then drive in a square drift and twist it until the broken part comes out, using a wrench for greater leverage. This method is a good one and quickly accomplished, but it has one objection: the drift used must be tapered to start it and fill the

A Lever Used to Steady a Drift and to Keep It from Working Out

hole as it is driven. The taper is the cause of the trouble, as it makes the drift easily loosened in the hole, and, once loosened, it will slip up a little and cut out the hole instead of starting the screw. A straight drift cannot be used for the reasons mentioned. The way to make the tapered one effective is to keep it in the hole and to avoid wriggling at the top, which loosens the drift. To keep the drift in the hole is simple enough by using a bar, a piece of board or a lever of any kind on top of the drift, and in almost every case the broken screw will come out. The sketch shows a piece of board fulcrumed on a shaft or any support and acting to keep the drift in place while it is turned.

### An Oil-Hole Cleaner

The cleaner consists of a light frame, made of galvanized iron, to form bearings for a ¼-in. shaft, the whole being fastened to a light wood handle of any convenient length. The shaft has collars attached just outside of the frame, to prevent it from shifting endways when it is turning. A strong cord, A, is given two or more turns around the shaft. Then one end is passed through a screweye, B, on the handle and tied to the end of a coil spring, C, the other end of which is fastened to the handle. The other cord end passes through another screweye and runs the full length of the handle, being fastened to the handle. The spring used was taken from a discarded curtain roller.

The end of the shaft is split and the parts are turned outward. This will pick up waste and clean out any dirt or gummy oil. A pull on the cord will cause the shaft to revolve rapidly, and a backward motion is given by the spring when the cord is released.— Contributed by C. R. Van Keuren, Famoso, Cal.

❧Inspect all belts frequently and keep them in a condition to avoid accidents.

### A Brush Holder

A sheet of corrugated strawboard, rolled up with the corrugations on the outside and held with rubber bands,

The Corrugations in the Strawboard Keep the Brushes Straight and Absorb the Moisture

makes a good brush holder for water-color brushes. The ribs prevent the brushes from bending and becoming deformed. The porousness of the strawboard also assists in absorbing the moisture after the brushes are washed.

### Protecting Shade Trees from Destructive Insects

To prevent ants and other insects from crawling up and gradually injuring valuable shade trees, encircle the tree about 1 ft. above the ground with sticky fly paper. Carpet tacks may be used to fasten the paper in place, and where the edges lap, the blank margin should be trimmed away so as to make the circle sticky all the way around. Where spaces or crevices occur beneath the paper—as will be the case with a very rough tree—they should be stuffed with cotton. If this remedy is tried out for a week, the insects will desert the tree.—Contributed by Chas. K. Theobald, Vicksburg, Miss.

### A Garage-Key Holder

A small hasp is just the thing to attach to a garage or stable key if it is to be kept in the house. The hasp part is used, and the key is attached

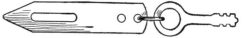

The Hasp Makes a Hanger for the Key and is Much Better Than a Stick of Wood

to it by using a split key ring.—Contributed by A. A. MacCready, E. Orange, N. J.

## A Pressure Regulator for Acetylene Gas

The pressure regulator shown is for use in connection with tanks having a high pressure of oxygen or acetylene.

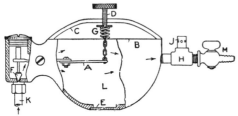

Pressure Regulator Constructed from a Discarded Carburetor for Delivering Gas to a Torch

It is constructed from a discarded carburetor. The float is removed and an arm, A, is attached in its place. A diaphragm, B, is soldered on top of the bowl to form a gas-tight joint. An arch, C, made of a flat piece of brass, is soldered at the edges, and a hole is drilled and tapped in the center, to receive a thumbscrew, D. A piece of brass is soldered over the hole E. A short piece of chain is fastened to the end of the arm A, and soldered to the center of the diaphragm B, allowing enough slack to let the valve F open $\frac{1}{64}$ in. The screw D compresses the spring G against the diaphragm B in making adjustment to obtain the desired pressure of gas to operate the torch. A ⅛-in. tee, H, is connected, as shown, and a safety valve, J, is turned into its side outlet.

In operation, the gas enters the pipe K, passing through the valve F into the chamber L and through the outlet M. When the set pressure is reached, the diaphragm B closes the valve F. When the torch is shut off, the valve will be entirely closed. If the regulator is well made, there will be only a slight variation in the pressure us d in the torch, regardless of the amount of pressure in the main supply tank.—Contributed by F. Elmer Wurzburger, Fairbury, Ill.

❧The arrangement of a belt, rope and cable transmission should be such that it may be easily guarded.

## To Prevent Hollow Porch Columns from Rotting

Hollow porch columns may be prevented from rotting at the bottom if two or three holes about ¾ in. in diameter are bored through the porch floor and the base of the column. This will allow the air to enter the inside of the column.

In building the column paint the inside with white lead and oil mixed thinly. The painting will prevent them from cracking open at the stave joints, as is often the case. If the column is finished, the painting can be done with a swab made of a piece of rag tied to the end of a stick long enough to reach halfway through the column.—Contributed by L. G. Burnand, Lyons, Iowa.

## Clamping Screw for Calipers

The locking device on the ordinary dividers or calipers not being satisfactory, I made a substitute, as shown in the sketch, that can be set quickly and will hold without slipping. It consists of a knurled nut with a part of it  threaded and slotted, similar to a draw-in chuck. A second knurled nut, with an internal tapering thread, closes the parts on the threads of the bolt, thus clamping it solidly.—Contributed by Chas. G. England, Washington, Pennsylvania.

## Duster Made of Hemp Rope

Procure a piece of 1-in. hemp rope, about 18 in. long, and bend it in the  center, then bind about 5 in. of the two parts together with a strong cord to make a handle. The remaining unbound part is loosened and combed out to form a brush. This makes a good duster for a shop bench.—Contributed by Samuel D. Laurie, Hannibal, N. Y.

## Paper Holder for a Paper Hanger's Pasting Table

Paper hangers have considerable trouble in keeping paper from curling and rolling when matching and cutting the lengths on the table. The illustration shows how a holder can be made for each end of the table. The holders are placed near the edge so that they can be operated with a finger. The holder A is cut to the dimensions shown from a piece of $\frac{1}{16}$-in. sheet steel. A piece of pipe, B, is fastened to a lever, C, which is loosely bolted to A and D. The pipe is weighted so that it will pull the holder down on the ends of the paper firmly. The bar C is hinged to the block D, which is fastened to the under side of the table

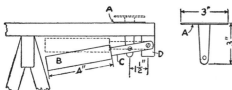

The Holder Grips the Ends of the Paper Lengths As They are Cut from the Roll

top. The device can be operated with one finger while pulling the strip of paper into place.—Contributed by J. V. Loeffler, Evansville, Ind.

## Boiler-Arch Forms Made of Metal

An excellent substitute for the wood arch supports in building an arch over a tubular or firebox boiler is a form made of old carriage tires. These can be procured cheaply from a carriage shop. Cut and bend them to the shape of the arch and turn each end out to make a rest to set on the side walls. These are placed 6 in. apart for the entire length of the boiler, and the bricks can be laid on them neatly. This saves

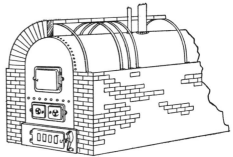

The Tire Metal is Easily Shaped and Makes a Better Arch Than Wood

burning out the forms, as is necessary when wooden supports are used.—Contributed by John F. Vidler, Portland, Ore.

## Pulling Truck Out of Mud

One of the best methods I have found for getting out of mud holes and slippery places with a motor truck is to carry a device like that illustrated. A piece of plank, 3 in. thick, 4 ft. long and as wide as the tire, is tapered at one end, and a notch is cut

The Pull of the Tire Chain will Draw the Plank beneath the Wheel

crosswise with the width at the end of the slope. The notch takes the tire chain, and when the power is applied, the chain draws the plank under the wheel. Iron bars are fastened across the plank underneath, to strengthen it. —Contributed by Harold A. Hawes, E. Weymouth, Mass.

## A High-Tension Switch

In order to make use of a battery and jump-spark coil for starting a gasoline engine equipped with a high-tension magneto, it is necessary to have some kind of a high-tension

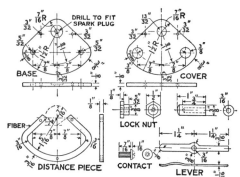

The Parts are Composed of Fiber and Brass Which are Well Insulated to Prevent Shocks

switch. The sketches show such a switch, which is absolutely shock-proof and at the same time very easily constructed.

Referring to the sketches, it will be seen that the base, distance piece, cover and handle are made of red fiber; the lever is of spring sheet brass; the lock nut, of hexagon brass bar, and the contacts are round-head machine screws. The only other material required is some $\frac{3}{32}$-in. copper rivets and two brass terminal nuts, such as are used on dry batteries.

After making the parts shown the contacts are put in place in the back where they are held by the terminal nuts. The base, distance piece and cover are then assembled and held in place with the rivets. The handle is put on the lever and held with sealing wax. To place the switch on the en-

gine, the terminal nuts on the spark plug are removed, the assembled body, with the lever in place, is put over the terminal screw and the lock nut put on and tightened up. All that now remains is to connect the cable from the magneto to one contact and the high-tension cable from the coil to the other.

To operate, throw the lever to the battery side and start the engine in the regular way. After the engine is up to speed, throw the lever over to the magneto side. To stop the engine throw the lever to the center position.

In testing the spark, move the lever over until there is about $\frac{1}{16}$ in. between the lever and the contact and turn the shaft over. If it is well adjusted, a spark will be seen through the observation holes in the cover.

With this switch in use it is impossible to injure the magneto by accidentally running the battery current through the magneto, and at the same time the battery is always available for starting or running in case of anything going wrong with the magneto. —Contributed by J. R. McCallum, Lansing, Mich.

## Feeding Moist Air to a Carburetor

Finding that the carburetor of the automobile I was driving gave better results in wet or damp weather, I made an attachment to feed moist air to it to produce the same results. A sleeve of fine wire netting, 4 in. long, was made to fit tightly over the auxiliary air intake, thus extending the intake about 2½ in. The screen was covered with an ordinary round lamp wick and the whole then covered with a sleeve of thin sheet iron, to hold the wick in place and to force the air to be drawn through the front opening.

The base and burner of an old lamp were procured and the base was filled with water and fastened to a bracket. The wick of this burner was attached to the wick of the sleeve. The wick in the lamp siphoned the water to the wick in the sleeve, thus keeping it damp all the time, and the air drawn into the auxiliary air intake must absorb a portion of it before entering the carburetor.

The wick in the lamp base can be raised out of the water in damp weather to get the same results. The evaporation of water is so small that it is only necessary to fill the lamp base once in about three months.

While this arrangement may not save any gasoline, the motor shows but little carbon deposits, while, with the usual method, I had to scrape carbon every three months.—Contributed by Walter Broeker, Chicago.

### Locking Bails Vertically on a Glue Pot

A very effective method of keeping the bails of the glue pot in an upright position is to bend the one on the inner glue receptacle square at the upper part and make a slight bend in the straight length to catch on the bail of the outer water can, as shown. This will prevent them both from falling down and from getting too hot to handle.

### Preventing Ants from Entering Lunch Pail

Being troubled with ants getting into my lunch, I provided a hanger to keep them out. This hanger, as illustrated, consists of a can having a wire run through it and oil placed on the inside. The wire is soldered where it passes through the can bottom. It is simple to make and is an absolute protection for the lunch. —Contributed by C. R. Van Keuren, Famoso, Cal.

### Homemade Scraper

An excellent scraper for rough work may be made from a bench-plane iron in the following manner: Procure a

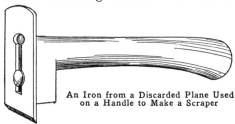

An Iron from a Discarded Plane Used on a Handle to Make a Scraper

piece of oak or any good hard wood, about 1½ in. thick, 3½ in. wide and 10 in. long, and shape it as shown. The long portion should be rounded and smoothed with sandpaper to form a handle for the scraper. Bore a hole for a ⅜-in. bolt at the place indicated in the sketch. The plane iron is fastened to the handle with a bolt.—Contributed by L. G. Burnand, Lyons, Iowa.

### Foundation for Soft Ground

A contractor secured a job of building a one-story factory building on some filled-in land that formerly was flooded once each year. The filling consisted of refuse, such as ashes, bricks, etc., about 12 ft. deep. To procure a solid foundation a trench was dug,

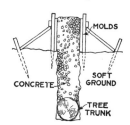

a little deeper than required, and trunks of trees, from 12 to 14 in. in diameter, were laid in the bottom. The concrete wall was made on top of the tree trunks. If, for any reason, a part of the ground gave way, the tree trunk would span the space and hold the weight, thus causing no uneven settling of the building.—Contributed by Joe V. Romig, Allentown, Pa.

⁋When a screwdriver slips from the screw slot, dip it in fine emery and it will hold.

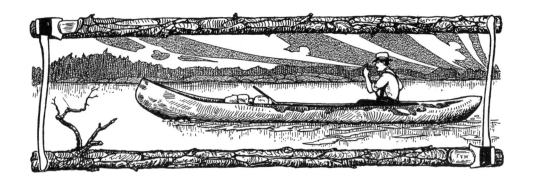

# How to Make a Log Canoe

### By G. O. SHIELDS

Persons traveling in the wilds often need boats to carry them and their outfits. The folding canvas canoe is popular and useful for such purposes, but that adds to the burden of the journey and can be eliminated if the traveler knows how, and if he travels in a timbered country.

Anyone who is handy with an ax can in two days fell a tree and dig out a canoe large enough to carry two men and a 30-days' supply of food, clothing, blankets, arms, ammunition, etc. In other cases a canoe is very handy where a camp is located near a lake or stream, and if campers only knew how easy it is to make a log canoe, more of them would be built and used. To make such a canoe means some hard work, but that is good for any person, especially those who have been shut up in an office.

The canoe illustrated was made at a camp among some lakes in Canada. Most of the forests in the region had been killed by fire, but fortunately there was a small patch of green spruce at the upper end of the upper lake where a few good-sized green trees were to be found. These were looked over the second day after arriving, and a tree, 26 in. in diameter at the butt, was picked out, which was straight as an arrow and free from branches up to about 30 ft. The next morning this tree was cut down and a log, 16 ft. long, cut off from the butt end. One side of the log was hewed off, and a flat, smooth surface, 16 in. wide, was made for the bottom. Be-

ginning about 2 ft. from each end, the log was rounded off from the bottom surface to the bark on the opposite side. This gave the curves for the bow and stern of the canoe.

The log was then turned over, and the bark was trimmed off on each side to a line that would give the canoe a depth of 16 in. The mark was made with a line dusted with charcoal, and the wood was notched down to it. This was a more serious undertaking than that of hewing and facing the bottom, for it meant the removal of a larger quantity of wood. About 2 ft. of solid timber was left at each end of the log, for bulkheads. This gave an open deckway of 12 ft. The notches were cut about 2 ft. apart, from the top of the log down to the charcoal line on the sides. When these notches were all sunk, the next thing was to split out the surplus wood. For this purpose a number of wedges were made from a small dead spruce, then an ax was driven into the end of each block, at intervals, from the top to the bottom, until the block started to split slightly, then a wedge was placed on each side of the block and driven in carefully with the poles of the axes. The blocks were easily removed in this manner.

With the entire top portion of the log removed, the excavating and removing of the wood from what was to be the interior of the canoe was begun. This required careful work, to prevent cutting through the shell and causing the canoe to leak. The axes were used

Removing the Bark from the Part to be Used for the Bottom

The Log is Lined and the Ends Left Partially Solid for Bulkheads

Notches are Cut in Log Down to the Line, Then the Wood is Split Out

The Canoe, being Light, is Easily Taken across Land to Another Lake

to remove most of the wood, but occasionally an adz came in handy for removing some pieces for close work. The surplus wood was gradually removed until the sides were thinned down to ¾ in. and the bottom to 1½ inch.

The thickness of each side and of the bottom was gauged with an awl having a file mark on it. This was driven in here and there from the outside, until the mark came flush with the surface. If the point showed through the inside, it indicated the proper thickness. It was an easy matter to plug these holes so that they would not leak. The inside as well as the outside was dressed with a jack plane. Three dry sticks, cut a little longer than the width of the boat, were inserted at intervals to spring out the sides of the canoe. When in place, a 20-penny nail was driven through the gunwale and into the end of each stick on both sides. These sticks prevented the wood from warping inward as the timber seasoned. A paddle was made from a dead pine, 6 in. in diameter.

### Attaching a Screen-Door Hook

A hook placed on a door casing for the screen door with the screweye in a horizontal position is likely to drop in

the way of the door and hold it open. A simple remedy for this is to turn the screweye until it stands in an almost perpendicular position. This insures a free swing of the hook in fastening as shown, but prevents it from turning over into the way of the door.—Contributed by F. R. Ritchie, Akron, Ohio.

### Starter for a Crosscut Saw

Starting a crosscut saw in the grain of wood is a difficult thing, and if accurate work is wanted, a starter should be provided. A very good starter, and one that will hold the saw at true right angles to the piece to be sawn, is shown in the sketch. It consists of a piece of

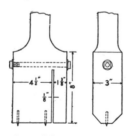

wood, 3 in. thick, 6 in. wide and about 1½ ft. long. A saw cut is made in one end, located as shown. The cut should be a little deeper than the widest part of the saw. The other end of the wood is shaped into a handle. A bolt is placed through the wood above the slot to prevent splitting. Two spurs are fastened into the end as shown.

In use, the saw is placed accurately on the line, the guide slipped over the saw back, and the spurs are pressed into the wood. It is impossible to make a slanting cut or for the saw to slip from the line.—Contributed by J. L. Bayley, Ione, Wash.

### Homemade Prest-O-Lite Tank Key

If the key is lost from a prest-o-lite tank one can be easily shaped from a cotter, as shown in the sketch. The eye of the cotter is shaped square by driving it on  a square-pointed tool. The spreading end is fitted with a small piece of wood for a handle.—Contributed by H. M. Smith, Douglasville, Ga.

### A Mottled Surface on Casehardened Articles

When casehardening with cyanide, a very pretty mottled effect can be produced by heating the piece, or pieces, to a bright red and then dropping them, one at a time, into water flowing at a good rate. The air bubbles give the effect. The bubbles can be made in the water by using an air hose, opening in the bottom of the vessel.

## Removing a Gummed Connection on a Bottle-Capping Machine

While endeavoring to remove a heavy brass connection on a bottle-capping machine, I found it so tightly gummed that it resisted all efforts to remove it with a large wrench. To start it with a chisel or hammer would have ruined the connection, and I tried heat, but having no blowtorch handy I poured a very strong and fresh lye solution in a can drawn up over the connection. In addition to expanding the metal, the lye worked its way in and acted as a dissolvent on the gummed deposit in the threads, so that the part was finally removed without defacing it.—Contributed by James M. Kane, Doylestown, Pa.

## Cover for an Electrical Lever Switch

The closing of an electrical lever switch at night or in a dark place is apt to give one a shock which may be

very dangerous at times, if the handle is missed and the open contacts touched with the bare hand. I covered my lever switch, as shown, and it is now impossible to touch any part of it except the handle.—Contributed by George M. Crawley, Jr., Newark, N. J.

## Producing a Second Crop of Strawberries

After strawberries have finished bearing or when nearing the end of the bearing period, they can be induced to produce a second crop in the following manner: Provide a metal ring, 1 ft. in diameter and about 5 in. high, for each hill. The ring can be made of stovepipe iron, and if well painted, will last a long time. The ring is placed over the hill and water is poured in to fill it. To water the plants without the ring will not produce results.—Contributed by J. W. Banholster, Gresham, Ore.

## A Spring Whiffletree for a One-Horse Vehicle

A whiffletree that will relieve a horse's shoulder of jerks and sudden jars when drawing a load is shown in

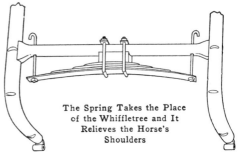

The Spring Takes the Place of the Whiffletree and It Relieves the Horse's Shoulders

the sketch. It is easily made of an old wagon spring and is fastened back of the crossbar of the shafts. Two rods, with ends formed into hooks for the traces, are run through holes in the crossbar and made fast to the spring. — Contributed by Abner B. Shaw, N. Dartmouth, Mass.

## Cutting Off Small Screws

Several hundred fillister-head screws of a special length were wanted quickly, and having on hand a quantity of screws, ⅛ in. longer, it was desired to make use of

them. To handle these small screws did not appear an easy matter, but it was made so with the use of the holder shown. A ⅝-in. rod was drilled out at one end to ⅜ in. in diameter, then a collar of ⅜-in. stock was made to slip in it freely, and a hole drilled in it centrally for the screws. Each screw was inserted in the collar and the collar dropped into the hole of the rod with the screw end projecting. It was now easy to grind the end off level with the collar end.—Contributed by Donald A. Hampson, Middletown, N. Y.

❧Equal parts of raw linseed oil and vinegar, thoroughly mixed, make a good restorer for linoleum.

## An Indicating Gasoline-Tank Gauge

The gauge shown in cross section consists of a vertical shaft, A, which is free to turn and has a needle, or indicator, mounted on its upper end that moves over a graduated scale, giving a direct reading in gallons. The movement of the vertical shaft is controlled by the height of the liquid by means of a float. The float is made from a piece of cork, mounted on a thin piece of sheet brass, shown at B. It is given a rotary motion by means of two small rods, C, bent into the form of a spiral of a little over one turn and passing through the two slightly oblong holes in the sheet of brass. This rotary motion of the float is transmitted to the vertical shaft by means of a piece of steel wire soldered across the center opening in the sheet of brass and passing through the slot D in the vertical shaft.

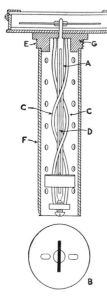

It must be borne in mind that the float and all parts that go inside the tank must be so dimensioned that they will pass through the opening in the tank. The opening might be provided with a threaded collar, soldered or brazed to it, so that the head of the gauge may be threaded as shown at E, to permit its being easily removed for repairs or inspection. The case in which the indicator or needle is mounted has a glass cover. The pasteboard scale is fastened in the bottom of this case by means of some shellac, or glue, and afterward marked.

A tube, F, is fastened to the piece G, to prevent sudden surges of the liquid in the tank from damaging the device. This tube, of course, should have numerous perforations in the side, so that the liquid may rise and fall freely within it.

After the device is completed and placed in the tank, it is calibrated as follows: Pour measured quantities of liquid into the tank and proceed to mark the position of the pointer on its scale for the various quantities of the liquid.

---

## A Split Hollow Mill

After I had made a set of 24 brass castings, as shown in Fig. 1, my customer desired a change which consisted in cutting off the shoulder, at the point A, ⅛ in., to make the round part longer. To make this change conveniently without removing the gate, a split hollow mill was made in the following manner: A piece of brass rod, ⅝ in. in diameter and 3 in. long, was procured, and a ¼-in. hole drilled centrally through it. Then the hole was enlarged in one end with a ⅜-in. drill for a length of 2⅜ in., and the end with the ¼-in. hole was tapered on the outside for 1 in. in length.

After these operations the piece was cut through on the dotted lines from B to C and D to C, as shown in Fig. 2. On one face of the remaining half two $\frac{1}{16}$-in. pins were fastened so that they projected ⅛ in. A steel blade for a

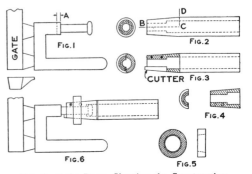

Details of the Parts, Showing the Construction of a Mill for a Special Work

cutter, having the thickness of the metal removed by the saw cut, was soldered to the opposite face, as shown in Fig. 3. The part removed, Fig. 4, was put back in place and held there firmly by means of a ring, Fig. 5. Two holes were drilled in this piece, of such size as to permit the pins to slip into them freely. The mill as it is used is shown in Fig. 6.—Contributed by Stephen Bona, Union City, Conn.

## Combination Drift and Hammer

The tool illustrated takes the place of a drift and hammer, and the combination can also be used as a center punch. The drift is forged from tool steel, and the shank is turned to fit loosely in a hole bored in the handle, which is also made of steel and has a ball formed on the end. A small collar is shrunk on the shank end, the outside diameter fitting the hole in the handle snugly, and another collar is pinned in the hole, at the handle end, with its inside diameter snugly fitting the shank. The hole in the handle should be bored out with a bottoming tool to make a flat bottom. The end

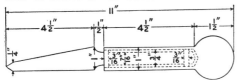

The Workman Loses No Time with the Combination Drift and Hammer, As They are Always Together

of the sloping part can be pointed for use as a center punch.

To improve the appearance, the ball can be polished and the straight part knurled. The end of the shank in the handle should be hardened to prevent its being burred over. A smart blow of the handle will remove a drill tightly fitting the socket. It only requires one hand to drive the drift, while the drill can be held in the other. —Contributed by V. S. Denison, Sandusky, Ohio.

## An Adjustable Spring Threading Tool

The threading tool illustrated is especially constructed for fine work, as it will not "dig" in and spoil the thread. It is made of tool steel throughout.

The cutter holder A is a bolt having

a conical head, which serves the two purposes of holding the cutter and of permitting adjustment. The block B, in which the cutter holder is fitted, has a groove in its curved upper part

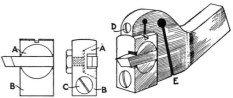

A Spring and Adjustable Lathe Threading Tool for Fine Tool-Room Work

to admit a clamping projection on the shank. The block revolves on the screw C, thus making it possible to adjust the cutter vertically, and is clamped when set with the screw D. The slot E makes a spring of the metal at the upper end, which will prevent the cutting tool from digging into the work.—Contributed by J. W. Eagan, Syracuse, N. Y.

## Lock for a Finger-Ring Case

It is a very easy matter for a thief acting as a prospective customer to take a ring out of the display tray without being seen. The illustration shows a safety device to prevent such a theft. From all appearances the ring case is the ordinary kind, but a wire slide is provided for each row of rings and a hook for each ring is fastened to the wire slide. When the wire is pushed in at the end of the case all rings are locked in their receptacles. The ends of the wires may be concealed so that a quick movement of

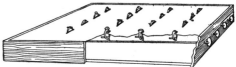

Each Ring is Locked in Its Place and cannot be Removed without being Released

the hand will release a ring without the customer noticing it.—Contributed by Francis Chetlain, Chicago.

⁋If dry cells run out quickly, examine the wiring system for a short circuit.

## Tape Holder for Electricians

A piece of wire, bent as shown in the sketch, makes a handy tape holder for electricians and linemen.

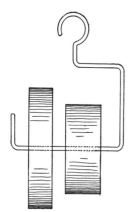

The tape is placed on the large hook and the small hook caught into a belt loop, or other convenient place. Different widths of tape can be carried on one holder.—Contributed by Patterson Merrill, Chicago, Ill.

## Remedy for Sticky Church Pews

Sticky church pews are caused by bad atmosphere, due to poor ventilation, more than to the character of the varnish, as a cheap varnish is usually, though not always, a quick and hard drier. Fish oil in the varnish, or resin oil, will cause stickiness. Varnishing over greasy seats is another cause. Apply two thin coats of brown shellac varnish where the original coating has failed to dry hard and ventilate the room well and often.

## Cutting a Left-Hand Thread with a Right-Hand Tap

When it is necessary to cut a left-hand thread and no die is at hand, a very good thread can be made with a right-hand tap in the following manner: Cut a notch in a piece of metal to admit one of the flutes in the tap, as shown at A, then procure a blank nut that will receive the rod to be threaded snugly and cut a slot in one of its sides

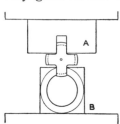

to admit the opposite flute, as shown at B. The threads on the flute should extend in the nut for their full depth. Slip the rod, or bolt, to be threaded in the nut the full depth, then draw the vise jaws together, to press the threads of the tap lightly into the metal, and turn the bolt to the left, at the same time giving it a slight downward pressure to start it in the proper pitch. After a few turns, the pressure is not necessary. The feed on the vise jaws is continued until a full thread is cut.—Contributed by F. A. Dowler, Lawrence, Kan.

## A Small Fire Extinguisher

Having need on several occasions for a small fire extinguisher for my laboratory, I devised an extinguisher which costs very little and is easy to make. An old bicycle pump, the handle and plunger of which were discarded, was used as the body of the extinguisher. The hole A, through which the plunger passed, was stopped with sealing wax. The small bottle B,

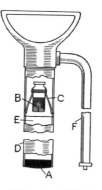

which is held in position by two small steel springs, C, made fast to the bottle with a small wire, is half filled with concentrated sulphuric acid. The pump barrel D is filled with a strong solution of baking soda, E. When the pump is inverted the acid acts on the soda solution, thereby forcing a stream of fluid through the tube F with considerable force. At one trial I found that the liquid was thrown 20 ft. The extinguisher contains enough fluid to put out any small-sized fire.—Contributed by Ellis S. Middleton, Washington, D. C.

❊Clean a dirty crack of a casting with a piece of caustic, and a weld can be made at once. Be sure to handle the caustic with care.

## Pneumatic Motor-Driven Flue Cutter

The cutting of flues in a great many small and moderately equipped shops is often an expensive job. The limited number of such jobs undertaken would, as a rule, not warrant the purchase of special equipment for this purpose and, therefore, the work is performed with hand tools, which, in holding irons, is a cheap and efficient source of power in any shop having compressed-air facilities. As the device is light and portable, it can be moved close to the job and thus eliminate a great deal of extra work in handling the flues. It is also convenient when it is necessary to cut flues of varying lengths for irregular flue sheets. The cutter can be used on

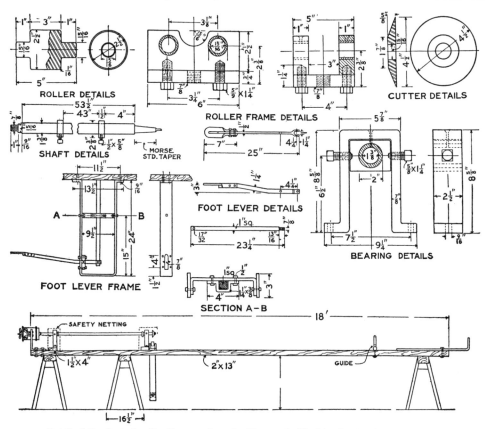

Detail of the Parts for the Construction of a Homemade Machine for Cutting Flues, Pipe or Any Light Tubing, the Power being Furnished by a Pneumatic Motor

most cases, is uneconomical from the viewpoint of both the shop owner and the customer.

The sketch is descriptive of a simple flue cutter, the parts of which are easily and cheaply made in any shop. The power is furnished by a pneumatic motor of almost any kind, the tool-shank recess slipping over one end of the cutter shaft turned to take it. The motor, when secured by suitable-angle pipe and almost all kinds of other light tubing.—Contributed by F. W. Bently, Milwaukee, Wis.

## Homemade Paper Punch

The need of a special paper punch of heavy construction brought about the making of the one shown in the sketch. It consists of a solid piece of steel, a sheet-metal handle and a steel punch. The solid piece of steel is slotted at one end to admit the thickness of the paper or cardboard, and a hole is drilled through the metal at

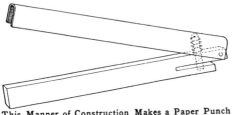

This Manner of Construction Makes a Paper Punch That will Stand Hard Usage

right angles to the slot. A tool-steel rod, snugly fitting the hole, is hardened and ground sloping on the end to be used for cutting, and the opposite end is made round.

A piece of sheet steel is bent in a V-shape and hinged to the slotted end of the solid steel, as shown. Before hardening the steel punch a small hole is drilled near the round end. A small coil spring is then slipped over the punch and one end is fastened in the hole. Pressure on the handle drives the steel punch through the slot and the paper inserted in it, and upon release of the pressure the spring draws it back together with the handle.—Contributed by Victor Arkin, Chicago.

## Noncalking and Water-Tight Joint in Wood-Stave Tanks

A good way to insure an absolutely water-tight fit between the edges of two boards in constructing a water tank or vat is as follows: Procure a round piece of iron, about half the width of the stave boards in diameter and about 6 in. long. Lay the iron on the board edge in the center and drive it into the wood to make a depression. Make this depression for the full length of the board, as shown in the cross section A. Plane off the raised portions to the level of the bottom in the depression. When two boards thus

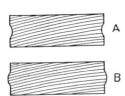

treated are placed edge to edge and drawn up with bolts, an absolutely water-tight joint is made without calking of any kind. The moisture will cause the compressed wood in the center to swell, as shown at B, and completely close the joint.—Contributed by J. G. North, Mountain View, Cal.

## An Adjustable Taper Gauge

The illustration shows a design of an adjustable taper gauge which is handy within its limits for reproducing taper pins, lathe centers, arbors, collets, and other tapered work of which duplicate pieces are required. The body A, which is made from a piece of tool steel, finished to $\frac{9}{16}$ in. in diameter, is $3\frac{1}{4}$ in. long and knurled

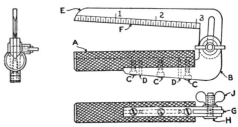

The Gauge can be Set for Any Taper, and Aids in Making a Perfect Fit

for its entire length. A V-slot, 90-deg. included angle, is milled lengthwise in the body A, and a flat place is finished for the piece B, which is held to the body by screws, C, and dowel pins, D.

The blade E is a piece of flat ground stock, $\frac{3}{32}$ in. thick and finished to the desired shape. The under side, at F, is beveled on both sides to $\frac{1}{32}$ in. in thickness at the edge, and is graduated its entire length, thus making it convenient in measuring the length of the taper. The end of the blade E, containing the elongated opening, is fitted in the slot G milled in the piece B, and is held in any desired position by the clamp screw H and wing nut J. With the use of this gauge, the cut-and-try method of fitting to a taper hole is eliminated, as the slightest error can be detected by holding the gauge to the light. — Contributed by E. P Fickes, Dayton, Ohio.

## Ridding a Pantry of Ants

To rid the pantry of a swarm of ants, a neighbor filled a sponge with sugar and placed it on a shelf among the sweet stuffs. When the holes in the sponge became full of ants, the sponge was thrown into a pan of boiling water, and the ants were soon exterminated.

No doubt other insects, not too large to enter the holes in a sponge, could be exterminated in the same way, providing the sponge were soaked with something they like.—Contributed by Joseph Patterson, Detroit, Mich.

## To Prevent Unlawful Use of a Fire Escape

To prevent the students of a school from stealing out by means of the fire escape a novel scheme was applied. Some tar was procured from a local gas company, and the railings and stairway were painted with it. The result was that the students after descending presented such an appearance that stealing out was not tried a second time. The tar remained in a moist condition quite a while and acted as an excellent preservative for the metal without preventing the use of the escape in case of an emergency.—Contributed by Geo. W. Gering, Annapolis, Md.

## Locking a Nut with a Wrench

The lock nut on the adjusting screw in the end of the exhaust-valve lever on a 100-hp. gas engine broke so that the  screw worked loose and turned out far enough to make the timing of the valve too late. The screw was put back in place, a wrench was put on the head and the handle bound to the lever with copper wire. In this way the run was finished without a shutdown.—Contributed by Earl Pagett, Coffeyville, Kan.

## Tapping Wing Nuts

In tapping wing nuts, provide a holder as follows: Procure a square or hexagon nut having a hole $\frac{1}{16}$ or $\frac{1}{8}$ in. larger than the outside diameter of the wing-nut body. Saw the nut in two and use it in the vise jaws as shown.—Contributed by John P. Kolar, Ithaca, N. Y.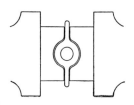

## Removing Tire Valve with a Cotter

 Where a valve cap is lost on a pneumatic tire the valve may be easily removed by the use of a small cotter. The cotter is placed in the valve, as shown, and turned with the fingers. In case of a tightly fitting valve, insert a nail in the eye of the cotter for a handle. —Contributed by M. B. Schweiger, Kansas City, Mo.

## A Box to Hold Powders

The mechanic's receptacle for holding any one of the powders, like emery or borax, that are occasionally used by him consists of a small pasteboard or metal box. I find one of the handiest receptacles for any powder is a tin can, with close-fitting cover, prepared as follows: A V-shaped notch is cut in the cover, and one in the can, in opposite directions. A slight turn of the cover makes an opening which can be increased in size up to the limit of the cuts. When not in use, the opening is easily closed by turning the cover.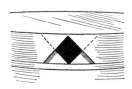

¶A pair of canvas gloves on the hands is better than a rag for washing a vehicle, as difficult parts and spokes may be easily reached.

## Safety Covering for Bevel Gears

Bevel gears are the most dangerous, because on account of their shape they are more difficult to protect. They are

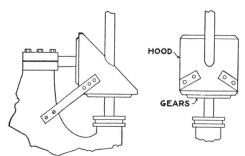

A Hood of Sheet Metal, Covering Bevel Gears on a Machine, to Protect the Workman

especially hard to safeguard where used on a shaft that extends both ways from the horizontal gear. The sketch is descriptive of a hood for covering such gears. The hood consists of a cylindrical piece of sheet metal, cut at an angle of 45 deg. at both ends so as to present a triangular form. The hole for the shaft should be so large that the shaft cannot touch the hood; the latter being anchored with supports which are shaped to suit the conditions.

## Drawing-Paper Holder and Cutter

The illustration shows a device that I am using in my drafting room for holding and cutting drawing paper. The paper used is 36 in. wide. The small rolls of the device are about 3 in. in diameter and 36 in. long. A piece

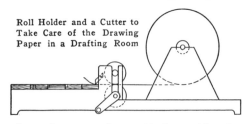

Roll Holder and a Cutter to Take Care of the Drawing Paper in a Drafting Room

of sandpaper, about 12 in. wide, is glued around each end of the lower roll and one piece around the center of the upper one. The weight of the upper roll keeps the paper in firm contact with the lower roll, which is

turned by means of a crank at the end. The end of the paper feeds out on the cutting board where a hardwood flapper is provided for the paper to pass under and which serves as a cutting edge.—Contributed by C. L. Orcutt, Akron, Ohio.

## Homemade Automobile Horn

A simple automobile horn that can be easily made and will give good results is shown in the sketch. The horn part is cut from sheet metal, and when complete, it should be about 8 in. long, 2 in. in diameter at the small end and 3 in. at the large end. Make a notched wheel from hard wood, about ¾ in. thick and 1½ in. in diameter. Holes are punched through the metal of the horn near the small end, and a piece of wire is run through them for an axle. The notched wheel is fastened to the wire in the horn. The end of the wire on one side is formed into a crank.

A strip of thin wood, ½ in. wide, is

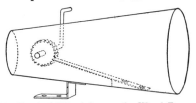

The Notched Wheel Causes the Wood Tongue to Vibrate and Produce a Loud Tone

fastened in the horn in such a position that its free end will touch the notched edge of the wheel. To prevent the axle from slipping endways, a washer is fastened to it on each side of the horn, or a little lump of solder will do. A quick turn of the crank will produce a loud sound, similar to that of an automobile horn. A bracket is fastened to the outside to provide a means of attaching it at a convenient place on the automobile.

❡Pneumatic tires should be large enough for the vehicle and for the load they are to carry. It is better to use tires that are over-size than those that are too small.

# Pattern for a Cored Piston

By J. A. SHELLEY

The castings for hollow, or cored, pistons do not vary much in design, but there is enough difference in the means used in building them to claim the attention of every one interested in patternmaking.

The best means is, of course, the use of a properly made pattern and core box, and these will be first considered in the construction of a standard pattern and core box for a 24-in. piston, shown in the illustration.

The constructive features of this pattern are shown in the sectional layout. The outside, or rim, is built of segments with the top and bottom heads recessed into it. These heads should be made of strips, 3 or 4 in. wide, with a space of about $\frac{1}{16}$ in. between them. They should be connected by a good strong piece, running across the spaces. This is to stiffen the pattern and provide a foundation for the rapping and the lifting plates.

The strips forming the heads should be first sawed to the proper diameter and then glued together with a $\frac{1}{16}$-in. piece between each strip, at the ends. When the glue has dried, plane one side, or surface, of each head perfectly true, then true up a faceplate of suitable size, and fasten one of the heads to it with screws. Rough-turn the edge of this head and fit the segment course No. 1 around it, then fasten with nails and glue. Face this off and apply course No. 2. This course should cover No. 1 and lap over on the head the same distance. Courses No. 3 and 4 are next applied, but before the course No. 5 is put on insert a stiffening piece and plane it off flush with course No. 4. The course No. 5 is then put in place, and a recess is turned to receive the bottom head. The head is cut on a band saw, to fit the recess, and then fastened with screws, or nails and glue.

Two prints will be required to carry the center core, one straight, on the

nowel, and the other tapered, on the cope side. The prints for carrying the compartment cores should be placed

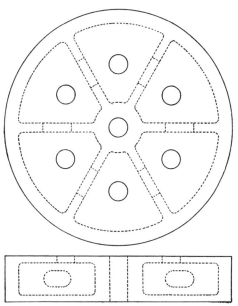

Layout for a Large Cored Piston from Which a Pattern is to be Constructed

on the cope side and need not be over $\frac{1}{2}$ in. in height. Hanging these cores in the cope does away with the necessity of using chaplets and enables the molder to vent these cores through the top of the mold. This makes a very substantial pattern which will stand a lot of hard usage.

Where only two or three castings are required, a pattern of much cheaper construction will answer just as well. In making a cheaper pattern, the heads should be constructed the same as for the standard pattern and securely nailed to three pieces, to keep them the right distance apart. The outside, or rim, of the pattern is made of narrow pieces of $\frac{7}{8}$-in. material, nailed to the heads. These pieces should be cut the exact length, to correspond with the depth of the pattern, but in nailing them in place, it is not necessary to be careful about the joints between the pieces. A little truing up with the block plane may be necessary to finish, but if the heads have been carefully laid out and sawn, and the strips are

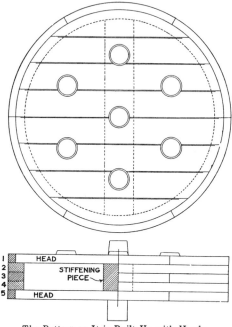

The Pattern as It is Built Up with Heads and Segments for the Rim

parallel and of equal thickness, the usual allowance for machining should be enough to correct any slight inaccuracies in the pattern. The prints for carrying the center core are used on this pattern, but those for carrying the compartment cores are not used, the molder locating and setting the cores in place by measurement.

The core boxes for both patterns are substantially the same, the only difference being in the length of the pipe-tap core where it cuts through the cope. This difference is due to the fact that one pattern has prints to carry the cores and the other not. The compartment box takes in a whole section and has half of the dividing ribs in each side. These dividing ribs are made in halves, the parting being through the center of the openings connecting the compartments. The bottom halves may be fast in the box, but the top halves must be loose so that the core can be taken out. A

point to bear in mind in making these boxes is to make the distance somewhat short in spacing off from the center of one rib to the center of the next, otherwise the molder will be obliged to file the ends of the cores to get them in place.

### Drilling Holes in Wood with Nails

A number of small holes of special size had to be drilled in some thin strips of hard wood, but drills of the proper size were not at hand, nor could they be obtained quickly. A way of making the holes with nails was tried out with good results in the following manner. The heads of the nails were cut off; the ends were flattened and pointed slightly as on a flat drill, and the nails were then used in the same manner. They did the work nicely, as the material was not over $\frac{1}{8}$ in. thick, but not so quickly as a drill.

Another time small holes were required in a set of lead-composition letters, to fasten them on wood patterns. The letters were only $\frac{1}{4}$ in. high, and consequently the body was narrow. Small nails, as described, were used to drill these holes.

### A Trapdoor Handle

Wishing to have a handle for a trapdoor that would not be above the floor level, I made one as shown in the sketch. A $\frac{3}{4}$-in. hole was bored, about $\frac{1}{8}$ in. deep, in the door where the handle was to be placed. In the center of  this hole another was bored, large enough to permit a chain, 5 in. long, to slip in it. On the upper side a button, such as used on uniforms, was secured to the chain end, and on the under side a weight was hung. The door is easily drawn up by lifting the button and grasping the chain.—Contributed by Wm. Trilling, Chicago.

## Cooling Air Entering Window Exposed to Sun's Rays

Many shops and factories have windows exposed to the sun's rays and the bricks on that side of the building become heated during the day and in turn heat the entering air, raising the temperature several degrees. A way to cool the bricks is to run along the tops of the windows a water pipe having small perforations made at each window opening. When the water is allowed to run through the pipe slowly, the bricks are moistened and this moisture rapidly evaporates, cooling the air so that it enters the building moist and at a reduced temperature.—Contributed by Loren Ward, Des Moines, Iowa.

## Making a Special Angular Cut

A number of special steel pieces were to be cut across their surfaces at an angle of 70 deg. Cutters for the

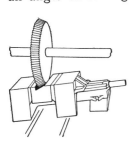

milling machine were available with a 60-deg. angle, but none of 70 deg. As no more such pieces were to be made, it was a question whether it would pay to purchase a cutter having the right angle, to alter an old one, or to plane the pieces instead of milling them. It was finally decided to do the work as follows:

The pieces were first clamped in the Miller vise, and a 60-deg. slot cut through them, then a shim was placed under one edge of the vise and the pieces were rechucked. The machine was set carefully so that the points of the cutter lined up with the extreme depth of the old cut, and the work was finished by passing the cutter over the face the second time. Raising one side of the vise made the cutter take off the angular side of the cut and increased its slope from the straight side which was a part of the original cut.

## Covering Tack Heads for Imitation-Rock Work

Sometimes paper is used to build imitation-rock work for temporary decoration, etc. If the paper is heavy, it often tears away from the tack; and if it holds, the tack will show. A remedy for this is to slip a piece of the same kind of paper on the tack, paste it on the under side and drive the

tack, then press the extending end down over the tack head after pasting the upper side. The piece of paper prevents the tearing of the heavy paper and effectually conceals the tack head.

## Locking an Automobile

The ordinary automobile may be safeguarded from theft as follows: The starter crank on almost all automobiles is from 5 to 6 in. in front of the axle. If a length of steel chain is passed around the axle and over the handle of the starter, then drawn taut

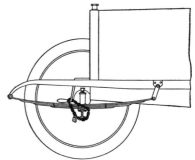

The Engine cannot be Started Until the Chain and Lock are Removed from the Crank

and the ends joined with a padlock, the engine cannot be cranked without removing the chain.

¶A little kerosene, poured into a box before running in the babbitt, will prevent the explosion that sometimes occurs.

## Finding the Wire Size to Use in Direct-Current Installation

The selection of the proper-size wire to use in conducting electricity between two points, a known distance apart, is governed by the current-carrying capacity, as established by the American Institute of Electrical Engineers, and by the voltage drop to be allowed when the circuit is carrying its full-load current.

The following simple formula, in combination with Ohm's law, is used in calculating the proper size of wire to use, so that the voltage drop will not be greater than the allowable value; and if the size of wire thus determined is capable of carrying the current, as determined from the table of current-carrying capacities, the calculation is complete. If the size of wire determined by calculation will not carry the current, then the size of wire, as given in the table of current-carrying capacities, which will carry the current, must be used.

$$R=\frac{K \times L}{C. M.}=\text{Resistance} \dots \dots (A),$$

in which K equals the resistance per mil foot and depends upon the kind of wire used, and its temperature. It is equal to 10.7 for copper under approximate working conditions; L equals the length of the wire in feet; and C. M. equals the area of the wire in circular mils, which is equal to the diameter of the wire in mils multiplied by itself (the mil is .001 in.).

Ohm's law gives the relation between the current in a circuit, the drop in voltage over a certain portion and the resistance of the same portion, and is usually written in the following form:

$$\text{Current}=\frac{\text{Drop in voltage}}{\text{Resistance}} \dots (B)$$

The above may be changed to read as follows:

$$\text{Resistance}=\frac{\text{Drop in voltage}}{\text{Current}} \dots (C)$$

Now, if the full-load current the wire is to carry is known and also the al-lowable drop in voltage, the resistance may be determined by dividing the drop in voltage by the current, as indicated in equation C. The resistance thus determined can then be substituted in equation A, and the required value of C. M. calculated. The equation A may be changed to the following form which is perhaps a little simpler:

$$C. M.=\frac{K \times L}{R} \dots \dots \dots \dots (D)$$

Since R equals volts lost divided by the current, equation D may be written in the following forms:

$$C. M.=\frac{K \times L \times \text{Current}}{\text{Volts Lost}} \dots \dots (E)$$

$$\text{Volts Lost}=\frac{K \times L \times \text{Current}}{C. M.} \quad (F)$$

$$\text{Current}=\frac{\text{Volts Lost} \times C. M.}{K \times L} \dots (G)$$

In the above equations, L is the length of the conductor in feet, which is twice the length of the circuit.

Equation E gives the value of the circular-mil area of a conductor to carry a certain current with a certain loss in voltage, the length of the circuit being $\frac{L}{2}$ feet.

Equation F gives the value of the volts lost in a circuit, $\frac{L}{2}$ ft. in length, carrying a known current and composed of a conductor of known circular-mil area.

Equation G gives the value of the current a circuit, $\frac{L}{2}$ ft. in length, will carry when the circular-mil area of the conductor is known and also the allowable volts lost.

Example: What size wire will be required for a 10-hp., 110-volt direct-current motor, located 200 ft. from the switchboard with an allowable loss in voltage of 4 volts? The voltage at the board is 115 volts and the efficiency of the motor is 85 per cent.

Solution: Since the motor has an efficiency of 85 per cent, its full-load input will be $\frac{100}{85}$ of 10 or 11.76 hp. One horsepower is equal to 746 watts, so that the watt input will be equal to

11.76×746, or 8,773 watts. The voltage at the motor will be equal to 115−4 or 111 volts, and the current input will be equal to the watt input divided by 111, or $\frac{8773}{111}=79.03$ amperes. Substituting, in equation E, this value of current, the voltage loss, which is 4 volts, and the value of L, which is equal to twice the length of the circuit, or 400 ft. in this case, one obtains:

$$C.\,M.=\frac{10.7\times400\times79.03}{4}=84,562$$

The diameter of the wire is equal to the square root of the value of the circular-mil area, which gives 291 mils. A No. 1 gauge wire has a diameter of 289.3 mils, so that if a No. 1 wire will carry 79.03 amperes, it may be used and will meet all the requirements. The allowable current a No. 1 rubber-insulated wire will carry, as given in the table, is 100 amperes, so that this size may be used.

If the length of the circuit had been 100 ft. instead of 200, the value of the circular-mil area calculated by means of equation E would be 42,281, and the diameter would be 205.6 mils, which corresponds to a No. 4 gauge. The allowable current-carrying capacity of a No. 4 wire is only 70 amperes, so it would be out of the question to use that size. A No. 3 will carry 80 amperes and it must be used.

It is apparent from the above that when the circuit was 200 ft. long it was the voltage drop that determined the size of wire to use, while with the circuit 100 ft. in length it was the current-carrying capacity.

The value of the voltage drop for a circuit 100 ft. long, composed of No. 3 gauge wire and carrying 79.03 amperes, can be calculated by substituting in equation F which gives:

$$\text{Volts Lost}=\frac{10.7\times200\times79.03}{52,630}=3.21\text{ volts}$$

The above calculations do not take into account any overload the motor might be called upon to carry which would require an increase in the current-carrying capacity of the leads.

The underwriters require the current-carrying capacity of the wire to be 25 per cent greater than the full-load current of the motor.

Calculations for lights are identical with the above, so that no examples need be given.

---

## Copper Faces for Chuck Jaws

It is often necessary to rechuck finished work in a lathe, and to prevent the jaws of the chuck from marring the finished surfaces it is necessary, of course, to place contact strips of some soft material between the jaws and the work. Anyone who has ever tried to get such strips hurriedly in place knows that it is 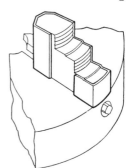 quite a provoking task. The sketch is descriptive of a form set of strips which can be quickly slipped over each individual jaw and which are so shaped that they will stay in place regardless of the jaw's position. These strips save the lathe man's time and patience, and take up little space on the tool rack.

---

## Re-Marking Steel Squares

Desiring to make the marks on a steel square black, I proceeded as follows: Some white-shellac varnish was rubbed into the marks with a piece of clean cloth, and the surplus on the surfaces was wiped off; then, after drying for a few minutes, lampblack was rubbed into the depressions with a stiff brush. When thoroughly dry, the surface was polished. This gave clear black lines on the scale.—Contributed by F. H. Tillotson, Chicago.

---

❡A cloth used for straining purposes can be held on a pail rim with clothes pins.

## A Chain Fastener

By those who use a chain, the hook shown, to make adjustable lengths, will be appreciated. The size of the

When the Hook is Placed in a Link of the Chain It is Held Solidly

hook will depend on the size of chain, the thickness at A being slightly less than the distance B, and the space C a trifle larger than the diameter D. The eye of the hook may be fastened to the chain with an extra link welded together or attached with a slit link.—Contributed by D. B. Templeton Bayonne, N. J.

## Preventing the Dripping of a Fountain Pen

Frequently it is necessary to use a fountain pen that is almost empty, and at such a time one is troubled with the ink dripping from the pen. The reason for this is that the additional amount of air in the pen is expanded by the heat from the hand, thus forcing the ink out when the pen is held in a writing position. To avoid this, clasp the pen in the hand and hold it in an upright position until it has become warmed by the hand and the air expanded and a portion passed out of the pen. Then the writing may go on without the troublesome drip.—Contributed by Bert H. Stanley, Portage, Washington.

## Marking Parallel Lines on Round Stock for Keyways

Parallel lines may be easily marked for keyways on round stock by the

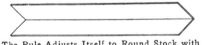

The Rule Adjusts Itself to Round Stock with the Edges Parallel to the Length

following method: Cut a piece of sheet metal 2 in. wide and about 1 ft. long, and bend it in the shape of the

letter V, carefully making the edges parallel and free from roughness. This will make a ruler which fits the shaft closely and can be slipped to any position, and the lines drawn along either edge will always be parallel with each other and with the axis of the shaft.—Contributed by Geo. Parke, Chicago.

## Gasoline-Engine Exhaust Muffler

A shop using a small gasoline engine for power was located near an office, and the exhaust annoyed the occupants of the latter. As the shop was to be moved in a short time, the owners did not care to purchase a muffler. The sharp report of the exhaust was temporarily muffled by using a forked pipe on the outlet.

A piece of pipe, 5 ft. long, was procured and its circumference divided into four equal parts. Lines were drawn on these marks lengthwise of the pipe and slots cut for almost the entire length, only allowing a sufficient solid and threaded end to be turned into the exhaust opening of the engine. The exhaust then resembled the exhaust of a steam engine.

## Oiled Insert for Automobile Springs

The leaves of automobile springs soon become dry and develop a squeak which is very annoying. An easy and effective manner to remedy this trouble is the following: Obtain some fine bronze-wire mesh and cut it into strips the same length and width as the leaves of the springs. Fill the spaces between the wires with hard oil or grease by placing the screen on a flat surface and using a putty knife or a flexible strip of steel to spread the grease. Take the springs apart and build them up again, inserting the greased mesh between the leaves. This will stop all squeaking and produce easier riding for a long time.

⟨A squeaking door hinge should be lubricated with graphite and a drop of oil.

# Testing Helical Springs

Two very simple, yet accurate, methods of testing helical springs are illustrated, which should be of great value to a garage owner or automobile repairman, where the accurate testing of a valve spring, for instance, is of vital importance. The testing of a spring consists of measuring the pressure it exerts when compressed to a certain length. For instance, a helical spring of 6 in. free length exerts a pressure of 100 lb. when it is compressed to a 3-in. length.

The method shown in Fig. 1 is only applicable to light springs of from 15 to 30-lb. capacity. It consists essentially of a circular flat plate to which is riveted a vertical rod. The spring to be tested is placed on the plate and weights are applied, as shown. Let it be assumed that the spring is to register 22 lb. when compressed to 1⅝ in. If the spring is correctly made of the right-size wire and wound to the correct pitch, the length will be 1⅝ in. when 22 lb. is placed on it.

Where it is necessary to measure springs of 80-lb. capacity, and upward, the foregoing method cannot be used, as it is impossible to apply enough weights for the test. For example, a spring having a free length of 4 in. should register 200 lb. when compressed to 2 in. in length. Place it on the platform of an ordinary scale and lay a strip of steel of sufficient size across its top as shown. Arrange two carpenter's clamps to hold the spring to the scale platform, as shown, but in drawing the clamp jaws together, do not compress the spring in the least. A weight representing 200 lb. is now placed on the beam end, and the clamps are drawn up until the scale registers the 200 lb. The spring is measured,

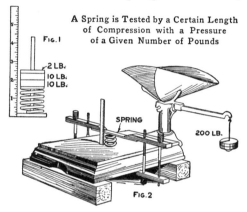

A Spring is Tested by a Certain Length of Compression with a Pressure of a Given Number of Pounds

and if the length is 2 in., it is perfect.—Contributed by Adolph Kline, Newark, New Jersey.

---

## A Decarbonizer

A decarbonizer is for use in removing the carbon from the interior of a gasoline engine with the least expense possible, as it does the work without the necessity of taking the engine apart or removing any parts whatever, except the spark plug. An inexpensive outfit for this work can be made at home as follows:

Procure a piece of copper tubing of the iron-pipe size, 3 in. in diameter and 6 in. long. While a brass tube will do, the copper is much better. Thread each end of the pipe and fit on 3-in. pipe caps. In the center of one cap drill and tap a hole for ⅛-in. pipe, and fit on a globe valve, as shown. Then fasten the copper tube on two supports made of bar iron, shaped to be fastened on a baseboard. The sup-

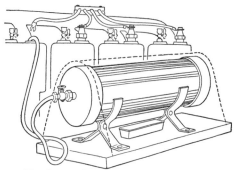

The Oxygen Gas Given Off by Heating the Chemicals Decomposes the Carbon Deposit

ports should be of such length as to raise the tube about 2½ in. above the base.

Make a burner of a shallow pan, about 4 in. long and 1½ in. deep. Fill the pan with strips of asbestos and set it on the baseboard beneath the tube. Bend a piece of sheet iron to form a hood which covers the tube and fasten it to the base, so that there will be about ½-in. space on top between it and the tube. Attach a piece of rubber tubing, about 5 or 6 ft. in length, to the valve outlet.

To use the decarbonizer, remove the cap not having any connection and fill the tube two-thirds full of a mixture consisting of 3 parts potassium chlorate and 1 part of manganese dioxide. Then screw the cap in place. Place some wood alcohol on the asbestos in the burner and ignite it. Remove the spark plugs on the cylinders successively and insert the open end of the rubber tube and then open the globe valve. It will clean out every particle of carbon in the cylinders in a short time, leaving them as clean as if they had been taken apart and cleaned by hand.

When through with the decarbonizer put out the fire and close the valve; the remaining chemicals will keep for further use. Never close the valve while the fire is burning, as the gas pressure will burst the tube.—Contributed by A. H. Waychoff, Koenig, Col.

## Releasing Pressure in Cylinder Oil Cups

The pressure on an oil cup comes from the power stroke of the engine by gas passing the piston rings. This will cause the oil to be continually stirred up in the cup, and will retard the feed as well as make the sight feed so dark that it is impossible to know whether the oil is feeding at all.

The remedy for this is to place a horizontal check valve between the cylinder and the oil cup so that the pressure from the cylinder will close the valve. The suction on the back stroke will open the valve sufficiently to allow the oil to pass through to the cylinder.—Contributed by E. Trusheim, San Diego, Cal.

## Double Cutting with a Power Hacksaw

As the sketch illustrates, a second saw frame is added to carry another blade which cuts in the opposite direction to the regular blade. The extra frame is fed upward by springs on top of the frame A, which is fed downward by its own weight; on the edge of the lower frame, at B, notches are cut, and a pawl, C, is used in them to hold the frames apart while feeding in the stock.

When the cut is about complete, the lower frame is "hooked up" with the

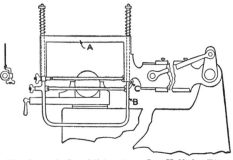

The Stock is Cut Off in About One-Half the Time of Cutting with the Ordinary Saw

pawl, and the cut is finished with the upper saw blade.—Contributed by Chas. Walte, Louisville, Ky.

## Finding Weight of Castings without a Scale

Improvised methods in accomplishing a great many things give as good results as if done with the aid of regular implements for the purpose. Some time ago I was called upon to get the weights, as closely as possible, of a considerable number of irregular castings. There were no scales handy, as the castings were at a place some distance from the shop. However, one of the smaller castings was a product of the shop, the weight of which was known exactly.

A light beam was secured, and the weights were obtained very accurately by means of the laws of leverage. The weight A, multiplied by the length B and divided by the length C, will equal the weight of the object D. The loca-

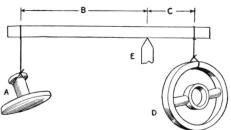

Weighing Objects by Means of the Laws of Leverage Where Only One Known Weight is at Hand

tion of the fulcrum E makes the balance and determines the lengths B and C.—Contributed by F. W. Bently, Jr., Milwaukee, Wis.

## Revolving Substitute for a Bench Drawer

Where a number of small parts are handled frequently on a bench, a wheel with a number of receptacles to take the place of a drawer will be found very handy. The wheel can be made of a board, revolving on a bolt fastened to the under side of the bench top. The edge of the wheel should come flush with the edge of the bench.

The upper surface of the wheel is fitted with as many receptacles as it will hold, made of discarded tin fruit

cans, or with small V-shaped boxes. A notch is cut in the bench top large enough to uncover one receptacle at

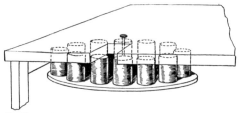

No Part of the Wheel Projects in Front of the Bench When Taking Parts from the Receptacles

the outer edge. The notch can be fitted with a hinged cover so that trash will not enter any of the receptacles.—Contributed by Lisle H. Scneder, Topeka, Kansas.

## Supplying Air to a Diver

The simple mouthpiece shown in the sketch provides a way to supply air to a diver. It consists of a metal tube, A, with a hose connection, B, at one end and an outlet valve, C, at the other and a mouthpiece, D, in the center of one side. The outlet may have any type of a check valve. The mouthpiece has a small wire soldered on both sides at the edge to provide a ridge that the diver can grip between his teeth. The part entering the mouth should be covered with a thin sheet of rubber to protect the mouth.

A hose of sufficient length is attached at B and an automobile tire pump fastened to the other end. In diving it is best to place a clip on the nose, then the breathing is free through

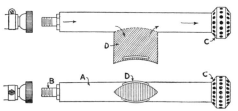

The Mouthpiece is Supplied with Air Pumped through a Tube from the Surface

the mouth. With this device a diver can stay under water a considerable length of time.—Contributed by C. Le Beuf, Jr., Westmount, Can.

## Strength of Cast Iron

Cast iron has great compressional strength but is weak in tension, the proportion being about 4½ to 1. In

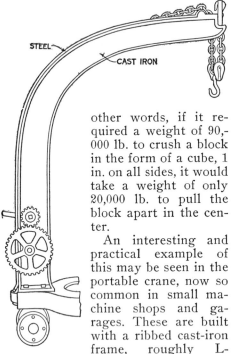

STEEL

CAST IRON

other words, if it required a weight of 90,000 lb. to crush a block in the form of a cube, 1 in. on all sides, it would take a weight of only 20,000 lb. to pull the block apart in the center.

An interesting and practical example of this may be seen in the portable crane, now so common in small machine shops and garages. These are built with a ribbed cast-iron frame, roughly L-shaped at the upper and outer end on which the weight is lifted. When a weight is suspended it has a tendency to bend this frame; that is, the back or outside tends to be stretched or "put under tension," and the inside, to be closed up or "put under compression." The back is less than one-fourth as strong as the front. To prevent fracture of the frame, steel bands, or straps, are bent around the outside and drawn up very tightly with nuts on the ends. This subjects the steel, which is strong in tension, to the strain, and relieves the cast iron where it is the weakest.

## Cooling a House in Hot Weather

The cooling of foodstuffs in hot and dry climates by means of water absorbed in burlap which hangs over the sides of a box inclosing the edibles, furnished the idea of cooling a house in hot weather. To try out the method, common cheesecloth was used on the screen frames for the windows and water run over it. The cooling effected was beyond expectations, but the cloth obstructed the light and would not last very long.

The cloth was removed and brass screen wire used in its place. The water was supplied through a system of ¼-in. pipe, which was perforated and run along the frame just above the screen. A small metal trough, at the sill of each window, caught the water and conveyed it to the drain, so as to prevent damage to the building.

It was found that the thermometer within the house registered lower on extremely hot days than on cool days. This was due to a more rapid rate of evaporation, which produced the cooling factor. The temperature of the rooms was at times lower than the temperature of the water before it reached the screens. The water supply for this system was an ordinary windmill and tank, neither of which was of unusual size, but proved adequate for the purpose.—Contributed by H. R. Spangler, Boulder, Col.

## Cutting Green Poles for Rafters

When using poles for rafters, it will be found quite difficult to cut the slopes at the ends so that each pair will fit at the center and rest properly on the plates. A simple but very efficient method of accomplishing this is the following:

Select small trees that will cut the right length and thickness, taking care to get them as straight as possible. Remove the bark and cut off the limbs

Green Poles Make Good Rafters for a Cabin, If the Angles are Cut Properly

close to the trunk. A drawshave is the best tool to use for removing the bark on this kind of timber. After making the poles ready, select a 2 by 6-in. timber, about 2 ft. longer than the desired rafter, and make a miter box at each end, as shown. Figure out the cuts on the side of the miter boxes in the same manner as for a pattern rafter of sawed material. Make saw cuts in the miter boxes according to the measurements.

For projecting rafters, with a notch to fit on the plate, make the cuts in the lower miter box about 4 in. apart at the bottom. Cut the top of the rafter first, the upper cut of the lower notch next, then move the rafter back 4 in. and make the other cut. In moving the rafter lengthwise be sure that it does not turn.

Before placing the rafter in the miter box, sight along it and lay it with the straightest side down in the box, then wedge it tightly in place. This method will make a rafter as good as a sawed one, and will give a good surface for roofing boards.—Contributed by A. J. Harstad, Lenia, Idaho.

### Raising an Automobile Top

When a person is riding alone and it becomes necessary to raise the top, it is almost impossible to get it in place single-handed. The sketch shows

The Connecting Wire between the Two Brackets Guides the Bow End to Its Position

an attachment that overcomes this difficulty, and one person can raise the top as quickly as two. A piece of wire is stretched from the rear bow on one side to the front-bow support. The bow to be moved forward has a loop attachment enabling it to slide along the wire. Raise the opposite side in the usual manner and the other bow will slide along to the front where it can be easily put into the bracket.—Contributed by Abner B. Shaw, N. Dartmouth, Mass.

⁋In applying more than one coat of shellac varnish to patterns, sandpaper each coat before putting on the next.

### Holding Work on a Drill-Press Table

The device illustrated will hold small work firmly in position on a drill-press table for drilling. It consists of

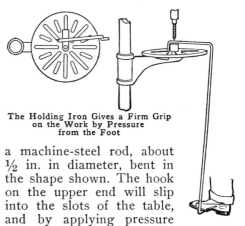

The Holding Iron Gives a Firm Grip on the Work by Pressure from the Foot

a machine-steel rod, about $\frac{1}{2}$ in. in diameter, bent in the shape shown. The hook on the upper end will slip into the slots of the table, and by applying pressure with the foot on the other end, the work under the horizontal part will be held tightly in place, so that both hands are free to operate the table.—Contributed by D. C. Goff, Knoxville, Tennessee.

### Heavy Roughing Tool for a Lathe

A very strong roughing-tool holder may be made by shaping a piece of steel to fit in the tool post of a lathe and boring a standard taper hole in one end, to receive a tool made from the taper shanks of broken end mills, which are usually made of high-speed steel. When they break the taper shanks can be used for tools in this holder which will last a considerable length of time. When the cutting edge is ground down too low, the shanks can be driven out and others substituted.—Contributed by Charles Homewood, Cedar Rapids, Iowa.

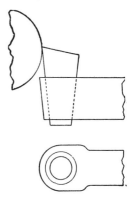

## A Substitute Surface Grinder

While working on a job in the woods, some castings were received which were only partly finished. Their

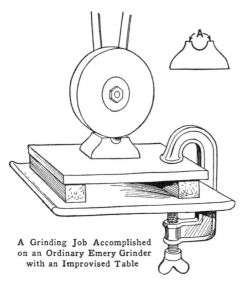

A Grinding Job Accomplished on an Ordinary Emery Grinder with an Improvised Table

bottoms were planed off, but the surfaces A on top were still in the rough. These had to be finished very accurately, and there was neither time to return them to the city nor a machine at hand to do that kind of work. As there were 30 castings, to chip and file them was out of the question. An emery wheel mounted on an iron stand was found in the mill's equipment, and it was decided to do the work on it.

An iron plate that had one machined face was found, and two blocks of wood were sawed out to pass under it so that, when placed on the pan of the machine, the top of the plate was approximately the desired distance below the emery wheel. The plate was held by a clamp. The castings were sorted and the highest ones shoved along the plate under the wheel. Then thicknesses of paper were put under one of the blocks so that the grinder would remove more metal. All the castings were finished in this way, and very quickly. A good, true-ground surface was the result, the paper layers giving a fine adjustment for close fitting.—D. A. H.

## Card-Writing Pens Made of Wood

Instead of using brushes or shading pens, procure three pieces of soft white pine, about the size of a lead pencil, and sharpen one end to a feather edge, like a slender wedge, making them into three widths, $\frac{1}{32}$ in., $\frac{1}{16}$ in., and $\frac{1}{8}$ in., respectively.

These three pieces, with a 1-ft. rule and two triangles, will make a good, durable and efficient outfit. The wood brushes are dipped in the ink, drawing or card-writer's ink, and used as a lettering pen. When these pieces of pine become filled with ink, they will retain a sufficient quantity to do considerable work, but the main advantages, over either pens or brushes, lie in the fact that anyone, with no experience, can do good work, making sharp, clear-cut letters easily and rapidly. These brushes improve with use, and if one is broken, another can be quickly made.—Contributed by J. B. Murphy, Plainfield, N. J.

---

## An Automobile Clutch Pedal

An automobile mechanic was called upon to make a clutch pedal to replace a broken one. A forge and anvil were at hand, and although not a skilled blacksmith, he made a very serviceable pedal in the following manner: The main part was bent up from a piece of $\frac{3}{4}$ by $1\frac{1}{2}$-in. steel. The footplate was made

from a piece of $\frac{1}{4}$-in. flat steel. It was fitted to the end of the arm part and fastened with a $\frac{3}{8}$-in. countersunk-head screw, in the center, and two $\frac{1}{4}$-in. dowels. It proved to be a substantial job.

---

❡Incase the ends of revolving shafting and avoid an accident.

# Rough Check for a Direct-Current Watt-Hour Meter

### By ARTHUR MOORE

The watt-hour meter is an instrument for measuring electrical energy used by a customer in a given time. The principle of the ordinary watt-hour meter for direct current is as follows: The current passes through two coils of wire, A, Fig. 1, and thus produces a magnetic field between them, which will vary in strength with the current. A very light armature, B, is mounted on a vertical shaft, C, between the coils, and this armature has a current run through it which is taken directly from the main line. The resistance of the armature circuit is high and hence it takes a very small current; and since its resistance is constant, the current through it varies with the electrical pressure between its terminals, which is the voltage of the main circuit.

When there is a current in both the armature and stationary coils, there will be a torque excited on the armature, causing it to rotate. The value of this torque will depend upon the value of the currents in the two circuits, or it will vary directly as their product; and since the current in the armature circuit varies as the voltage of the line, the torque varies as the product of the voltage and the current, which is the power in watts. The energy in any circuit is equal to the product of the power and the time; thus if the power taken by a certain circuit is 10 watts and it is constant for one hour, the energy would be equal to 10 watt hours. If the power taken by the circuit is 20 watts, then the energy in one hour will be 20 watt hours. Since the meter is to record the energy, it is obvious that the record shown on the dial D must vary directly as the power, when the times are the same, hence the speed of the meter's armature must vary as the power.

Some sort of a load must be put on the armature shaft so that its speed will vary directly as the torque. Such a load is provided by a copper disk,

E, revolving between the poles of permanent magnets, F. The torque required to drive such a disk varies directly as the speed, and as a result there will be the proper relation between the speed and the power. If the armature shaft be connected to a train

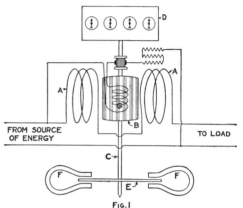

FIG. 1
Diagram of an Ordinary Watt-Hour Meter Showing Connections and Manner of Construction

of gears by means of a worm gear, the total revolutions of the armature may be registered with pointers mounted on the shafts of the gears and arranged to move over suitable dials. The total number of revolutions of the armature indicated on the dial, multiplied by the watt hours required to produce one revolution, will give the total watt hours of energy. In the majority of cases, the dials are direct-reading, and no constant is required.

A stationary coil, G, is connected in series with the armature, and it should produce a magnetic field of sufficient strength to almost cause the armature to revolve when there is no current in the coils A. If this adjustment is properly made, the armature will start to revolve when a very small current is sent through the coils A, and the meter will register for low loads; otherwise a considerable current would have to be sent through the coils A before the armature would start to turn. When the magnetic effect of the coil G is too great, the armature will rotate when there is no current in the coils A, and the meter is said to "creep" when this is the case.

The disk constant of the meter is the

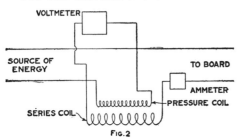

FIG. 2
**Wiring Diagram Showing Where the Voltmeter and Ammeter are Placed for Recording the Current**

number of watt hours required to produce one revolution of the disk. It bears a definite relation to the value of one division, in watt hours, on the lowest reading dial and is often called the "gear ratio."

In order to test a meter, it is necessary to know the current passing through it and the voltage impressed on the pressure circuit. An ammeter and voltmeter will be required to make the measurements accurately, and the connections for a two-wire meter

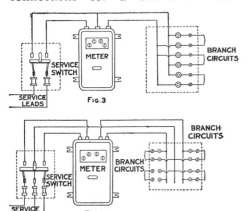

FIG. 3

FIG. 4
**Diagram Showing the Connections for a Two-Wire and a Three-Wire Watt-Hour Meter**

should be made as shown diagrammatically in Fig. 2. The load current should be maintained constant while the armature makes a certain number of revolutions. The time required for the armature to make a number of revolutions should be carefully noted; and

the accuracy of the meter may be determined as follows: The current indicated on the ammeter, multiplied by the value of the voltage indicated on the voltmeter, gives the power. This product, multiplied by the fractional part of an hour required for the armature to make a certain number of revolutions, gives the value of the watt hours the meter should indicate.

The disk constant of the meter, which is usually marked on the dial, multiplied by the revolutions of the disk, gives the indicated watt hours. The difference between the true and indicated watt hours is the amount the meter is in error. For example, suppose a 220-volt, 25-ampere, two-wire watt-hour meter, having a disk constant of 2, gives the following results under test on a load of 25 amperes: Average voltage, 220; average current, 25 amperes; time taken for the disk to make 120 revolutions, 3 minutes. Since the disk constant is 2 and the armature makes 120 revolutions, the indicated watt hours will be equal to $120 \times 2$, or 240. The power is equal to $220 \times 25$ or 5,500 watts. The time is $\frac{1}{20}$ of an hour, and hence the true watt hours will be equal to $\frac{1}{20}$ of 5,500, or 275. The meter then reads $275 - 250$, or 25 watt hours slow when the true watt hours are 275, and the per-cent error is equal to $(25 \div 275) \times 100 = 9.09$.

When an ammeter and voltmeter are not available, an approximate check may be made by using lamps, whose current consumption is known, and assuming that the voltage remains constant. This, however, is very unsatisfactory and should be used only in extreme cases.

The connections of an ordinary two-wire meter are shown in Fig. 3, and those of a three-wire meter, in Fig. 4. The three-wire meter should be checked when the load is balanced.

¶An old sprinkling can, with the sprinkler head removed, makes a convenient device for filling an automobile radiator.

## Relieving Jar of Hammer Handle

When using a small hammer on quite heavy work, it often happens that the handle vibrates and causes a very unpleasant feeling in the hand. To remedy this, bore a ⅜-in. hole, about 2 in. deep, in the large end of the handle and fill it tightly with beeswax. Long handles in large sledges can be treated in the same manner, but the hole should be larger and deeper and completely filled with the wax.—Contributed by E. C. Stevens, Detroit, Mich.

## A Bench Gas Heater

The illustration shows a type of gas heater which, in many instances, takes the place of the forge in hardening and tempering small tools, such as taps, drills, counterbores, etc.

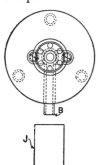

The base A is made of a casting, 4½ in. in diameter and ⅜ in. thick. A $\frac{5}{16}$-in. hole is drilled at B for the gas intake, and the stem is turned to fit a piece of ½-in. rubber hose. Holes are then drilled and tapped in the posts C for the flange D, and for the gas tip E. The flange D, which is held to the

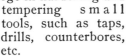

base A with screws F, is bored to fit the piece of tubing G, which is 4 in. long. The casting H is bored to fit the top of the tube G, and to receive the cupola J, which is made from a piece of 1¾-in. tubing, 4½ in. long. Holes are drilled in the under side of the casting H for admitting air.

With a good volume of gas and the mixer K properly adjusted, the burner will heat a piece of steel, ⅜ in. in diameter and 1 in. long, in a short time.—Contributed by E. P. Fickes, Dayton, O.

## Removing Screw Tops on Fruit Jars

An old broken pair of shears can be made into a useful tool that will come in handy during the canning season, or at any time that a fruit can is to be opened. The broken ends are ground to make them rounding, and a hole is drilled in each end large enough to allow a wire, about ⅛ in. in diameter, to pass through them. The wire is formed as shown, and the ends are fastened in the

holes. It should be of such length as to reach over the fruit-jar cover when the shears are opened. Place the wire over the cover and close the shears with a good grip. The wire then takes a good hold on the cover, and it is an easy matter to tighten or loosen it.—Contributed by J. J. Kolar, Maywood, Illinois.

## Small Hole in Stud Bolt

A broken stud presents a difficult job to repair. The remaining end is hard to remove without doing damage to the threads in the metal where it is fastened. A very good plan is to drill a small hole in the stud when making it; then, if it breaks, it is not a hard job to make a large drill follow the small hole, and a drift can

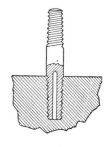

be used in turning out the shell.

❡When out of cast-iron flux or scaling compound for welding, fine common salt makes a good substitute.

## Desk Block for a Watch

In a great many places where it is necessary to know the time at any moment, a watch is a very convenient guide. If the watch is placed flat on

The Block Places the Watch in Such a Position That It is Easily Seen

the table or desk, it is not always easily seen, and then, too, it is liable to be pushed off and broken. The sketch shows a desk block which was used with a great deal of satisfaction.

The recess in the top of the block is for the chain, which need not be taken from the watch. The slight angle of the block, which is hollowed out to receive the watch, makes the dial clearly visible from almost any point of view. For convenience and safety in connection with the continual use of a timepiece this suggestion is hard to excel. The block is easily made and finished to present a pleasing appearance on any desk.

## A Tire-Fluid Gun

The sketch shows the way I connected a 12-in. tire foot pump to a tank so that it would take tire fluid from

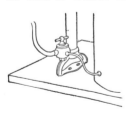

the tank and force it into a tire. The plunger of the pump was equipped with double leathers, and a three-way valve was attached at the base. The tank and foot pump were fastened solidly to a baseboard, and a ¼-in. copper tube was connected between the valve and tank.

The operation is simple. Turn the valve to make connections between the tank and pump cylinder, then draw out the plunger. This will draw a charge of fluid into the pump. The valve is then turned, to connect the hose that is attached to the tire valve, and the plunger is forced down the same as for filling the tire with air.

The device is always ready to use, can be attached quickly, and a tire treated in a very short time.—Contributed by Hill, Pasadena, Cal.

## Taking a Drill Chuck Apart

The ordinary drill chuck is so cheap and durable that one seldom gives its construction a thought. Occasionally, however, it is necessary to take one apart for some purpose, and the person who is not familiar with its construction will find this a hard task. Such a chuck is illustrated herewith. A knurled sleeve, drilled for the spanner, surrounds the body, and turning this sleeve loosens or tightens the drill in the jaws. There is no sign of threads, setscrews, or pins, to hold this sleeve

on, but still it stays in place and turns around.

This outer sleeve is pressed on and a movement longitudinally will remove it. After it is off, the assembly of the chuck is readily apparent. The chuck is assembled by pressing the sleeve back into its proper place. Sometimes the sleeve becomes loosened after long service and slips when a drill must be held very tightly. The remedy is to remove it and shrink it up a little. To do this, heat the metal to a red heat and immerse in cold water. Repeat this operation if the piece is very loose. Press it back in place, and the sleeve will hold like new.

¶A reamer should not be turned backward in a hole.

# Patterns for Cylinder Flanges

By J. A. SHELLEY

Flanges for small cylinders are usually sawn from a solid piece and fitted over the prints after they have been turned to size, but in some instances grooves are turned for the flanges, as shown in Fig. 1. This makes a good job, but one that has been discontinued on account of the difficulty in removing the flanges for alterations, especially if they have been nailed through the ends. The plan of fitting directly over the prints is better in all cases, as it provides for easy alteration and the fitting and fastening of the flanges without removing the cylinder from the lathe centers.

For thick flanges of large diameter, segments are the proper thing. If the

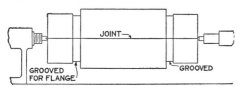

Fig. 1—Grooves Turned in the Core Prints of a Pattern for Receiving the Flange

combined thickness of the flange and fillet is not too great, one course will do, but it will need to be strengthened at the joint where the segment ends come together. There are several ways of doing this, and the most common one is to saw grooves in the ends and fit a feather with the grain running directly across or at right angles to the joint. Another way is to bore holes part way through the segment ends with the joint for the center and glue pieces of dowel pins in them for feathers. Both these forms of feathering are illustrated in Fig. 2.

Very thick flanges, or those with large fillets, will have to be built of two or more courses of segments on a faceplate, and should be rough-turned before fitting to the barrel prints, but if there is a good band saw at hand, do not try to turn the inside to fit over the prints, as it can be sawn to fit in a fraction of the time required to turn it.

In building one course of flanges, make an allowance inside and out for sawing after the glue has set. Glue it up in halves after jointing, and clamp

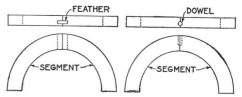

Fig. 2—Two Methods of Feathering, to Strengthen the Joint of the Flange Parts

it to a straight plate. If they are to be grooved on the circular saw for feathers, be sure to mark the joints before taking them apart, as there might be some mistake in putting the right segments together. If a dowel is to be used, do not attempt to bore the hole until the glue has thoroughly dried.

It sometimes happens that the lathe has sufficient swing between centers to turn the barrel and prints, but not the flanges. In this case the flange will have to be finished completely on the lathe faceplate and fitted to the barrel after it has been removed from the lathe centers, or it may be that the lathe is long enough to turn the barrel but not the prints or flanges, and in this case they will have to be built together on a faceplate and fastened to

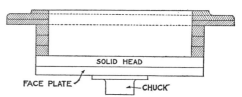

Fig. 3—A Section of a Core Print and Flange Made in One Piece on a Faceplate

the barrel after it is taken from the lathe. A section of a print and flange built together is shown in Fig. 3.

⟪A mechanic should never wear jewelry on the hands while working at a machine, as it is apt to catch on the work and cause a serious injury.

## Cuspidor Carrier

The time required to empty, clean and return a large number of cuspidors was greatly reduced by using a carry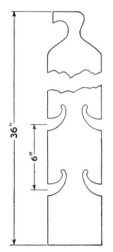ing device which permitted more than one vessel to be taken at once. The material used in the construction is maple, about ¾ in. in thickness, the length and width depending on the size and number of cuspidors to be handled.

The notches cut in the edges are about 1¼ in. wide at the opening, and are made the shape of the rim on the cuspidor. The shape of the handle shown is one selected from several as being the most satisfactory to take hold of without an uncomfortable position of the hand.

Each notch receives a cuspidor, which is easily hooked into position and taken out by lifting with an outward turn of the bottom.—Contributed by D. L. Converse, Erie, Pa.

## Drafting-Table Inkstand

A very handy holder that will prevent the spilling of ink on a drawing may be easily made as shown in the sketch. The holder consists of a piece

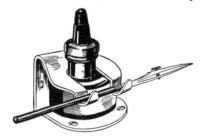

The Holder Prevents the Spilling of the Ink and Provides a Place for the Pen

of sheet brass, about No. 16 gauge, bent to the proper shape. If the ends of the spring arms are turned up

slightly, they will provide a place for the pen when it is not in use. Holes are drilled in the bottom and back of the holder so that it may be fastened with screws to the wall or table.—Contributed by C. A. Allen, Whetinsville, Massachusetts.

## Towels for Mechanics

Printers, garage men and machinists are very hard on towels. The ordinary bath or crash towel quickly wears out under the treatment which it receives in the shop. If a mechanic cares more for utility and economy than for appearances, a more serviceable towel can be made from a grain sack. These sacks can be procured cheaply from a feed store. A large-size sack will make two towels.

## Making Loose Packing Nut Hold the Gasket

In many instances where the hole through the packing nuts, used on water or lubricator glasses, is too 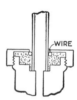large for the glass, the gasket is easily squeezed through the space between them, and a leaky connection soon develops. This is also apt to cause the breaking of the glass. The sketch is descriptive of a quick method of overcoming the difficulty and making the old nut as serviceable as a new one.

A piece of No. 12 or 14 gauge copper wire is bent in a circle to the exact outside diameter of the glass. It is then wound with a cord to prevent breaking the glass. The body of the wire prevents the gasket from passing up through the opening caused by the oversize of the nut, and the pressure of the gasket keeps it firmly in place. In places where a new nut cannot be readily made or procured, this kink will eliminate a great deal of trouble.

⟪Be sure to oil the surface of work to be knurled.

# A Hot-Rivet Catcher

### By ALVIN L. YOUNG

Hot rivets are usually caught in a bucket or keg when they are thrown by the person at the forge. The men throw these rivets quite accurately, but if one goes aside, then there is some danger to the person trying to catch it, especially if he is standing on a beam. This bad feature is entirely eliminated by using the catcher shown in the sketch. It not only catches the rivet, but places it without having to pick it up with the tongs.

The general make-up of the catcher is similar to a large pair of tongs, with the jaws in half circles, to make the opening about the size of an ordinary bucket, the two parts, A, coming closely together when the handles are closed. The device for adjusting the opening B to any certain rivet is shown in the detail sketch. The disk D is of irregular shape, having several straight edges, each of which is at a different distance from the hole that forms the axis. This disk is riveted to a clip, E, fastened to one of the handles as shown, so that it can turn slightly upward. The disk is not riveted so tightly but what it can be turned. A slanting piece, F, is fastened to the opposite handle to receive the edge of the disk.

The sides of the jaws, from the round

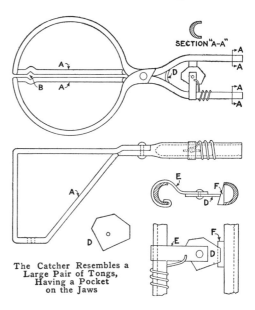

The Catcher Resembles a Large Pair of Tongs, Having a Pocket on the Jaws

part to the lower sloping pieces, are covered with wire netting or asbestos. When a hot rivet is caught in the pocket thus formed, it falls to the bottom where it easily drops into the hole B, which is adjusted to its size by the disk D. With a good grip on the handles, the disk D and its holder, E, are forced up the slanting piece F, and the rivet is gripped so that it can be placed.

---

## A Homemade Check Protector

A device that will effectually prevent the raising of the amount written on a check can be made from two pieces of metal, hinged like a nutcracker and having a series of notches filed in the edges of their inner surfaces. The pieces are about 6 in. long and ⅜ in. square. A slot is cut through one end of each piece and a small, thin piece of metal is fitted in them. When riveted loosely in place it forms a substantial hinge. The notches should be stepped off and filed accurately so that they will mesh closely together. After

the amount is written on a check it is placed between the pieces and pressure applied, which will roughen the paper

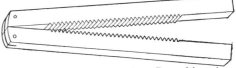

The Roughened Inner Surfaces Pressed into the Paper over the Written Amount Effectually Protect It

in such a manner that the amount cannot be readily changed.

---

❡Kerosene oil is a good lubricant for reamers used in aluminum.

## A Scissors Holder for Paper Hangers

Scissors are a troublesome tool to keep in sight and in a handy place when wanted, and especially so for the paper

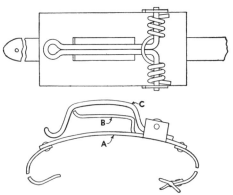

The Holder is Strapped in the Right Position to Receive the Scissors from the Hand

hanger. The illustration shows a holder to take the place of a pocket in the overalls. It consists of a strip of metal, A, to which is attached a clip, B, for holding the scissors, and a spring, C. Straps are riveted to the ends of the metal, A, to be used in attaching the holder to a limb of the user. The scissors are easily slipped behind the spring by the natural swing of the arm and it is not necessary to look where to put them.—Contributed by F. C. Myre, Tacoma, Wash.

## Leather Hand Protectors

Workers handling hot irons or carrying heavy objects, such as a stove, use some kind of pad to protect the hands.

One of the best things I have seen for this purpose is a piece of leather, cut from a boot top and with slits made in it, as shown, so that it will slip over the wrist and the little and forefinger of the hand.—Contributed by James M. Kane, Doylestown, Pa.

## A Rubber Sanding Block

When smoothing boards with sandpaper the usual method is to wrap the paper around a block so that a better grip for the hand may be had and at the same time covering the surface more evenly than could be accomplished without it. On uneven work the block would only touch the high spots and for this reason it is better to use a block of soft rubber about 5 in. long, 3 in. wide and 1½ in. thick. Its surface is yielding and with the pressure of the hands it forces the sandpaper into the low parts and smooths them as well.

## Clamps for Holding Polished Pipe

A pipe coupling makes a good gripping device for highly polished brass or nickeled pipes. A pipe coupling is

procured that will allow about ¼ in. space between its inside diameter and the outside diameter of the finished pipe to be gripped. Take a piece of smooth pipe the same size as the nickeled pipe and place it centrally in the coupling. The ends of the openings are stopped up in the same manner as in babbitting a shaft, and the space is filled with melted lead. When cold, cut the coupling in two with a hacksaw. The clamps may be used in tongs or in a vise.—Contributed by W. C. Loy, Rochester, Ind.

## Changing Resiliency of Automobile Springs

The reason that an automobile of the roadster type is hard-riding is as follows: The manufacturers use one chassis for both its runabout and touring bodies and naturally expect that the touring car will be required to carry a greater passenger load in addition to the extra weight of the body. The same springs are used for both bodies, and to protect himself, the manufacturer makes them strong enough for the larger load, with the result that there is not enough resiliency for the lighter car. To "soften them up," shock absorbers are used, but before applying them, it will help still more if the lower leaf—the short one—is removed from the lower half of the spring. After doing this, the motorist should be careful not to overload his car.—Contributed by Donald A. Hampson, Middletown, New York.

### Drawing Work Tightly on the Lathe Live Center

It often happens that the steady rest has to be used when doing a lathe operation on a piece of work. If the piece has been previously turned up on the centers and subsequent operations must be accurate, the end which is usually placed in a chuck should be fastened snugly against the live center. This can be quickly accomplished in the following manner.

Attach a dog, or driver, on the part to be worked, and place it between centers in the usual way, with the steady rest in the correct position, and unscrew the faceplate about three turns. Procure a piece of rawhide belt lace, about 3 ft. long, lace it tightly around the driver and through the faceplate, and tie it firmly. It is obvious, that when screwing the faceplate back in place against the shoulder on the spindle it will draw and hold the work securely against the live center. The tailstock can then be removed and the work begun.

### An Eraser Cleaner

The eraser cleaner consists of a box with solid ends and the four sides covered with coarse wire mesh. The boards, set at an angle in the corners, and the axle serve to beat out the dust in the erasers as they fall from one to the other when the box is revolved.

The ease with which erasers are cleaned in this manner makes it possible to run them through often, which

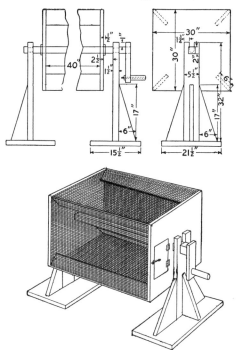

The Chalk Dust in the Erasers is Easily Knocked Out as They Roll in the Box

will reduce the amount of dust in each room of a public school.—Contributed by John L. Cooley, Farmington, Me.

### Finding Air Pressure in a Bell Jar

In the course of some experiments I had occasion to determine with some degree of accuracy the air pressure in a bell jar from which the air was partly exhausted by means of a vacuum pump. I was without a suitable manometer tube and likewise without the wherewith to construct one, but solved the problem in a very simple and satisfactory manner by making use of a steam gauge which was at hand.

For the purpose, the inlet pipe of the gauge was plugged, a pipe coupling having been screwed on the nipple and a plug inserted in the end of the coupling, the joints being made tight with red lead to prevent leakage. The gauge thus arranged, was introduced into the jar. The air pressure within the coil of the gauge could not change as the pressure of the atmosphere in the jar

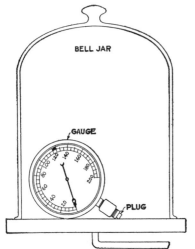

The Plugged Coil of the Steam Gauge Records the Air-Pressure Reduction within the Jar

lowered, but the confined air acted in the same manner as air under pressure with the gauge used in the ordinary manner. The hand, of course, registered the drop in pressure or the difference in pressure between the air in the jar and the air in the coils of the gauge. Subtracting this reading from the pressure of the atmosphere, as determined by a barometric reading, gave the exact pressure of the air in the jar which was desired.—Contributed by J. Naveman, Brooklyn, New York.

### Slip Bushings for Jigs

Parts that are drilled and reamed in a jig at one setting usually require slip bushings, one each for the drill and reamer, and sometimes more for subsequent operations. Unless some means is provided to prevent it, the bushings will turn with the tool, which rapidly wears both the stationary and slip bushings. It is obvious that the accuracy of the jig is quickly lost under these conditions. The sketch shows some of the different methods used, which are simple and inexpensive and will give satisfactory results.

That shown in Fig. 1 is perhaps the

simplest of them all: the straight pin prevents turning, but does not keep the bushing from working upward. It does very nicely where there is a limited number of parts to be worked, or in extreme cases where the cost of the tool is the first consideration.

A method that is much used and gives satisfaction is shown in Fig. 2. The cutting of the step makes this one a little more expensive than the others. The rotation of the tool keeps the notched part of the bushing solidly against the finger.

A method that gave better results than any of the others is shown in Fig. 3. A slot is cut on an angle of 45 deg., which was found ample to keep the bushing firmly seated and at the same time not wedge itself to prevent turning with the fingers in the opposite direction for removing.

The one shown in Fig. 4 is kept in place with a pin and plunger. It may be further improved by adding a small spring, to prevent any tendency of the plunger to work out. Its principal advantage is the simplicity of work on the bushing, although the plunger and housing are more expensive to construct than the other similar devices.

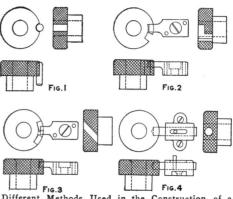

Different Methods Used in the Construction of a Holding Device for Jig Bushings

It is sometimes advisable to leave the dowels out of the fingers shown in Figs. 2 and 3. In case the tool catches or sticks in the bushing, it will turn, using the screw as a pivot, and prevent breaking the end from the finger.—Contributed by A. Dane, Pottstown, Pennsylvania.

# How to Make a Battery Charge-and-Discharge Indicator

### By R. A. McCLURE

A cross section of the complete indicator is shown in Fig. 1. It consists of a coil of wire, A, mounted inside of a metal case, B, and provided with two terminals, C, with a permanent magnet, D, mounted on a horizontal axis inside the coil and having its position controlled, when there is no current in the coil, by the soft-iron yoke E. A very light tube of nonmagnetic material is attached to the permanent magnet and is, as a result, rotated as the position of the magnet changes by the action of a current in the coil. The surface of this tube moves past an opening in the dial of the instrument, and its position will serve as an indication of the direction of the current in the coil when the proper marks have been made for currents of known direction.

The principle of the instrument is the following: The permanent magnet D assumes the position shown when it is perfectly balanced and there is no current in the coil. When a current passes through the coil, a magnetic field is established within it, whose direction depends upon the direction of the current in the coil, and whose strength increases or decreases with the current. The permanent magnet is turned from the zero position due to the action of the current, and if the effect of the yoke E were entirely removed, the magnet would come to rest in a vertical position. If the current in the coil be reversed, the magnet would then be turned through 180 deg. The turning of the magnet is limited by two stops, F, and as a result the yoke E is always tending to bring the magnet back to its original position, and when the current in the coil is reduced to zero, the magnet again assumes its initial position.

When a storage battery is being charged, the current is sent through the circuit in the reverse direction of that in which the battery discharges. Thus,

if the coil of the indicator be connected in series with the battery, it is obvious that the magnet will turn in one direction when the battery is charging and in the opposite direction when it is

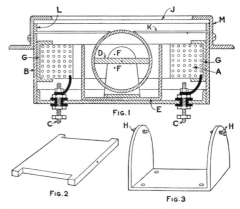

FIG. 1
FIG. 2
FIG. 3

General Arrangement of the Parts for Constructing a Battery Charge-and-Discharge Indicator

discharging. Under these conditions, the position of the cylinder affords a suitable indication as to charge and discharge, and the words "charge" and "discharge" may be printed on the surface of the cylinder, so that one or the other appears when the cylinder is at either of its extreme positions. The word "neutral" may also be printed on the surface of the cylinder so it will be in sight when there is no current in the coil.

The diameter of the containing case is 2¼ in., and the various parts are in about the same proportion as shown. The wire used in the coil should have sufficient cross section to carry the maximum current that may pass through it without undue heating, and its resistance should always be as low as possible, so as to prevent an excessive loss in winding. The coil may be fastened inside the containing case by means of four pieces of thin brass, soldered to the inside surface of the case so that the ends may be bent down over the sides of the coil as shown at G. Both terminals of the coil come out on the same side and are fastened to two terminals, mounted on the back of the containing case and insulated from it.

The exact form of the magnet is shown in Fig. 2. It should be made from a very good grade of steel and well magnetized after having been properly tempered. Two small recesses are made in the sides of the magnet, to accommodate the points of the trunnion screws that are to support it.

A thin tube of insulating material, as long as the magnet is wide and having an outside diameter equal to the maximum length of the magnet, should be obtained. Two small notches are cut in each end of this tube to accommodate the four projections on the magnet, whereupon the tube is sprung over the magnet.

A soft-iron yoke is made from a piece of iron, a little narrower than the magnet, so that it may be mounted within the coil. The part resting on the back of the containing case may be made as broad as the base of the U-shaped support for the magnet. This

support is shown in Fig. 3. Two small steel screws, H, with their ends ground down to a fine point, are placed in two threaded holes in the upper ends of this piece. This piece and also the soft-iron yoke may be fastened to the back of the case by means of two or more screws passing through holes in them and into threaded holes in the back of the case. The back of the instrument may be fastened to the shell of the case, by means of small machine screws, with their heads countersunk so as to be below the surface of the case.

A glass cover, J, is placed over the top of the instrument and raised above the piece, K, by means of a narrow ring, L. This glass cover, the ring L, and the disk K, are all fastened to the shell of the case, as shown, by means of a ring M. The projection on this ring will serve in mounting the indicator on a board, a hole being drilled in the face of the board equal in diameter to the outside diameter of the main part of the case. All electrical connections to the indicator can then be made back of the board.

## A Stud Extractor

The extractor consists of a sleeve with a hexagon head, the bottom part of which has a projection carrying a disk with a knurled and hardened circumference pivoted off center to make an eccentric.

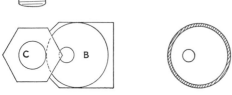

The Gripping Part of the Extractor Takes Hold on the Stud Where It Has No Threads

The advantage of this extractor is that the gripping part comes in

contact with that portion of the stud A having no threads, which is in the center or close to the joint. The threaded portion of the stud is protected inside of the extractor. The grip of the eccentric disk B will be tighter as the pull is applied to the hexagon part C, and is easily released by a slight backward turn.—Contributed by Richard Flagen, Cardiff, England.

## Care of Automobile Drive Chains

The wear that comes on exposed drive chains is caused mostly by dust and grit settling on and mixing with the lubricant on the chain. This wear is more noticeable on trucks than on any other vehicle. It is a fact that chains will last nearly twice as long if they are removed and thoroughly cleaned in gasoline, and then boiled in paraffin wax. When cool, the wax becomes hard, and keeps the bearings and moving parts well lubricated. This stops the rattle, and furnishes a coating to which dust will not adhere readily.

## Base Trimmer for Paper Hangers

Various styles of devices are used for trimming wall paper at the edge of the baseboard and around casings. One of the best things for this purpose is a shoe knife with a serrated cutting edge. The paper is temporarily pasted to the baseboard or casing, and with a sawing motion of the knife held in line with the baseboard edge, the paper is neatly cut. The paste adhering to the woodwork should be wiped off before it dries.

## Solid Expanding Arbor

It is often convenient to have an expanding arbor for use in light facing operations, finish-turning cuts, and

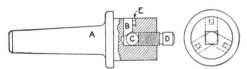

The Three Points of Contact are Forced Out Equally from the Center with the Screw

similar work, to be held and driven by the lathe spindle direct. The one shown in the illustration has proven that it will hold the work perfectly true with the bore after long and hard service. The shank, or body, A, was made of tool steel, but not hardened. The three expanding figures, B, are hardened tool steel, beveled on one end to 30°, with a small pin, working in the slot E, to prevent their turning in the holes. The projecting ends were turned off in position, to make them perfectly true, so that they would grip the finished bore of the pieces to be mounted on the arbor without marring them. The turning up of the setscrew D drives the ball bearing C with equal pressure on all three fingers B, which hold with a firm and positive grip.

⟪Never set a plane flat on a bench.

## Glass Tops on Desk Slides

As I was in need of a glass top for my desk and without means to get one, I hit upon the idea of making glass tops on the arm rests, or slides, over the top drawers. The slides were taken out and

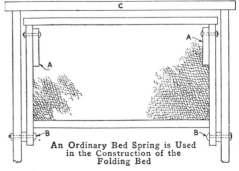

The Glass is Set into the Wood Slides Deeply Enough to Protect the Sharp Edges

a recess cut in them to receive a piece of double-strength window glass. A hole was bored in the end of the slide, large enough for a finger to be inserted from the under side to raise the glass. This provides an excellent place to keep data.—Contributed by Peter J. Theisen, Denver, Col.

## Homemade Folding Bed

A comfortable folding bed can be made from an ordinary wood-frame bed spring. A frame is built around the spring frame of 1-in. material, the

An Ordinary Bed Spring is Used in the Construction of the Folding Bed

edges projecting above the spring for holding the mattress, and below for the folding legs, A. The end pieces extend beyond the frame to receive the bolts, B, that act as a hinge.

The outside frame, or cover, C, can be made plain or ornamental to appear like a mantel. It consists of two ends and a top, and is fastened to the wall. The front is draped with a curtain divided in the center.

### Rack to Hold Automobile-Engine Hood While Painting

When repainting or varnishing an automobile it is very difficult to have the hood stand upright without falling

The Shape of the Sawhorse Holds the Hood in the Right Position for Painting

over and spoiling the paint. To have it fall would mean doing the work over. A simple way to overcome this trouble is to secure a wood sawhorse and lay the hood on it, as shown in the illustration.—Contributed by Carl Kaufmann, Santa Ana, Cal.

### An Adjustable Tap Wrench

A very efficient tap wrench, that answers the purpose well, can be made as shown. A piece of cold-rolled steel, A, about ⅜ in. thick and 1¼ in. wide, is cut long enough to allow two round disks, about ¼ in. thick and 1 in. in diameter, to be fitted on it. Notches are cut or filed into the disks B so that, when two notches of equal size are opposite each other, they form a square opening. The disks revolve freely on the screws D, which are turned into the plate A. A hole, large enough for the largest tap, is drilled at C. Handles are attached to the holder ends as shown. When a tap is in the notch the disks cannot turn.

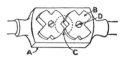

### Portières Made of Corn Kernels

Desiring to have a portière a little different from the usual kind, I experimented with kernels of corn and found them to be far superior to the beads or paper tubes used in making the Japanese kind. Ordinary field corn was selected and shelled and the kernels were placed in a pan, and enough boiling water was poured in to cover them. This softened the corn and prevented worms from eating into the kernels. The corn was allowed to soak for 24 hours. Too much at a time should not be prepared, as it will become sour.

The kernels are strung on No. 8 cotton thread, as it comes double from the needle, about 1 ft. longer than the opening where the portière is to be used. The extra 1 ft. will take care of the shrinkage. Use only sound kernels and thread them on in one way; that is, each kernel in the same position as the previous one, using care not to push them on too hard to cause them to split.

The corn will shrink some in drying, and each string should, therefore, be looked over and the kernels pushed together. Make a loop at one end of each string to fit the pole, and be sure that all strings are of the same length. They are then ready for varnishing, which is done by dipping a few at a time in varnish warmed a little. They are then hung on a stick or old pole to drain and dry. Allow them to dry thoroughly, but not rapidly. When dry, they are hung in place on the pole. The ends of the threads can be trimmed even with shears, as the kernels will not slip off.

The kernels may be dyed any color desired and designs worked in with different colors of corn, although this is not so pretty as the plain color. The length of the strings may be varied to suit the taste. One very nice method is to make the strings quite short at the center of the curtain and gradually increasing in length toward the sides.—Contributed by Earl Zander, Three Rivers, Mich.

# A Small Portable Oxyacetylene-Welding Outfit

### By ALBERT H. WAYCHOFF

The small welding outfit shown is especially adapted for light and portable work where the larger outfits would be cumbersome and almost useless. Both gas generators are alike in construction. The size can be changed if desired, but the dimensions given are for an outfit suitable for all-around work.

To make the gas generators, procure two pieces of seamless steel tubing, 6 in. in diameter and 8 in. long, having $\frac{1}{16}$-in. walls, and cut a fine thread on each end. The flanges A are made of thick boiler plate and threaded internally to fit on the threads of the tubes. When they are in place on the ends of the tubes they are soldered, or, better still, brazed; then, if possible, turned up on a lathe. The latter operation is not essential, however, providing a good thick gasket is used in the joint between the head and the flange. Plates for heads are then fitted to both ends and fastened with cap screws.

The plates used for the tops have three holes drilled and tapped for pipes, for attaching the safety valves B, the feed-water pipes C, and the gauges, D.

A cup, E, is made of sheet tin, or better still, aluminum, to fit snugly inside of each of the tubes F. These cups should have a central perforated tube fastened to the bottom and extending to the top, similar to a cake pan. The perforated tube should be about $\frac{3}{4}$ in. in diameter.

The water tanks G are made in the same manner as the tanks F, their size being 4 in. in diameter and 6 in. long. Drill and tap centrally the bottom plate of each tank for a $\frac{1}{4}$-in. pipe,

and provide a tapped hole for a plug in the top plate.

The $\frac{1}{4}$-in. pipes C are 10 in. long with a number of small holes drilled

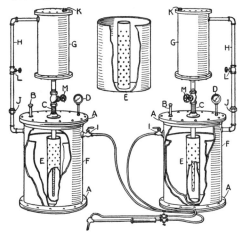

Each Pair of Tanks is Made and Connected Alike, the Operation Being the Same for Each Chemical

in one end for a length of 7 in., and the other end threaded for about 3 in. Screw this end of the pipe into the head of the tank F, from the under side, until about 2 in. of the threads extend through on the upper side of the plate. A $\frac{1}{4}$-in. globe valve is attached on the upper end of the pipe, and a short nipple connects it with the water tank G. Both pair of tanks are made alike.

About 2 in. below the top of the tanks F, drill and tap holes for $\frac{1}{4}$-in. pipe on the two sides of the tanks facing each other. Provide each opening with a gas cock so that hose may be attached connecting to the torch.

The outside of the tanks are drilled and tapped in like manner for connecting a ⅛-in. pipe line, H, from the water tanks G to the gas chambers F. These outside pipes equalize the pressure so that the water feeds equally at any pressure of the gas.

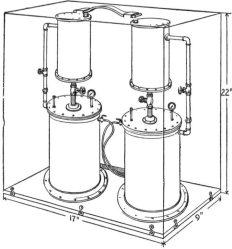

The Tanks can be Attached to a Base over Which a Cover is Placed for Carrying

A small gauge, having a 3-in. face, is attached at D. Such gauges are used on gasoline-lighting systems.

To use the outfit when it is assembled, fill the cups with chemicals, using calcium carbide for the acetylene gas and sodium peroxide for the oxygen. Place the cups in their respective tanks and fasten the top plates on the tanks F. The unions J are placed in the pipe lines to enable disconnection when removing the cover for filling and cleaning the cups. Fill the water tanks through the hole in the top after removing the plug K, making sure that the valves L and M are closed.

In use, open the valves L a turn, then slowly open the valves M, allowing the water to enter the cups through the perforated pipes C where it will come in contact with the chemicals. The valves are only opened a little for light work. The safety valves B should be set for 15 lb. above the working pressure to prevent loss of gas. The chemicals must be kept in air-tight cans, as the air and dampness will spoil them.

The tanks should be painted or labeled so that the proper chemical is always used in the same tank. Also take care not to exchange the cups; always use carbide in the carbide cup and tank, and peroxide in the peroxide cup and tank.

A very good method is to mount the tanks on a base and make a top that will fit over them, which is fastened to the base with hooks and eyes. A handle is attached to the top and the whole outfit can be carried where it is to be used.

### Operating Roller Shades on Casement Windows

Casement windows are rapidly coming into general use. Home builders have come to realize that with this form of a window it is possible to get the full benefit of the entire window opening, whereas with the usual sliding-sash window only 50 per cent of the space is available for maximum ventilation. The one disadvantage of this form of window is the difficulty of operating the usual roller shade, due to the pull cord becoming caught between the top of the casement and the window as the latter is opened and closed. Under these conditions a long stick with a nail in the end is usually brought into play. A little forethought, however, when the shades are put up, will avoid all this trouble and will render their operation just as satisfactory on this form of window as any other.

To accomplish this, simply place a

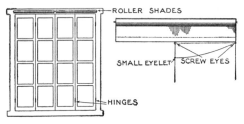

Pull Cord Attached to the Casement for Drawing the Shade Pull to One Side

small screweye, or staple, near the end of the stick in the bottom of the shade. Slip a small ring on the pull cord;

attach this ring to a second cord and then run the latter through the new screweye. Referring to the sketch it will be noted that this additional cord

use the hoist clear of the truck platform.

The frame consists of three parts, each constructed of two standards

The Track for the Chain Block is Supported at the Top by an Angle-Iron Frame, Which does Not Interfere with the Loading, the Chain Block Enabling One Man to Do the Work of Several

hangs somewhat loose when the pull cord is being, or has just been, pulled, but when the shade is up, it is merely necessary to pull on the side cord to pull the center cord over to that side. On account of the friction and the fact that the cords are about of equal weight, either one will remain where placed. When both are over to one side the window may be opened without further thought, and when it is closed, a slight pull will bring the pull cord again to the center so that the shade may be drawn down. The lower end of the side cord may be attached with a small tack at a point about halfway down on the casement, thus distinguishing it from the pull cord.

### Chain Block and Runway on a Truck

Where a truck is used for hauling heavy objects the burdensome task comes in on the loading and unloading of the pieces. A truck driver having a considerable amount of this work to do built a frame of light angle iron on the truck platform to support an I-beam centrally, on which a chain hand hoist could be run. The I-beam extended out at the rear far enough to

joined together at the top similar to the gable of a house and trussed to keep them from spreading. The three parts are joined together with a ridge and two side bars. All connections are riveted.

### Corn Cutter on a Shoe

A piece of an old crosscut-saw blade constitutes the cutter which is attached to the shoe sole with screws. The blade is formed as shown and the edges of the V-shaped notch are ground sharp. The advantage of this cutter is that the operator has both hands free to hold the stalks. The cutter is adapted only for use in cutting drilled corn where there is only one stalk in a hill. It could not be used on corn where several stalks grow together.— Contributed by F. L. Patterson, Lockwood, Cal.

## Locating Keyholes in the Dark

A particularly useful device for people who are forced to stay out late at night is the key guide illustrated. The

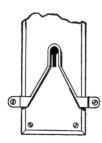

little guide is made in such a manner that it is capable of being applied to a d o o r without any change in the construction. The device is placed over t h e escutcheon so that the diverging arms form a tapering passage through which the key will be guided to the keyhole by placing the point of the key between the arms and moving it upward until it enters the keyhole. This is a simple device and should prove very useful in places where it is impractical or impossible to have a light to illuminate the keyhole.—Contributed by H. Kaye Martin, Washington, D. C.

## Combination Safety Inkwell

Every draftsman knows how easily the usual bottle of drawing ink tips over, yet does not care to litter up the

board with more than one heavy cast-iron holder, such as are sold to prevent spilling. Having occasion to use the red and black drawing ink and also the common writing fluid caused me to provide three bottles for them. In order to prevent overturning and at the same time arrange the three bottles so that they could be shifted about together, the very simple device here illustrated was contrived. A piece of ¾-in. ribbon brass, about 12 in. long, such as is used to hold the asbestos covering on steam pipes, was procured. These strips usually have a narrow ring attached to one end. The three bottles were placed together, the brass wrapped around them and drawn up tightly, the free end being drawn

through the ring and bent over. It was originally expected that the bend would have to be loosened every time a bottle was changed, but this was found unnecessary throughout the year that it has been in use. In fact, the metal band acts as though it were quite springy, and the bottles never become loose or rattle. For desk use it is best to cut off the tops of the stoppers as shown.—Contributed by John D. Adams, Phoenix, Ariz.

## To Prevent Book Leaves from Sagging

The leaves of large books will sag down and cause the book to lose its original shape. A way to remedy this

is to mount a set of blocks that are beveled and rounded in front so that the book will slide upon it easily. The block keeps the leaves up, and the book will retain its shape. Blocks of proper thickness may be glued directly to the surface of the shelf or mounted on a thin board.—Contributed by John V. Loeffler, Evansville, Ind.

## Pointed Ends for Small Lathe Boring Tools

When making small, fine tools like reamers, mandrels, staffs, etc., it is hard to turn them up on an ordinary

lathe center. When the center in the work is large enough to hold it well while turning, it makes a hole too large in proportion to the work and is also inconvenient in other ways. If the tool is to be hardened, the first place that will develop a crack will be around the large center end. If the tool is fluted, as a reamer or tap, the danger of cracks developing is further accentuated.

A remedy is to use male centers for the work and have a pair of female centers for the lathe and the grinder. The sketch illustrates such centers on a reamer. The piece can be turned as readily as if the holes had been drilled in the ends. In hardening, the risk of cracking is slight compared with what it would be if center holes had been used instead of the pointed ends.—Contributed by Donald A. Hampson, Middletown, N. Y.

## Substitute for Long-Spout Oilcan

An extension can be made to an ordinary oilcan spout if a piece of wire be put through the spout extending the desired distance on the outside. The inner end should be coiled around a pencil and the coil placed securely in the spout, thereby holding the wire in place. The oil will follow the wire to its outer end.—Contributed by Robert Byer, Chicago, Ill.

## Loading Sod on a Scraper

In making a ditch with a plow and scraper, the first plowing in sod is difficult to load on a scraper. The only

A Stable Fork Remodeled to Handle Sod in Loading a Road Scraper

way to load the scraper is by hand. An improvement on this method was accomplished by the use of an ordinary stable fork, which was bent at the shank as shown and provided with a handle, fixed in connection with the regular handle. The chunks of sod could be easily picked up and moved without stooping.—Contributed by A. S. Thomas, Amherstburg, Can.

## Turning Over a Scow

Having occasion to turn over a capsized scow, which floated bottom side up with only about 6 or 8 in. extending above the surface in the harbor, we proceeded as follows: When there was slack water two hawsers were lowered with weights, each hawser being supplied with an eye splice by means of which a loop was formed and slipped over the stanchions at either end of the scow on the off side, as shown in the illustration. A turn or two of the hawsers was taken around the stanchion on

the tug and a strain was put on slowly with the tug until both hawsers were good and taut. Then the tug was "hooked up" on what marine engineers term "a strong gingle," full speed ahead. The result was that the strong pulling power of the tug and the "quick water" from the propeller forced against the near side of the sunken scow turned it right side up. It was then towed to a dry dock.—Contributed by W. F. Quackenbush, New York City.

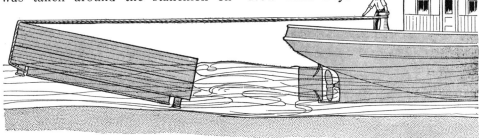

After Attaching the Hawsers to the Off Side of the Scow, They were Drawn Taut with the Tug, Then the "Quick Water" Striking the Under Side of the Scow Forced It Over and Right Side Up

## Locking Device for Shifter Lever

In the ordinary belt shifter, it frequently occurs that the belt will creep from the loose to the tight pulley,

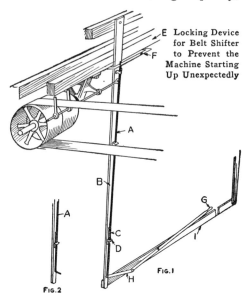

E Locking Device for Belt Shifter to Prevent the Machine Starting Up Unexpectedly

FIG. I

FIG. 2

thereby endangering the operator, who may be caught and injured in the revolving machinery. The locking arrangement shown in the sketch effectually prevents any such creeping. It consists of a latch rod, A, Fig. 1, attached to the shifter lever B so as to have a free, vertical movement. To this rod is attached a spiral spring, C, which, pressing against the lower angle bracket D, tends to keep A in one position. To the overhead beam E is fastened a U-shaped lock bar, F, with a hole at each end, of sufficient size for rod A to pass through freely. Sufficient distance must be allowed between the parallel sides of the U-shaped bar to allow lever B to shift the belt from the loose to the tight pulley.

The device is operated by pressing down on the lower L-shaped end of rod A, Fig. 2, thereby disconnecting it from the lock bar F, after which the lever may be shifted as desired and again locked in position by releasing rod A, the spring forcing it to enter the corresponding hole in the lock bar F when hole and rod are in line.

If the device is to be attached to a long lathe or machine where the operator could not always stand in reach of the shifter lever B, an arrangement of levers G and H, Fig. 1, can be attached to the horizontal bar I, usually found on long-machine belt shifters. By this connection, any downward pressure on the long end of lever G will cause a downward pull on rod A, disengaging it from the lock bar F. Releasing G will again cause the latch rod to resume its usual locked position when in line with one of the lock-bar holes.—Contributed by Joe Bovey, Houston, Texas.

---

## Tanning a Hide

To tan a hide spread it out carefully, with the flesh side up, as soon as possible after skinning, and rub, or sprinkle, on equal parts of saltpeter and powdered alum mixed together; roll up the hide and lay it away for a few days. Unroll and remove the surplus flesh, then stretch it out tightly on a frame to dry. Rub on some neat's-foot oil, which is afterward rubbed out by means of a wedge-shaped paddle. Some trappers stretch the skin against a building where the sun's rays will strike it, and when warm rub out the grease or oil.—Contributed by A. Ashmund Kelly, Malvern, Pa.

---

## Marking a Wire-Gauge Size

Where it is necessary to use one certain size on the wire gauge a great many times it will be convenient to mark that opening to quickly find it without referring to the figures impressed in the metal, which are hard  to see. The marking may be made by placing rubber bands around the narrow metal between the gauge jaws, as shown, and the opening can be found quickly.

# A Loud-Speaking Telephone

### By HAROLD HINTON

An instrument that is rapidly replacing the old-style megaphone has been perfected and is extensively used for announcing the score at baseball games, interesting events, to give commands in the turrets of a battleship, etc. This instrument is known as the loud-speaking telephone, and the receiver closely resembles an electric automobile horn.

In the transmitter A the quality and articulation are largely dependent on the mechanical dimensions of the diaphragm and the manner in which it is mounted. In any diaphragm, a certain tone will be found which is fundamental to it, and as the weight of the moving part, which is attached to the diaphragm, is increased, this tone becomes emphasized. If the moving mass is not kept exceedingly small, this tone interferes with the proper production of the words transmitted.

The problem of designing an efficient transmitter for this service has been that of making use of the largest possible mechanical proportions, in order to permit large currents, without making the moving parts so heavy that the distinctness of articulation is destroyed.

While the loud-speaking telephone is very similar in operation to the regular common-battery telephone, the one particular point followed in the design of the loud-speaking apparatus has been to obtain a method of construction which will give greater emphasis to the harmonies of the voice and less to the fundamental note. Altogether, this method will give better results as far as intelligibility is concerned, and it has been followed out consistently in the construction of both the receiver and transmitter.

In the transmitter, the articulation of the receiver is governed largely by the mechanical characteristics of the diaphragm and the method in which it is mounted.

In the receiver, the diaphragm B has been corrugated and mounted on rubber cushions, C, along the line of phonograph construction, the sound being concentrated and delivered from a

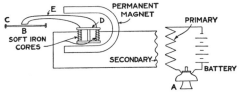

Parts Used in the Construction of a Loud-Speaking Telephone That Are Different from the Ordinary

small metal megaphone-shaped horn. One of the usual features of the modern receiver construction has been departed from, in that metal other than iron is used for the diaphragm. This would be impossible but for the iron armature D, which is acted upon by the pole pieces and thereby allows a phosphor-bronze diaphragm to be used, as this metal produces the best results. A lever arm, E, connects the diaphragm to the armature.

By employing the magnetic principles used in the construction of polarized ringers, the efficiency of articulation was found to be still further increased. A two-way positive action of the diaphragm has become possible by the use of a differential magnetic circuit in the receiver. In the normal condition of the receiver, the diaphragm is practically free from all tension, and this has the effect of greatly increasing the efficiency of construction, due to the fact that a much smaller air gap may be used. It is these new and entirely original constructive features which have produced a loud-speaking telephone that combines clear articulation with a maximum of sound volume.

---

⟪Bookbinder's varnish is made of 8 parts gum shellac, 3 parts gum benzoin, and 2 parts of gum mastic. These are pulverized and placed in 50 parts of denatured alcohol and ½ part of oil of lavender.

## A Rein Holder

A piece of strap iron, ⅞ in. wide, is bent as shown and fastened to the side of the seat with screws. A peg,

or bolt, is attached to the seat, back of the opening in the strap iron. If a bolt is used, it s h o u l d have t h r e a d s long enough to permit a nut to be placed on each side of the seat end, allowing the head to extend on the outside. The ends of the reins can be doubled and inserted in the opening of the bent iron, and then looped over the bolt or pin.—Contributed by Leo F. Wright, Warren, Ill.

## Holder for a Motorcycle Tank-Filler Cap

A holder which will prevent the loss of the filler cap on a motorcycle gasoline tank is shown in the sketch. It

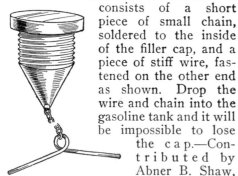

consists of a short piece of small chain, soldered to the inside of the filler cap, and a piece of stiff wire, fastened on the other end as shown. Drop the wire and chain into the gasoline tank and it will be impossible to lose the c a p.—Contributed by Abner B. Shaw, North Dartmouth, Mass.

### Steady-Rest Bearing for Brass Rods

It is frequently necessary to machine a long bar of brass in a lathe and in some instances the only method of supporting the loose end of the brass rod is in the steady rest. Having such a job to do where the brass rod was of the exact required diameter of the

finished piece, I used the following method to prevent scoring by the steady-rest jaws:

A bushing was made twice as long as the diameter of the brass rod, with a hole to snugly fit it. The walls of the bushing were left a thickness equal to one-quarter of the diameter of the hole and slotted lengthwise through one side with a $\frac{1}{16}$-in. milling cutter. This was slipped over the end of the brass rod and held in the steady rest. With a few drops of oil applied occasionally the rod may be worked for any length of time without danger of the surface being marred.—Contributed by M. B. McGall.

## A Draftsman's Eraser

Break off one side, or nib, of an ordinary steel pen, then sharpen both

sides of the remaining one, and a very good eraser for ink lines will be had. It is used in a penholder the same as a pen.—Contributed by H. Cranston, Ottawa, Can.

## A Solder File

Procure an old 8-in. square and anneal it; then file teeth on one surface about $\frac{1}{16}$ in. deep and eight teeth to the inch. The file can be tempered again or used as it is annealed. This makes a fine solder file for metal-cornice workers.—Contributed by Wm. J. Tolson, Lyons, Ia.

## Pliers for Holding Screws

Where it is necessary to handle screws or studs with the ordinary pliers the threads are apt to be damaged. T h e n,

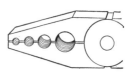

too, it is difficult to hold and handle a round object in flat jaws. A screw-holding plier can be made from the ordinary kind by clamping the jaws together and drilling four or more holes with their centers on the line or joint between the jaws. These holes are then tapped for standard threads. When a screw is taken up in the pliers, the threads are not damaged and the holding power is greater. The surfaces on the jaws should be ground slightly after the holes are finished to make them clamp tightly on the threads of the screw or bolt.—Contributed by J. J. Kolar, Maywood, Ill.

## Tube for Preserving Blueprint Paper

Wrapping and unwrapping the roll of blueprint paper every time a print is desired is a good deal of a nuisance. The covering soon becomes torn and frayed so that neither light nor moisture is excluded. A long tube with a screw cap may be satisfactorily made in the manner indicated in the sketch.

Procure one of those strong cardboard containers with a tin bottom and a screw cap made for mailing bottles and powders. This should be about 2½ in. in diameter and 4 in. or more long. Neatly cut this in two with a sharp knife, and then procure a cardboard mailing tube having an out-

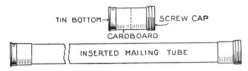

The Metal Ends of a Bottle-Mailing Tube Fastened to a Long Cardboard Tube

side diameter corresponding as closely as possible to the inside diameter of the container. Any slight difference may be remedied by sandpapering off the surplus or by applying a few turns of heavy glued paper if the mailing tube is too small. Having adjusted the diameters so that the two halves of the container closely fit on the ends of the mailing tube, fasten them permanently with glue and then varnish or shellac the entire tube. The container so formed is practically light and moisture-proof.

❡When replacing belts, put them on the driver wheel first.

## An Indicator for Machine-Tool Work

The use of a reliable indicator is almost indispensable for various chucking operations on a lathe, shaper or

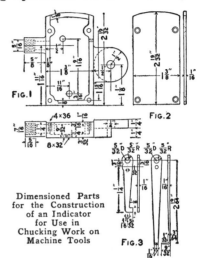

Dimensioned Parts for the Construction of an Indicator for Use in Chucking Work on Machine Tools

miller. The one shown has been in use for some time and has given the best of satisfaction. The body of the instrument, Fig. 1, is made of gray iron, or it may be worked out of mild steel and casehardened. The cover, Fig. 2, and the levers, Fig. 3, are made of sheet steel and casehardened. The shank A, Fig. 4, is of tool steel hardened and drawn to a purple. The body hinges on the shank, so that it can be rotated about 20 deg. of the circle, and is clamped in the desired position with a knurled nut.

The plunger, Fig. 5, is made of tool steel and tempered very hard on the end that comes in contact with the work. All other parts, Fig. 6, are made of soft steel and casehardened.

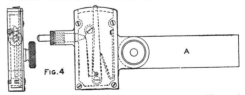

Shank with the Movable Head That can be Clamped Wherever It is Set

The graduations for the pointer may be spaced on a miller or laid off and etched by hand. Use a micrometer head in connection with this work, if extreme accuracy is required. The attachment shown in Fig. 7 is for internal work and places where the regu-

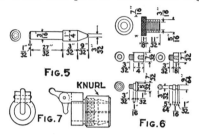

FIG.5

KNURL

FIG.7    FIG.6

The Smaller Parts are Made of Soft Steel Except the Plunger Which is of Tool Steel

lar contact point cannot be used. All parts are dimensioned so that its construction can be easily followed out. —Contributed by A. Dane, Pottstown, Pennsylvania.

## Multiple Tool Holder for Using Short Steel

The illustration shows a handy arrangement for using up short pieces of tool steel, suitable for small forming tools in light cutting operations, such as turning corners, fillets, etc. The tool holder A is enlarged at one end to the same diameter as the tool head, and is turned out to fit it. The round turret head B is slotted on the big end for the desired number of tools, to such a depth that a portion of the tools will project above the top of the head. The round washer C is likewise slotted,

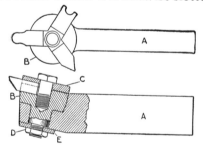

Turret-Head Tool Holder for Using Discarded Pieces of Steel on Light Cutting Operations

but to a depth merely sufficient to hold the tools in place, still forming a small clearance space between the washer and the head, when clamped into place.

The head B is locked in any desired position by the nut D and washer E, there being sufficient clearance between the lower face of B and the holder A.—Contributed by Jas. H. Rodgers, Hamilton, Ont.

## Screw-Slotting Jig

To hold a screw, or stud, without injury to the threads while slotting or doing other work on it is quite difficult, and where several such pieces are to be machined, it is best to provide a holder of some sort that is inexpensive to make. As such parts are of one size, a holder can be constructed quickly as follows:

A block of steel or iron is drilled to make a hole the same size as the screws, and if the jig is to be used in a milling machine, it is advisable to drill two or more holes, as shown at A. Then a slot is cut through the holes and ending at a hole some distance away and near the end of the block, to

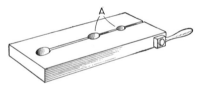

A Screw-Holding Jig to Prevent Damage to the Threads While Slotting the Heads

give spring to the parts and permit the screws to be readily extracted. The jig can be put in an ordinary bench vise, a machine vise, or a chuck, or it can be made an independent fixture, in which case a binding screw with a short pin handle is provided. If used in this manner, the block is clamped directly on the milling-machine table.

## To Light a Fuse

A very sure and quick way to prepare a fuse end for lighting is to split it through the core for about ¼ in. in length and insert the head of a match with a small portion of the stick left intact. The lighting of the match head will cause it to flash and instantly start the fuse.

# The Construction of Wood Flooring

### By WILLIAM GOODWIN

Wood is the material most commonly used in flooring, almost exclusively in private dwellings and for office floors, even in fireproof structures. It is comparatively low in first cost, can be laid with pleasing effects and is not cold nor hard on the feet, as is the case with composition floors of tiling and cement.

In the preparation for the floor, the joists must receive first attention. These depend in size on the load to be carried by the floor, the length of span, and the general proportions of the building. The allowable live load carried in various buildings, not including the weight of the materials of construction, should be estimated at not more than 70 lb. per square foot for dwellings, 100 lb. for office buildings, and 150 lb. for warehouses. The accompanying table gives the safe loads for white-oak beams, in tons of 2,000 lb. uniformly distributed. For woods other than white oak multiply the load figures in the table by .8 for hemlock, .9 for spruce, .9 for white pine, and 1.1 for oak and yellow pine.

Joists are usually spaced from 12 to 15 in. apart. To prevent their vibration and tipping tendency, herringbone

strutting, Fig. 1, or crossbridging of any rough material, about 1 by 3 in., is put in about every 8 ft. If solid

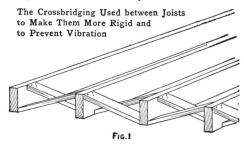

The Crossbridging Used between Joists to Make Them More Rigid and to Prevent Vibration

FIG. 1

blocks are used, the shrinkage of the joists will soon cause them to become loose, unless held in position by means of tie bolts, as shown in Fig. 2. The wall supports for the joists in brick or concrete buildings should consist of 2-in. planks, of the desired width for bearing surface, placed on the foundation walls, as shown in Fig. 3. If this piece be omitted and the joists placed directly on the walls, difficulties will arise in obtaining a level and smooth floor, and after completion serious warping and cracks will show up, due to uneven settling of the foundation. Should the length of the room be so great that the joists are not long

| SIZE OF TIMBER | DISTANCE BETWEEN SUPPORTS IN FEET | | | | | | | | | |
|---|---|---|---|---|---|---|---|---|---|---|
| | 6 | 8 | 10 | 11 | 12 | 14 | 15 | 16 | 17 | 18 |
| | SAFE LOADS IN TONS OF 2000 LB. UNIFORMILY DISTRIBUTED | | | | | | | | | |
| 2 X 6 | 0.67 | 0.50 | 0.40 | 0.36 | 0.33 | 0.29 | 0.27 | 0.25 | 0.24 | 0.22 |
| 2 X 8 | 1.19 | 0.89 | 0.71 | 0.65 | 0.59 | 0.51 | 0.47 | 0.44 | 0.42 | 0.40 |
| 2 X 10 | 1.85 | 1.39 | 1.11 | 1.01 | 0.93 | 0.79 | 0.74 | 0.69 | 0.65 | 0.62 |
| 2 X 12 | 2.67 | 2.00 | 1.60 | 1.45 | 1.33 | 1.14 | 1.07 | 1.00 | 0.94 | 0.89 |
| 3 X 6 | 1.00 | 0.75 | 0.60 | 0.55 | 0.50 | 0.43 | 0.40 | 0.37 | 0.35 | 0.33 |
| 3 X 8 | 1.78 | 1.33 | 1.07 | 0.97 | 0.89 | 0.76 | 0.71 | 0.67 | 0.63 | 0.59 |
| 3 X 10 | 2.78 | 2.08 | 1.67 | 1.52 | 1.39 | 1.19 | 1.11 | 1.04 | 0.98 | 0.93 |
| 3 X 12 | 4.00 | 3.00 | 2.40 | 2.18 | 2.00 | 1.71 | 1.60 | 1.50 | 1.41 | 1.33 |

Table for Determining the Sizes of Joists Necessary to Safely Carry a Load Uniformly Distributed

enough to span the distance between the partition walls, an intermediate supporting wall or girder will be neces-

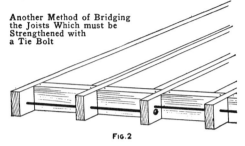

Another Method of Bridging the Joists Which must be Strengthened with a Tie Bolt

FIG. 2

sary. The joists then may be halved as shown in Fig. 4 by overlapping the ends. If the lengths are merely sufficient to allow the ends to butt, a construction as in Fig. 5 may be used. In figuring for lumber it should be kept in mind that lengths come in even feet, as for example 6, 8, 10, and 12 ft. If the joists fit into an unsupported girder or beam and this be weakened too much by the notches, constructions similar to Fig. 6 may be used.

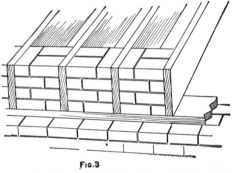

FIG. 3

A Plank is Placed in a Brick Wall on Which to Set the Ends of the Joists

In the usual construction of floors, laths are nailed directly to the joists. When girders or beams are used, special ceiling joists, Fig. 7, are frequently fastened to them, this construction preventing to quite an extent the transmission of vibration to the ceiling.

For sound-proof floors, filler strips may be nailed lengthwise with the joists and rough boards placed on them crosswise, the space between the boards and floor being filled in with sound-proof material, as sawdust, dry ashes, mineral wool, etc., as shown in Fig. 8.

A more expensive method, shown in Fig. 9, is to build special joists for ceiling and floor in such a way that no metal connection exists between the two sets. The sound and vibration are transmitted through the air medium only, which, in comparison with wood or iron, is a much poorer conductor. The simplest, though not such an effective, method of sound-proofing is produced by nailing strips of felt along the edge of the joists, the floor boards resting on these; by thus breaking the solid connection between the floor and the ceiling, a considerable amount of the

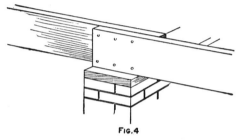

FIG. 4

Overlapping Joist Ends on an Intermediate Wall or Girder to Strengthen Them on a Long Span

vibration can be stopped and noise diminished. To avoid unevenness in the floor due to irregularities in the felt, laths may be first nailed to the felt, the flooring being put on the laths.

In very cheap floor construction, only one layer of board is usually put down, this being placed crosswise and at right angles to the joists. Even in that case, a fairly durable job can be made by taking care in the manner of laying the grain of the boards. With curved grain, the boards should be laid

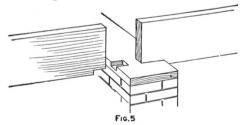

FIG. 5

Where Necessary to Butt the Ends of Joists on a Wall, This Method is Used

so that a natural arch is formed, as in Fig. 10. If this precaution is not observed, the floor will soon wear rough and the edges have a tendency to curl up. Unevenness in floors can frequently be reduced by means of thin strips nailed to the joists to level up their top edges.

The first layer of boards in a double-floor construction is usually placed at an angle of 45° with the joists, thereby producing not only better bracing but also providing a more uniform and level surface for the upper boards. Whenever butt joints are necessary in a floor they should be placed over a joist, to prevent the possibility of sagging. Between the top and under flooring should be placed a layer of building paper to protect the room against cold and moisture.

The top flooring usually is made of hard woods matched on the edges and, in the best construction, also at the ends. Three grades of wood are adopted by hardwood dealers: Clear, No. 1, and factory. The clear wood is adapted for the best construction; No. 1, for service in stores and public buildings, and the factory grade, for rough wear, as in factories and warehouses. Three thicknesses can be obtained: $\frac{3}{8}$ in., in clear and No. 1 only; $1\frac{3}{16}$ and $1\frac{1}{16}$ in., for all three grades. The widths of the stock vary from 1½ to 3¼ inches.

The top boards should not be laid until the plastering is completed and dry, so as to avoid the chances of the flooring absorbing the moisture, causing warping and buckling. The top boards, if properly prepared, should have been thoroughly dried at the factory. It, therefore, is best not to accept flooring unloaded or delivered in wet weather. Neither should it be stored in freshly plastered buildings, damp places, or sheds with open sides, where the moisture would affect the exposed ends of the boards. If the boards are put down while damp, they will warp and expose large cracks after having been seasoned in a warm room. The top flooring should not be placed directly on the building paper, for by doing so the paper will wrinkle up and enter the grooves when the boards are being drawn up, thereby preventing a

close fit between tongue and groove. The difficulty can be overcome by placing laths or thin strips on top of

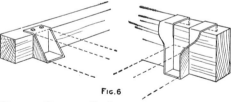

Fig.6

Straps or Shoes are Used on an Unsupported Girder for the Joist Ends

the paper and laying the matched boards on these.

It is advisable not to allow the flooring to fill the space close up to the walls, as in that case any expansion of the boards would result in bulging the surface or spreading the walls. The molding or baseboard will cover up the space allowed for expansion. Special care should be taken to lay the

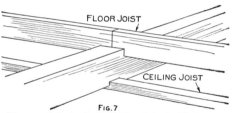

FLOOR JOIST

CEILING JOIST

Fig.7

Manner of Fastening a Ceiling Joist to Girders to Prevent Vibration of the Ceiling

first top board square with the sides of the room and each succeeding strip the same way; otherwise the end matching will be thrown out of line, exposing cracks. The boards should be drawn up tight against one another by placing a piece of two-by-four against the tongue and striking it with a sledge or heavy hammer.

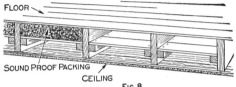

FLOOR

SOUND PROOF PACKING

CEILING

Fig.8

A Part of the Space between the Joists Filled to Make Sound-Proof Floors

In fastening the boards, the nails should be driven at an angle of about 60°. If they are driven too perpendicularly, the tongue is liable to split off; if at too small an angle, the floor will be liable to buckle. The ⅜-in.-

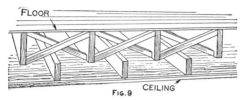

FIG. 9

Another Construction of a Sound-Proof Floor Where the Ceiling Joist is Separate from the Floor Joist

thick flooring should be nailed every 8 to 10 in. with 3-penny nails; the $\frac{13}{16}$-in. should be held down by 8-penny cut flooring brads, approximately 16 in. apart. The nails, after being driven nearly their entire length, should be set by as few final blows as possible, any light tapping with the hammer having a tendency to loosen them. Bruising the edge of the board must be avoided, as such places cannot be easily fixed. If proper care is taken in the selection of the strips, the appearance of the floor can be improved by not putting together colors of great or striking contrast.

Due to irregularities in the under boards, a perfectly smooth surface cannot be obtained on a finished floor without first scraping and sandpapering it. This should be done in a lengthwise direction with the grain, and, in the absence of a regular scraping machine, may be done by means of a planer blade or broad chisel.

In finishing the floor, having thoroughly cleaned it with a dry rag, it should first be given a coat of filler carefully rubbed. This is especially

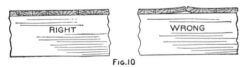

FIG. 10

The Right and Wrong Way of Laying a Floor: The Former Prevents the Board from Warping

necessary with soft woods having large pores. Then several coats of alcohol shellac should be applied, each being allowed to dry before the next is put on, after which the finishing coats of varnish may be added, letting each dry

thoroughly as before. If it is desired to obtain a wax finish, use a light-colored floor wax instead of the varnish, taking the precaution to rub each coat in thoroughly before adding the next. Maplewood floors are frequently given coats of boiled linseed oil thoroughly rubbed into the surface with woolen cloths. For softwood floors, stains are frequently desired and should be put on after the filler coat, to get the best results.

## Homemade Automobile Whistle

A simple exhaust whistle for an automobile may be made as follows: In a 10-in. length of ¾ or ⅞-in. piece of brass tubing, A, cut a notch, as shown, about 1 in. from the end. A wood stopper with one side shaved off flat, as in a toy whistle, is then inserted in the notched end and the other end completely stopped with a plug.

Procure two blocks of hard wood, B and C, 5 in. square and ¾ in. thick, and in the center of the block B bore

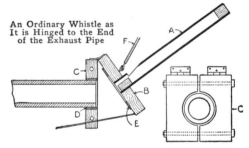

An Ordinary Whistle as It is Hinged to the End of the Exhaust Pipe

a hole so that the brass tube will be held snugly when driven in. In the other block C, cut a hole to fit the exhaust pipe from the muffler, and drill two $\frac{5}{16}$-in. holes through it edgeways for ¼-in. bolts. The block is then sawed in half so that it can be clamped over the exhaust pipe. A strip of asbestos, D, is placed around the pipe under the wood to insure a good grip when the bolts are drawn up. The blocks are hinged together so that the block B can be swung down flat against the block C. A thin, flat ring of asbestos, E, is fastened on the block to prevent leakage around the sides. A light screen-door spring, F, is stretched from the block B to any convenient point under the car to draw the whistle end away when not in use. A wire, run over pulleys to the driver's seat, operates the device. The wire may be fastened to a pedal or to a small handle. The block may be secured to the muffler pipe in any position, with the hinges on the top or at the side, according to the space requirements under the car.—Contributed by B. A. Thresher, Lakeville, Conn.

## To Repair a Felt Roof

During the winter months snow and ice on the roofs present some unusual problems. One factory roof, with none too much pitch, was covered with a felt-composition roofing. Usually the snow was removed with shovels, but conditions after one snowfall of about 1 ft. were such that this was not cleared off and a few days later there was a troublesome leak developed on the lower side. The warmth from within heated the roof so that part of the snow melted and the water run slowly down and froze near the eaves, thus forming a dam. To chop off this ice meant to cut some holes in the roofing, and it appeared as if the only thing to do was to let it leak until the entire lot had melted and run away.

One of the carpenters asked permission to try an experiment, which was granted. Some cement was taken to the roof and a spot found where a lot of water was standing somewhat higher than the point of the leak. A quantity of the cement was poured into the water which carried it under the ice and snow to where it was escaping through the hole causing the leak. Enough cement was deposited in the hole to close it in two hours and the leak was entirely stopped in a short time afterward.—Contributed by Phil Wood, Rochester, N. Y.

❈A knob formed of friction tape on the end of straight tool handles will aid in guiding the tool as well as prevent its slipping from the hand.

## Gear-Blank Pattern from an Old Gear

To avoid the necessity of making a gear-blank pattern, particularly for a rush job, when the old gear is at hand,

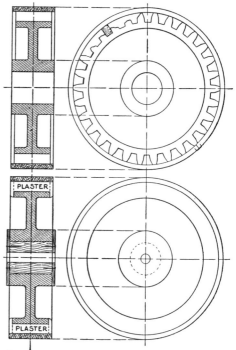

Leather is Placed on the Addendum Line and the Spaces are Filled with Plaster of Paris

proceed as follows: For small gears, up to 12 in. in diameter, place a single thickness of leather around the old gear—belt leather will do very well—and join the ends by means of staples. For large wheels use double thicknesses of leather, to allow for shrinkage of the casting, and for finish. If necessary to finish the sides of the gear, the leather should be cut ¼ in. wider than the face. If the gear is badly stripped, small pieces of wood, as high as the depth of the teeth, should be placed between the casting and the leather, so the circumference will remain true. Plaster of paris can then be poured between the teeth and finished off even with the sides or leather band. The plaster can be stopped off from entering the side space by means of molding sand, wood, or clay. A plug is driven into the hole in the hub and the necessary thickness of wood or leather for hub finish tacked on. The dowel-pin holes for the core print are then drilled in the plug, and the pattern is ready for the foundry. By having some one prepare the plaster while the rest of the pattern is being made, a very quick job can be accomplished.—Contributed by N. H. Parry, Jr., Kenosha, Wis.

## Holders for Barricades Surrounding Street Excavations

The combination flagpole, lantern lock, and barricade holder is made of pipe fittings throughout, except for the

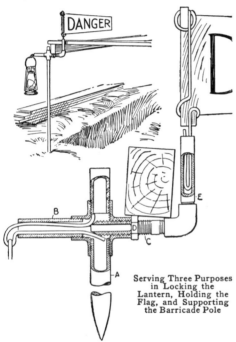

Serving Three Purposes in Locking the Lantern, Holding the Flag, and Supporting the Barricade Pole

lantern and flag holder. A cross, having a ¾-in. straightway opening, one ⅜-in. side outlet, and the other ½ in., makes an excellent head for the post. The pipe A, of sufficient length, is pointed to enter the ground. The projecting ½-in. nipple B carries a ⅛-in. steel spring wire, bent as shown. When the spring is inserted in the nipple with the lantern swinging on the outer end, it is locked in place by the beveled end of the ⅜-in. nipple C. The locknut D holds it tightly. The el and nipple E make a standard for the flag wire and provide a place to lay the barricade pole.—Contributed by J. D. Westman, Pensacola, Fla.

## Large Hole in an Aluminum Crank Case Closed by Welding

There was a large hole broken in an aluminum crank case and the piece had been lost. From all appearances the cost of repairing would be considerable, but by adopting the following method it was accomplished at a very reasonable price.

Back of the hole, which was about 5 in. across, and on the inside of the case I placed a thin sheet of aluminum; then a sufficient amount of waste was forced in behind to make the sheet conform to the contour of the inside of the crank case. The aluminum sheet and edge of the hole, which was previously filed level, were greased. The hole was then filled with plaster of paris which was molded to the shape of the lost part as near as possible. When the plaster had set it was removed, shellacked and used as a pattern. From this pattern a piece was cast that exactly fitted the hole. The welding was then a simple matter.—Contributed by P. D. Merrill, Chicago.

## A Vine Cutter

Having need of a vine cutter with which to reach the tops of hop vines, I made one that gave remarkable results by fastening a mowing-machine sickle blade to a long pole with bolts. With an upward and a downward slash it will cut vines or branches 1 in. in diameter better than they can be cut with a pruning tool.—Contributed by L. Pedrose, Seattle, Wash.

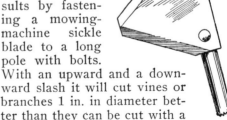

### Remedy for Sprains

A reliable remedy for a slight sprain is the application of something cold to the injured member. Wring out a towel soaked in cold water, wrap it lightly about the injured part, covering all that is swollen. Cover this with a dry bath towel and securely fasten it. Allow the patient to remain under cover to keep warm and prevent the towel from drying out. This will remove the inflammation rapidly.—Contributed by L. Alberta Norrell, Gainesville, Ga.

### A Saw Clamp

A carpenter being hindered in his work of placing hanger blocks by the dullness of his saw and having no way to sharpen it, happened to have a file, but the clamp was in the tool box about

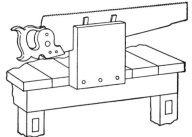

The Back of the Saw is Inserted in the Groove and Firmly Held with Wedges

a mile away. A piece of timber was ripped with the saw and the saw dropped back downward into the groove. A couple of wedges were whittled and forced into the groove with the saw which held it firmly in place. The block was nailed to the end of a bench and the saw then filed as neatly as if held with a regular saw clamp.—Contributed by F. W. Bently, Milwaukee, Wis.

### Tool Holder for Grindstone

The illustration shows a simple device whereby chisels and similar tools may be ground rapidly and to the desired taper. It consists of a U-shaped frame, A, with a roller attached at each end and a holding arrangement

for the tool. Thread spools, with the flanges removed, will do very well for rollers. The tool is held in place on

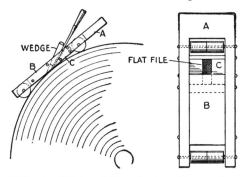

Holder for Chisels and Plane Irons to Sharpen Them Evenly on a Grindstone

the two tapered pieces, B and C, by means of a wedge, as shown. If a piece of a flat file is imbedded in the block C, the tool will be held more firmly. Variations in the taper of the tool point can be had by using a different size of roller at one end of the frame.

### To Prevent Spilling Oil from Tipped-Over Can

Oilcans are easily turned over when working about machinery, and a considerable amount of oil is wasted before discovered. A very simple little device to overcome this trouble can be made by anyone in a few minutes. Solder a disk of sheet metal on the upper surface of the base on the spout. The disk should be a little larger in diameter than the bottom of the can. This will prevent the oil from running out of the can when upset.—Contributed by Stanley Radcliffe, Laurel, Md.

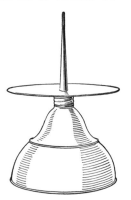

¶A machine should never be stopped by grabbing the belt.

## Adjusting Slack of a Belt

The slack of a belt running straight between two pulleys can be easily taken up by means of the adjuster

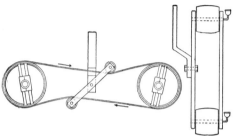

The Slack in the Belt is Taken Up Evenly from Both Sides

shown. The adjuster consists of a frame, carrying a small pulley at each end, supported loosely at its center. The pull of the belt will keep it taut.—Contributed by J. Harger, Honolulu, Hawaiian Islands.

## Finding Gear Diameter with Only a Broken Piece

It is often necessary to find the diameter of a gear of which only a piece of the rim remains. This can be accomplished as follows. Place one point of the dividers on the extreme circumference, at A, and strike an arc near the center at B; then set one point of the dividers on the right side, at C, and strike another arc at B, being careful not to change the dividers. Do likewise on the point D. The point where the three arcs intersect at B

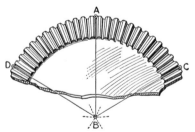

Locating the Center with Dividers to Find the Diameter of a Gear

will be the center of the gear, from which the diameter may be found.—Contributed by Russel E. Hollis, Chicago.

## Cleaning Carbon Commutator Brushes

A very easy method to clean carbon commutator brushes is to insert a piece of sandpaper between the brush and the commutator with the abrasive side to the brush. Draw the paper back and forth until all the dirt is removed. It is not necessary to remove the brushes from their position, and the paper takes the curve of the commutator. After cleaning the brush, be sure to remove all grit from the brush end and the commutator bars to prevent scoring.

## Tape-Measure Holder

In measuring the distance between iron or brick columns, piers, walls of buildings, etc., it is necessary to have an assistant to hold the tape end. Many times no one is at hand and the measurement can only be made with difficulty. For such work I constructed

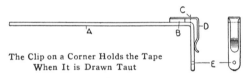

The Clip on a Corner Holds the Tape When It is Drawn Taut

a clip for holding the tape end as follows:

A strip of brass, A, about $\frac{1}{4}$ in. wide and 4 in. long, was obtained and a square bend made about 1 in. from the end. A block of metal, B, small enough to fit inside the tape ring, was soldered on the long piece near the bend, allowing sufficient distance, C, from the end to permit the tape ring to come in line with the inside of the bend. On this block was soldered a piece of spring brass, D, for the purpose of keeping the tape ring on the block.

In use, the tape ring is slipped under the brass spring clip and over the block. The device may be put on the corner of a building or edge of a pier, and if the tape is held fairly taut, measurements can be made. The device can be used in any position on flat or horizontal surfaces, and can be placed on square or round corners. If for any reason it is desired to keep the holder in place after measurements are taken, a hole can be drilled at E, and a tack driven into the woodwork or mortar joint.—Contributed by Geo. L. Brown, Albany, N. Y.

## An Emergency Pipe Coupling

While doing work in the oil fields I found it difficult to keep a sufficient quantity of pipe couplings on hand and in their absence I have made quite a few of these fittings in the following manner: The threads of the pipe ends were thoroughly cleaned and given a coat of black lead. A piece of brass tube was procured having an inside diameter ⅛ in., or more, larger than the outside pipe size. A hole was bored in a piece of hard wood to receive the brass shell which was cleaned and dipped into soldering fluid, then while hot it was driven into the hole bored in the wood. The tube with the wood was slipped on one pipe and then the pipe ends were brought together. A piece of copper wire of a size to let it halfway into the threads was procured and dipped in the soldering fluid. The wire was wrapped in the threads, beginning on one pipe and finishing on the other. Then the brass tube was moved centrally over the pipe threads, the ends stopped up with clay similar to babbitting a box on a shaft, allowing a vent at one end and a gate at the other, and babbitt poured in. This made a good, serviceable coupling and the wire made a steam-tight thread.—Contributed by J. B. Murphy, Plainfield, N. J.

## Drilling Holes Straight Through Diameter of Shaft

It is impossible to drill a hole in a round shaft accurately unless some sort of a jig is used. One of the best and least expensive methods for this work is to make a collet of the same outside diameter as the shaft to be drilled, and bore a perfectly central hole through it the size of the drill used in drilling the hole through the shaft. The shaft is placed in a

vise and the collet set on top of it, as shown in the illustration, and both are clamped together. The drill is then

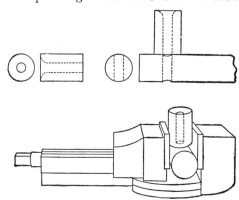

The Vise Grips Both Stock and Collet, and the Drill Must Enter Straight

run through the collet hole, which guides it for drilling the hole in the round stock.—Contributed by G. T. Du Bois, Detroit, Mich.

## Putting on Buggy-Axle Clips

A very handy tool for putting on buggy-axle clips can be made of a joint taken from a discarded buggy top. The shape of the tool is shown to the right, and in applying the clips it is used as shown at the left. The tool is not difficult to make. One end of the

The Yoke Ends are Easily Drawn Together with the Tool and This Clip Slipped over Them

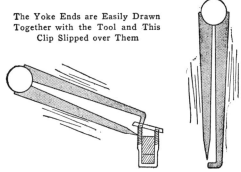

hinged forging is sharpened and the other turned in at right angles.—Contributed by H. T. Mitchell, Tayah, Texas.

⟪Before starting a machine look it over carefully to make sure every part is in working order.

## Magnet Support for an Electric Trouble Lamp

When one is working about a gasoline engine he is usually in his own light and some one must hold the lamp

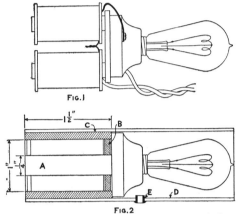

FIG. 1

FIG. 2

**The Lamp with the Magnet Base will Remain in Any Position on Iron**

so that its light will fall where it is most desired. The simple device shown in Fig. 1 does away with the extra person for holding the lamp, as the electromagnet will hold it any place on an iron support. The winding of the electromagnet is connected in series with the lamp and it will be energized only when the lamp is being used.

The electromagnet is similar to the ones used in the ordinary vibrating bell; in fact, the one shown was taken from a discarded bell and the lamp socket mounted on it, which with the lamp and wire constituted the complete device. A suitable protection should be provided for the lamp, so that if the circuit happens to be broken the lamp will not be broken when it falls.

If a better-appearing outfit is desired, one may be constructed at a very small cost, as shown in the cross section, Fig. 2. The magnet instead of having two windings, as shown in Fig. 1, has a single winding around a soft core, A. One end of the spool on which the winding is placed is made from a piece of soft iron, as shown at B. The completed spool is inclosed in a short piece of soft-iron pipe, C, and is held in place by means of several small burrs made

on the inside edge of the pipe after the spool is in place. The magnetic circuit in this case is through the core of the magnet, the end of the spool, the piece of iron pipe and the metal connecting the core and the pipe at the left end, where it is placed against some iron object. The terminals of the winding are brought out through two insulated holes in the metal washer. The lamp is mounted on the end of the spool in such a way that it will not interfere with the terminals of the winding.

The whole device is inclosed in a piece of brass tubing, D, which fits on the outside of the pipe C, and extends out a sufficient distance to protect the lamp as shown in Fig. 2. An opening is cut out in the brass pipe through which the flexible cord connecting the device with the source of energy may pass. The opening is provided with a small insulating bushing, E. The spool is wound full of No. 22 gauge cotton-covered copper wire.

## Replacing a Detachable Tire Rim

It is a more difficult job to replace an automobile tire rim than to remove

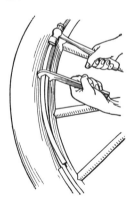

it, but this can be made much easier with the use of an open-end wrench usually supplied with the tools in the box. Such a wrench with an opening to fit over both rims, as shown in the sketch, can be driven around the wheel, thus forcing the tire rim in place.—Contributed by W. W. Slocum, Buffalo, New York.

❡To prevent burning the hand with steam while filling a hot teakettle, run the water from the faucet through the spout.

## Fountain Mucilage Can

Any handy person who has a soldering outfit can construct a fountain mucilage can out of a regular mucilage
pot or ordinary preserving jar, some
tin cans, and several pieces of brass or
iron tubing. Make a suitable opening
in the tin cover of the jar A, and solder
onto it a small can, B, or short cylinder,
open only at the end connecting to A,
but having a hole near the closed end
suitable for attaching a square or
round pipe, C. This is soldered to the
cross pipe D, which should have a hole
in the center to fit C, so that any
mucilage from the jar A is free to pass
through B and C and flow out at the
ends of D. A simple way of making
connection for C and D is to use an
ordinary pipe tee with the pipes
screwed into it as shown at G. The
brush cans E are punctured near the
bottom to admit pipe D and then soldered to it. This practically completes
the fountain. The wires F may be

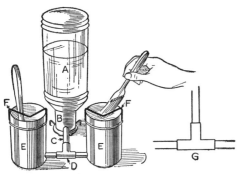

The Small Cans will be Kept Filled to a Certain
Level at All Times

soldered to the cans E for the purpose
of brushing off any surplus paste.
Coating the cans, wire, and brush
handles with paraffin tends to keep
them cleaner.

## Torpedo Fork for Railway Flagmen

The device shown in the sketch is
known as the torpedo fork. It allows
a person standing on the rear end of a

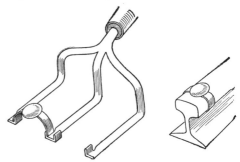

Fork for Holding the Spring of a Torpedo to Place
It on a Rail behind a Train

train to place torpedoes on the rail
while the train is in motion.

The tines are spaced wide enough
apart and are so shaped that the rail
head will pass up between them. The
ends of the tines are flattened and bent
as shown, while the whole fork is
fastened in a handle of suitable length.

In operation the torpedo spring is
opened and slipped over the clips on
the tines. The fork is then lowered
over the rail. When the torpedo
strikes the rail it is knocked off the
clips, and the spring grasps the rail
head.

These forks can be made single if
desired, but the double fork is more
convenient where it is required to set
two torpedoes close together.—Contributed by Clyde L. Adams, La
Grange, Ill.

---

¶A help in starting an automobile
motor in cold weather is to soak a rag
in hot water and wrap it around the
carburetor and intake manifold.

## Speaking Tube with Both Transmitter and Receiver

It was necessary for me to communicate with the workmen on the second floor at times, and I was compelled to go up, as there were no telephone or speaking-tube connections. Knowing it was useless to ask for material, I found some old pieces of pipe in the scrap and connected them up to make a speaking tube, as shown in the illustration. The transmitting mouthpiece at each end was made of a tin funnel soldered in a nipple which was turned into the side outlet of a tee fitting, and the receiver consisted of a funnel attached to a piece of rubber gas tube fastened to the end of the tee. This made it possible to listen and talk the same as with a telephone. Rapping on the pipe in one room could be plainly heard in any part of the other one.—Contributed by J. O. McDonnell, Toronto, Can.

## Gauge for Determining Density of Salt Water

For protection against fire in manufacturing plants, barrels of salt water are frequently set around in various places. If the brine be of sufficient density, freezing of the water will be prevented in cold weather. A handy gauge for determining the density of the solution can be readily made out of a lath or strip of wood and any ordinary nut. Cut the lath tapering, as in the sketch, with the small end rounded off to fit the nut securely. The stick should be cut off a little longer than the depth it will sink

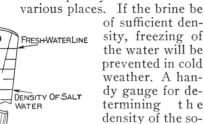

FRESH WATER LINE

DENSITY OF SALT WATER

to in fresh water. This should then be marked for the fresh-water line, after which it may be placed in a salt solution of the necessary density and the depth again marked. The loop of string at the upper end is for carrying it. If the gauge is to be used frequently, it would be better to varnish it, to insure against water-logging.—Contributed by M. Clogston, Terre Haute, Ind.

## Homemade Revolution Counter

For average accuracy and speed the revolution counter shown in the illustration will serve as well as a manufactured article. It consists of a wooden frame of convenient and sufficient width and length to contain two wire spindles. These should be made of stiff wire, pointed at one end and provided with a centering plug at the other. Solid-metal washers are fitted in the frame and countersunk slightly to serve as bearings for the pointed ends of the spindles. Holes are drilled at the opposite sides of the

A Homemade Revolution Counter or Speed Indicator for Finding the Speed of Shafting

frame to allow the spindles to pass through easily. In order to hold the spindles in place with sufficient stiffness so their momentum will not cause them to revolve after the frame is removed from a rotating shaft, collars are provided and held in place by soldering, or with pins placed through holes drilled in the spindle. At one end of each spindle a hole is drilled for fastening the end of a thread so that, when assembled, the holes will be at opposite ends of the frame. A strong, fine thread of sufficient length to produce a large number of turns is fastened to the spindles and wound up. If too much string is used, the coils will be too close together. It is advisable to put on sufficient string so that the total number of coils is divisible by 10. When using the counter, the exact number of coils on each spindle must be known before starting; it is therefore best to start with one full spindle and the other empty. The length of time required in getting the speed will be determined largely by the number of coils available. If the speed is high the spindle will be wound up rapidly and a short time must be figured on, or the spindle will wind up all the available thread and break it at the end. Full minutes, or convenient fractions thereof, should be used in taking the speed. The tedious work comes in counting the coils. This can be partly overcome by placing a small knot on every tenth coil. It will then only be necessary to count the knots, multiply that number by ten and add the several coils wound up outside of the last knot.—Contributed by P. A. Baumeister, Easton, Pa.

## How to Make an Electric-Fuse and Lamp-Trouble Tester

A great many good fuses and electric globes are thrown away for the simple reason that there is no device for testing them out. The sketch is descriptive of a simple device for testing plug fuses, inclosed fuses, opens in circuits, and incandescent lamps.

The base is made from a piece of insulating material, such as slate or, preferably, a composition that is not easily broken, approximately 8 in. long, 5½

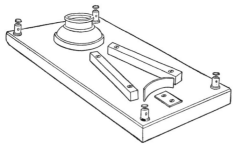

The Parts as They are Located on an Insulated Base to Make a Trouble Tester

in. wide, and ⅝ in. thick. Four binding posts, with back connections, are mounted in the four corners, as shown.

The screws fastening these binding posts in place are countersunk on the under side, and a washer is provided under the head

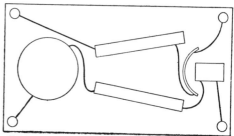

Wiring Diagrams Showing Manner of Connecting the Parts from the Back of the Base

of each screw. A lamp receptacle is mounted on the face of the base, in the center and near one end, as shown. Two pieces of brass, ⅜ in. square and about 4 in. long, are mounted on the base by means of suitable screws with their upper ends closer together than their lower ends. A piece of thin sheet brass is bent into a curved form and mounted on the lower end, and a small piece of strap brass is mounted inside of the curved piece, as shown.

The various parts of the device are connected as follows: Starting with the upper left binding post, connect it to the terminal of the socket; connect the other terminal of the socket to the left piece of brass, and from this to the piece of brass in the center of the curved piece at the lower end of the base; thence to the lower left binding post. The upper right binding post is connected to the right piece of brass, then to the circular piece of brass and to the right lower binding post. The wires used in making these connections should be imbedded in grooves cut in the under side of the base. Place an ordinary 110-volt lamp in the receptacle and connect the two upper binding posts to the source of current and the device is complete.

Lamps and plug fuses may be tested by placing their two terminals in contact with the curved piece and flat piece mounted in its center. If the circuit through the fuse, or lamp, is complete, the test lamp at the upper end of the board will glow, and the degree of its illumination will depend on the amount of resistance introduced in the circuit. Thus, if a lamp of the same kind and candlepower as the test lamp is being tested, both will be subjected to one-half its normal voltage, while a fuse will introduce practically no resistance in the lamp test,

and it will burn up to the full candlepower if the fuse is good.

Inclosed fuses may be tested by placing their terminals in contact with the two strips of brass set in a V-shape. Flatirons, electric heaters, motors, etc., can be tested by connecting them to the two lower binding posts.

### Replacing Paper-Box Covers

The replacing of a cover on a paper box is not easy, especially if it contains small heavy articles, such as screws 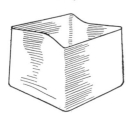 or small nuts. Many articles in the hardware trade are put up in these boxes. A little trick that will enable anyone to quickly cover the box is shown in the illustration. Push inward slightly on the sides of the box to bend them in, as shown, and the cover will slip on easily.

### Fastening Fiber Knobs to Screws

A number of small adjusting screws, with fiber knobs securely fastened to them, were required, and, as they were 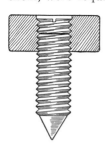 to be used on high-tension electrical apparatus, it was, of course, out of the question to secure the knobs to the screws in the usual manner with a pin driven through the fiber and screw, as this would present an uncovered metal part where a shock could be received through the hand.

After some experimenting, I hit upon the following plan, which was to drill and tap a hole through the center of the fiber knob and turn the screw in about two-thirds of the way. Setscrews of the proper size were procured and one of them was turned down on the screw in each knob. The

setscrew was allowed to sink below the surface of the knob. The recess thus formed was filled with a highly insulating compound.—Contributed by G. N. Garrison, E. Orange, N. J.

### Paper Stencils

As I had a job of numbering some benches and was unable to make the figures neatly, I thought of cutting  some stencils, but had no numbers to draw the outlines. In looking among the things stored in my desk I found an old calendar pad and from this I cut out the figures in stencil form, which served the purpose as well as regular stencils. A brush, cut short, and some thick paint were used.—Contributed by Chas. D. Morgan, Dayton, O.

### A Twine Cutter

A very simple twine cutter can be made from a common screwhook, by filing the inner side of the curved end to a cutting edge. With the hook screwed into a convenient place, the twine may be cut easily by drawing it over the sharp edge.—Contributed by U. B. Gilroy, Marysville, Cal.

# How to Make an Aerial Propeller

## By JOE V. ROMIG

A great difference of opinion in designing the various parts of an aeroplane seems to exist regarding the proper construction of the propeller. No one propeller will work equally well for all cases. In the following description will be given the approximate formulas and proportions of propellers suitable for driving homemade gliders, canoes, and wagons, together with a method of constructing them.

The principle of a propeller action may be compared with that of a bolt turning in a nut, the turning bolt acting as the propeller while the stationary nut takes the place of the air. In actual practice, only a small section of the bolt A, Fig. 1, is taken. In order to balance this section, an exact duplicate of it is set on the opposite side, thus forming the two-bladed propeller of Fig. 2.

The "pitch" of a propeller can be best explained, by referring to Fig. 1, as that distance through which the bolt would move in a lengthwise direction during one turn, or equal to the distance B.

In the case of the bolt and nut every turn, no matter how slight, will move the bolt lengthwise a corresponding amount. It hardly need be mentioned that the propeller cannot act in the same way, due to the yielding nature of the air. The difference between the distance a propeller would move through, theoretically, and the distance it actually moves forward, is called its "slip." In the bolt and nut no slip occurs; in water the slip may be as low as 20 per cent, but in air it is greater, averaging about 50 per cent, or, in other words, the propeller theoretically covers twice the distance it actually passes through. Slip will vary with the design and care in the construction of the propeller. Some well-known makes have reduced the slip to 25 per cent.

By "thrust" is meant the amount of push or pull that a propeller can exert.

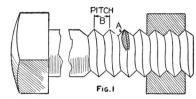

Relation Existing between the Pitch of an Ordinary Bolt Thread and That of a Propeller Blade

It is frequently given in pounds per engine horsepower, varying with the different designs of propellers. A fair average value may be taken as 10 lb. per horsepower; thus, if it required a pull of 20 lb. to draw a wagon at a rate of five miles per hour, the engine horsepower to drive the same wagon with a propeller would be 20 ÷ 10, or 2. For driving an aeroplane, an average thrust equal to $\frac{1}{6}$ the total weight can be assumed; thus, for a 1,500-lb. machine a thrust of 1,500 ÷ 6, or 250 lb., is required. Knowing the amount of thrust, the necessary theoretical engine horsepower may be figured from the following formula:

Hp.= thrust × speed in feet per
  hour ÷ 60 × 33,000 . . . . . (1)

For a biplane a speed of about 30 miles per hour is necessary to raise it off the ground; in a monoplane the speed must be greater. Assuming a machine of 1,500-lb. weight, requiring

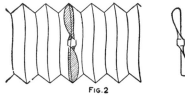

FIG.2

A Two-Blade Propeller and Its Similarity to the Threads of a Double-Threaded Bolt

a thrust of 250 lb., and traveling at a rate of 30 miles per hour, the necessary theoretical engine power would be found by substituting in the above equation, as follows:

Hp.= 250 × 30 × 5,280 ÷ 60 ×
  33,000 = 20;

but assuming losses in engine friction

and transmission to propeller of about 50 per cent, the actual horsepower would have to be double, or 40.

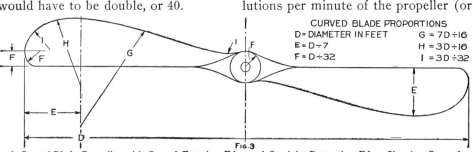

CURVED BLADE PROPORTIONS
D = DIAMETER IN FEET
E = D ÷ 7
F = D ÷ 32
G = 7D ÷ 16
H = 3D ÷ 16
I = 3D ÷ 32

FIG.3

A Curved-Blade Propeller with Curved Entering Edge and Straight Retreating Edge, Showing General Proportions Used in Designs Suitable for Propelling Homemade Gliders, Boats, and Ice Boats

The thrust available with a propeller may be approximately found by this formula:

Thrust $= .0019688 \, D^2 \times V^2$ . . . (2),

in which D equals diameter of propeller in feet, and V the velocity of the air leaving propeller, which, in turn, is equal to the pitch of the propeller in feet times its revolutions per second, times the efficiency of the propeller. The second equation can also be written:

$D^2 =$ desired thrust $\div V^2 \times .0019688$ (3),

hence $D = \dfrac{1}{V} \sqrt{\dfrac{\text{Thrust}}{.0019688}}$.

The diameter of a propeller is limited by its peripheral speed or the linear distance the extreme outside edge would travel. The peripheral speed, ordinarily taken, varies from 12,000 to 40,000 ft. per minute. Assume a speed

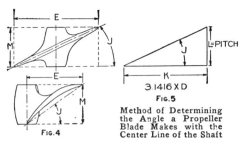

FIG.5

Method of Determining the Angle a Propeller Blade Makes with the Center Line of the Shaft

FIG.4

Difference between a Flat-Blade and a Curved-Blade Propeller, Showing Method of Obtaining Thickness of Hub

of 20,000 ft. per minute and an engine speed of 1,000 revolutions per minute, then the diameter of propeller can be figured as follows:

$D = L \div 3.1416 \times$ R.P.M. . . . . (4),

where L is the assumed linear speed of the propeller tip, and R.P.M. the revolutions per minute of the propeller (or engine, if direct-connected). Hence

$D = 20,000 \div 3.1416 \times 1,000 =$ 6.4 ft.

For any desired speed, the necessary pitch, P, of the propeller can be determined by the following formula:

$P = M \times 5,280 \div 60 \times$ R.P.M. $\times E$ . (5),

where M equals the actual distance covered, in miles per hour; R.P.M. equals the speed of the propeller in revolutions per minute, and E equals the efficiency of the propeller; that is, the ratio of the distance the propeller actually moves forward to the distance it theoretically would move forward if there were no slip.

In the example of the speed of 30 miles per hour for the aeroplane, and an efficiency of 50 per cent at a speed of 1,000 R.P.M. for the propeller, the pitch would be

$P = 30 \times 5,280 \div 60 \times 1,000 \times .5 =$ 5.28 ft.

With the diameter and pitch of the propeller thus figured, the thrust could be found by substituting in the second formula:

Thrust $= .0019688 \times 6.4^2 \times (\tfrac{1,000}{60} \times 5.28 \times .5)^2 = 156$ lb.

But as this thrust is smaller than originally figured, a larger diameter and higher speed must be taken.

The engine horsepower necessary to drive the propeller can be determined by substituting in the first formula:

Hp. $= 156 \times 30 \times 5,280 \div 60 \times 33,000$.

Since there are many different designs for propellers, general proportions may be assumed as given in Fig. 3.

How to determine the thickness of the hub parallel with the direction of the shaft will be described later on.

In the simplest but least efficient propellers, the blades can be made flat instead of curved. In the flat blade, the angle J, Fig. 4, is determined as in Fig. 5. Lay off a distance, K, equal to 3.1416 times diameter of propeller in feet. The distance L is laid off at right angles to K, and is equal to the pitch of the propeller in feet. Having decided on the width, E, of the blade, the thickness of the hub M, or necessary thickness of block, may be found by laying off the triangle, as in Fig. 4. In a flat-blade propeller, one-half is usually placed on each side of the center line, as in Fig. 6. In a well designed propeller, the blade changes its angle from tip to hub and is also curved to correspond to a theoretical screw.

In Fig. 1 it is seen that every point of the bolt must move exactly the same distance in a lengthwise direction for any rotation. A point on the outside of the bolt will move through that distance by passing through a large circle; a point at the bottom of the thread will have a much smaller and sharper

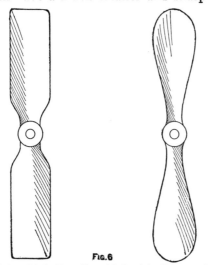

Fig. 6

A Flat-Blade Propeller with Straight Edges, and the Same with Curved Edges

curve to pass through, while a point at the center of the bolt would simply move in a straight line, parallel with the axis. In other words, due to the

pitch remaining the same, the blade angle should increase from tip to hub. This angle, for various points on the propeller, may be determined as in

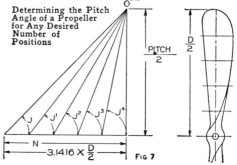

Determining the Pitch Angle of a Propeller for Any Desired Number of Positions

Fig 7

Fig. 7. Lay off a distance equal to 3.1416 times one-half the diameter of the propeller; at right angles to this line draw one equal in length to one-half the pitch, then by connecting the two ends of the lines thus drawn, the required tip angle is determined. Any number of blade sections may be determined by dividing one-half the blade into the desired number of equal parts, dividing the length N into the same number and connecting these points with O; the angles indicated by J, $J^1$, $J^2$, $J^3$, etc., are the required angles of the blade curve. To these values should be added small and regular increases from 2 deg. at the tip to about 5 deg. at the hub, to increase the efficiency of the propeller.

If the propeller is to be made out of one piece of wood, select a piece with the grain as straight as possible and from a strong wood that can be shaped with a drawshave, such as poplar or spruce. The desired shape of propeller should be laid off on the block of wood and cut out. Templates of cardboard should be made corresponding to the required angles, as found in Fig. 7. After laying off the required distances from the center on each side of the blade, notches should be cut at an angle exactly corresponding to the templates, as at J, Fig. 8. Then the shaping can be done, starting at the hub and working toward the tips, being careful at all times of the grain, so as not to split the wood. Fig. 8 represents the blade with one side beveled off. This should then be given the proper curve as represented by Fig. 9.

With the front side finished, the back

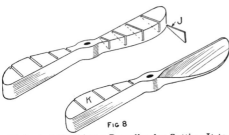

Method of Notching a Propeller for Cutting It to Shape, and One Blade Shaped

side may be shaved off and the thickness calipered frequently by means of outside calipers. The blade should come to a rather sharp edge on the straight, or retreating, edge; the thickest portion should be at about one-fourth the width of the blade from the entering, or curved, edge. The blades in a propeller must be as nearly alike as is possible to make them, in order to prevent vibration.

After the blades have been cut to shape, they should be scraped and sandpapered. To prevent splitting, especially with soft woods, a fine strong cloth should be glued over the surface.

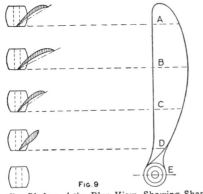

Propeller Blade and the Plan View, Showing Shapes of Blade at the Different Points in Sections

The efficiency of the propeller can be improved by giving it several coats of varnish, evenly put on, thereby reducing the skin friction.

❡To set cutting tools in a moving machine is exceedingly dangerous.

## Taper-Shank Drills Used in a Chuck

In the machine shop of a felt mill several miles from town only straight-shank drills were used, because they were easily obtained in the small town. One day the errand boy brought back six taper-shank drills, and some of them had to be used immediately.

The one lathe in the shop was a small affair with a solid tailstock, and we had no way of boring a taper hole, but as there was no time to send the drills back for exchange, we made sockets interchanging with the straight shanks in the following manner: Copper wire was wrapped around the drill shank, that had been previously rubbed with black lead, one layer deep, the size being about that of ordinary wire used for baling hay. The wire was tied with fine wire, to hold it in place, and then dipped in soldering solution.

A straight hole was bored through a block of wood, the wrapped drill shank placed centrally in the hole, tang down, and the lower end was packed with clay, whereupon melted hard solder was poured in around the drill shank. When cool, the shank and its copper-and-solder socket was removed from the mold by splitting the wood.

A hole was then drilled through the side of the socket and part way into the drill shank, to make a good countersink, and the hole threaded. A setscrew was used in the hole to clamp the drill in the socket. The whole collet was then turned up in the lathe. No attempt was made to drive the drills by the shanks; they were driven with the setscrew.—Contributed by J. B. Murphy, Plainfield, N. J.

## Preventing Noise on Automobile Drive Chains

A customer came to a shop one day with an automobile having a set of extremely noisy drive chains, the noise being caused by the chains slapping on the sprocket teeth as they came into mesh. The following simple repair eliminated this trouble: A strip of leather, of such thickness as to barely touch the chain, was fastened on the circumference of the brake drum. Each chain link touched the leather lightly as it engaged its proper tooth, and in this manner the noise due to the contact was muffled to a considerable degree, and the result was a very quiet set of chains.

## Tool for Removing Shingles

When, in repairing old roofs, shingles must be removed without disturbing others surrounding them, a shingle hook made as shown in the sketch is a handy tool to use. The shape of the shank end is such that it can be driven in either direction. The edges of the notches are sharpened for cutting the nails. The tool can be used to cut nails holding shingles below

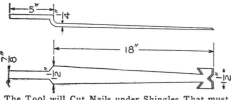

The Tool will Cut Nails under Shingles That must be Removed and Replaced with New Ones

others that need not be removed.— Contributed by Otto V. Vaughn, Belfast, Maine.

## Fastening an Anvil to a Block

When it is necessary to fasten an anvil to a block one common way is to spike it. The spikes soon work loose and usually do not hold very well after that. One device for making an adjustable fastening is given in Fig. 1. It consists of two U-shaped bars, strapped around the anvil at each end. The ends of the bars are bent at right angles and drilled to receive bolts, which, by means of strong spiral springs, connect the straps with similarly bent pieces fastened to the block. Any wear or vibration of the anvil is thus automatically taken up by the springs.

Additional means of securing anvils

are shown in Figs. 2 and 3. In Fig. 2 the fastening consists of closed loops fitted to pass around the anvil and block. The loops may be of whatever

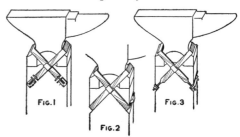

Three Ways of Making Adjustable Straps for Fastening an Anvil to Its Block

length required, and should be hung in place around the anvil when this is ready to be set on the block. The loops are driven into place in notches previously cut in the block at the proper distance. Any looseness, or adjustment for wear, can be taken up by driving wedges between the block and loops.

In Fig. 3 is shown an adjustable fastening consisting of two U-shaped bars with round rods welded on the ends, which are threaded for standard nuts. Cross bars of sufficient width to extend beyond the sides of the block are drilled for the threaded ends of the U-straps. When fastening the anvil on the block, the straps are put in place, the bars slipped over the threaded ends, and the nuts put on. Any adjustment for wear can be readily made by simply turning the nuts.—Contributed by James Hughes, Mexico, N. Y.

## Pulling Gun Trigger with Mitten-Covered Hand

The sketch is descriptive of a method of firing a gun used by myself while out hunting on cold days. Gloves are not as warm as mittens and I attached a strap to the trigger as shown so that I could take hold of it with a mitten-covered hand.—Contributed by Bob Warman, London, Canada.

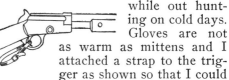

## Glass of Water as a Holder for a Candle

In the country where neither gas nor electricity is available, it is often necessary to use a candle for illumina-

tion. If it is desired to light up a corner or part of some mechanism and both hands are to be used, a simple holder for a candle can be improvised by inserting a nail in the lower end of it and placing it in a glass, three-fourths full of water. The candle will rise gradually as it is consumed, and no tallow will be spilled on the lighted object.

## Holding Irons for Carrying Sheet Metal

Large sheets of metal can only be handled conveniently by hand in a hor-

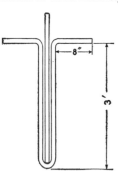

izontal position, and this is very dangerous, as the fingers are liable to be cut or jammed in passing through doors.

The sketch illustrates a holding device that can be used for carrying the metal in an upright position. The metal in this position more readily keeps its form, so that it may be carried through many places where a great deal of trouble would be experienced if carried in a horizontal position.

The holding irons can be made in any size and strength, to suit general conditions. For convenience and safety in moving any of the heavier forms of unwieldy sheet metal, they are hard to beat.—Contributed by F. W. Bently, Milwaukee, Wis.

## Selecting Wood for Making Patterns

In spite of the advance in prices of material and the introduction of cheaper kinds of lumber, pine still retains its position as the leading wood used in the making of patterns, and justly so, for it is soft but not brittle, works nicely under the hand and machine tools, and is not easily affected by atmospheric conditions. These desirable qualities, however, are not characteristic of all pine nor of all boards sawn from the same log. Some boards may possess all these qualities and others not one. The selecting of suitable pine for pattern work should be intrusted to an expert and not left to the judgment of the lumber dealer.

One of the first things to be considered is that the lumber must be perfectly dry, as no matter how good the quality may be, if it has not been kiln or season-dried, the wood is of no value in patternmaking. The boards should be carefully examined on both sides to see that they are free from sap and sap wood, knots, worm-eaten holes, wind shakes, and fancy grain somewhat similar to quarter-sawed oak. The latter is an indication of extreme hardness. The presence of sap is easily discovered, as the board will be very heavy, yellow in color, and in some instances the sap will stand out in little globules on the surface. Sap wood is dead and spongy, and does not work well. It is almost always white in color, but sometimes runs from this to a reddish brown. A board should not be condemned, however, for a little sap wood at the edges, as this condition exists in some very good boards. The same holds good of worm-eaten parts. Some authorities state that the presence of worm-eaten holes is an indication of good lumber, the worms being the best kind of judge, but the usual practice is to discard such boards. A few knots, if they are small and not loose, will do no harm if the board is otherwise sound, but very few knots are found in the better grades. Wind shakes are those longitudinal slivery splits, which indicate that the log has been subjected to a severe twisting strain in the tree. Boards in which this condition exists are useless and should be avoided.

Two of the best indications of the quality of a pine board are the width and weight. Boards, 14 in. or over in width, are usually of good quality, which improves with the width. This is because the wider boards are from trees of mature growth, nearer the heart and farther away from the outside sap. Such boards will be light in weight, straight-grained and soft, while those from the younger growth will be narrow, hard and heavy, and consequently difficult to work.

Quarter-sawed boards are cut from the log in such a way that the center line drawn through the thickness would be a radial line cutting the center of the tree. There is little or no shrinkage to quartered stock and, both sides being affected equally by the atmosphere, they do not warp or twist. It is the ideal lumber for delicate patterns that must be made in a single piece. The end of a quarter-sawed board will always show the growth or year-ring marks standing at right angles to the surface.

In selecting pattern pine, one cannot expect to procure it all perfect, even if the stock is picked from that of first quality, but by keeping in mind the points mentioned there should be no difficulty in getting the best the lumber dealer has.—Contributed by J. A. Shelley, Brooklyn, N. Y.

## Numbering Inches on a Rule Both Ways

As draftsman in a large automobile-body works, I found the need of a new-style measuring rule that would save time in adding up lengths. For instance, by the addition, or continuation, of the numbers 37, 38, 39, 40, etc., up to 72, on a 3-ft. rule, two rules in one, a 3-ft. and a 6-ft. rule, were obtained.

To use the rule, measure the full length, then over to the point desired;

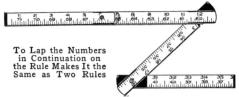

To Lap the Numbers in Continuation on the Rule Makes It the Same as Two Rules

say, for 44 in., just extend to the 44-in. mark. It is always sure and saves the time of turning the rule around and figuring the amount to make 44 in.— Contributed by Frank P. Reidhoar, Connersville, Ind.

## Bevel on Washer to Pick It Up Easily

The picking up of a washer on a flat surface cannot be easily accomplished, and when I had several hundred pieces to machine and washers to raise for each piece in clamping them in place, it presented quite a task. I found that, by filing the under-side

edge of the washer on a bevel, a slight touch on one side would raise it on the other sufficient to slip the thin piece under it.—Contributed by F. H. Hague, Jr., Chicago.

## Soldering-Copper Rest

To prevent a hot soldering copper from touching the surface upon which it is placed, attach a large iron washer to the shank as shown. This will act as a rest and keep the copper raised.

The Washer on the Shank Holds the Heated Copper End Up from the Surface

When doing work on a small space the washer can be slipped up to the handle and held there, then let down to its position for a rest.

### Lining Up Shafting

A very simple method of lining up shafting is as follows: The principle is to intersect two planes, the vertical and the horizontal. Proceed to locate the shaft in the vertical plane, then adjust it to the horizontal plane. If the work is carefully done, the center of the shaft in each plane will be straight.

The apparatus necessary is a plumb bob and cord, a string the length of the shaft, a level and leveling board, and three U-bars, about 5 ft. long.

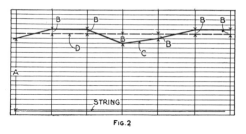

To adjust the shaft in the vertical plane, stretch the string on the floor parallel with the shaft and about 1 ft. to one side. At the location of each hanger drop the bob over the same side of the shaft and carefully measure the distance from the string to the

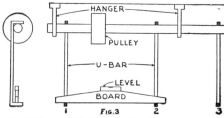

The Shaft is Plotted on Profile Paper and the Distances It Is Out of Line Recorded

point of the bob A, Fig. 1. Plot these results, as shown in Fig. 2, on a sheet of profile paper and relocate the shaft on it, taking the new line so that the adjustments will come within the range of the hangers. The distance B of the actual shaft line C from the required line D will give the amount of adjustment at each hanger necessary to place the shaft in the vertical plane. The results should be plotted to a large scale transversely, but longitudinally any scale may be used within the limits of the paper. The hangers should now be adjusted to the right or left as the amount, or distance, B indicates.

To adjust in the horizontal plane the level board and U-bars are used. The U-bars are necessary to get between and past the pulleys on the shaft, otherwise this adjustment could be made directly on the shaft. The U-bars are placed at convenient distances, about 8 ft. apart or the hanger distance, from each other, and the level and board placed on the first two, as shown in Fig. 3. The level board is then raised until it is level. The amount it is raised or lowered at the end from the starting point gives the adjustment. Next the level and board are placed on the second and third U-bars and the adjustment made in the same

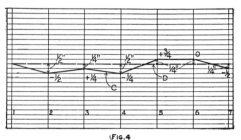

The U-Bars, with the Aid of a Level Board and Level, Locate the Shaft's Position Horizontally

manner. This gives the adjustment necessary with reference to the second U-bar. The first U-bar is then placed on the other side of the third U-bar, and the level again used. This is continued to the end of the shaft. The results are plotted with reference to the first point, as shown in Fig. 4. It must be remembered, in plotting, that each point is taken with reference to the one preceding it, the starting point being taken as zero. The new line of

The Plot of the Shaft in the Horizontal Position, Showing Amount of Adjustment at Each Hanger

the shaft is now drawn as in the previous case, and the distances measured. The hangers are adjusted to give the required horizontal center line. If the work has been carefully done, the shaft will be found perfectly alined.

In using the U-bars, the center on the leg of the bar must be directly below the center of the shaft, and the level board should be reversed each time to eliminate any possible error due to faulty construction of the level or board. In plotting the points for the horizontal adjustment, the results are cumulative, that is, if point 1 is zero and point 2 is —½ in., point 3 is +¼ in. with reference to point 2, but —¼ in. with reference to point 1. By this method the shaft can be adjusted for any required condition of parallelism.—Contributed by S. A. Peck, W. Lafayette, Ind.

### Uses for Left-Hand Drills

No doubt many mechanics have never heard of left-hand drills and would regard them as a joke, yet they are a useful thing in many shops. These drills have their flutes cut in the opposite direction to the ordinary, and to cut they must, therefore, be turned in the opposite or left-hand direction. They may be obtained from any drill manufacturer at practically the same price as the ordinary drill.

They are useful when, for some reason or other, a regular drill "digs" in or sticks in the cut. A common example is the drilling out of a hole that has threads in it. The points of a regular drill would catch in the threads and make a slow and poor job. A left-hand drill will cut over the angle of the threads, not into them, and do it easily and quickly.

### A Strong Box of Simple Construction

A shipment of small brass parts, weighing close to 200 lb., was sent to me in a square wood box of somewhat unusual construction, since it had no particular top or bottom, yet was remarkably strong throughout.

The box was made of six 12-in. lengths, sawed from a 10-in. pine

board, 1 in. in thickness. Two pieces stood parallel on their longer edges, and a third piece was nailed lengthwise across them. A similar piece was

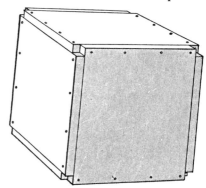

A Box without a Special Top or Bottom, Producing a Very Strong Construction for the Shipment of Castings

nailed across the bottom, and two others, one at each end, completed the box, which, as will be seen, was composed of the least number of pieces possible; and it would not have been stronger with twice that number.—Contributed by W. W. Slocum, Buffalo, N. Y.

### Penwiper Holder for a Drawing Board

About the most troublesome thing a draftsman has to deal with is the penwiper. A solution of this trouble is clearly shown in the sketch. The rag is held at the end of a string which passes through two small screweyes turned into the under side of the board, or table. At the free end of the string is tied a small weight. The rag, after

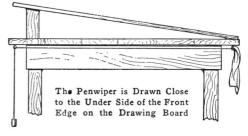

The Penwiper is Drawn Close to the Under Side of the Front Edge on the Drawing Board

using, is simply dropped and the weight jerks it into place. It is always where it can be reached, and out of the way as well.

## Blade Spreader for Elliptic Springs

The spreader consists of a piece of bar steel, bent into a U-shape as shown, with small projections on the inside of the lower ends. A bolt is run through holes drilled in the sides  and a thumb nut used on the threads. The projecting ends are filed to a chisel edge.

In use, the sharp projections are inserted between the blades of the spring and the nut is turned up. This will separate the spring parts so that oil can be readily placed between them.—Contributed by Albert H. Waychoff, Koenig, Col.

## Crude-Oil Burner Made of Pipe Fittings

An adjustable and practically smokeless crude-oil burner can be made of an ordinary 5-in. and 3-in. pipe cap con- 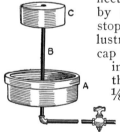 nected to the oil supply by a 1/8-in. pipe and stop valve. In the illustration, A is the 5-in. cap drilled and tapped in the center, from the closed side, for a 1/8-in. pipe thread; B is a piece of pipe 6 in. long, threaded the usual distance on one end but about 4 in. on the other. This is firmly screwed into A, allowing the long end to project above the cup side of the cap. The 3-in. flange C is drilled and tapped in the center from the cup side to fit the long threaded end of B so this will come flush with the top of the cap. The burner is now ready to be connected to the crude-oil supply by the necessary pipe fittings and stop valve, placing the burner lower than the supply, so the oil will flow by gravity.

To operate the burner, pour a little kerosene in the cap A and light it; then open the regulating valve, allowing the crude oil to flow out on top of the cap C and drip over the edges into the cap A, where it is burned. After a short time, the cap C will be sufficiently hot to ignite the oil, which will then burn with a steady and safe flame that can be regulated to suit.

## Starting-Crank Holder on an Automobile

A device for holding the automobile starting crank in a vertical position when not in use can be easily made of 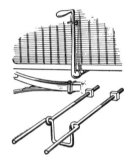 a 3/16-in. rod and two eyebolts. The bolts are run through the openings in the radiator and drawn up tightly. The rod for the holding device is bent as shown. The rod ends are raised, then dropped after the crank is placed in a vertical position.—Contributed by Abner B. Shaw, N. Dartmouth, Mass.

## Preserving Solid Ground Paints

To keep solid ground color in oil or japan without drying out and forming a skin over the top, prepare the can when opening it in the following manner: Cut out the can top carefully close to the sides, so that the entire diameter will be unobstructed, and place the part cut out on top of the paint. Cut  several sheets of cardboard, using the bottom of the can for a pattern, and place them on the tin top covering the paint. Cut a square opening at the lower part, in the side of the can, only severing the upper end and the two sides, then turn the piece down. Make a square plug to fit this hole and use it as a cork.

To take the paint from the can, remove the cork and press down on the cardboards and tin that cover the paint. This action is the same as in using a lead tube of color. Very little paint will be wasted, and the color will be preserved fresh and ready for use.—Contributed by W. M. Mitchell, Minneapolis, Minn.

### How to Make a Large Water Rheostat

It is often desirable, in testing generators and watt-hour meters, to have some means of providing a steady load on a line, and in such cases the water rheostat will be found exceedingly satisfactory, while the cost of its construction is very small. The essential parts are a suitable containing case, usually a wood box, a number of lengths of ordinary iron-fence wire, and a number of switches. The most expensive item is the switches.

A rheostat will be described that will take care of a load of 2,000 amperes at 220 volts. This will require approximately eight strands of wire, about .105 in. in diameter and each strand about 95 ft. long. These wires are coiled about a piece of pipe, 2½ in. in diameter.

The dimensions of the wood box are given in the sketch. An inlet hole, 1 in. in diameter, is bored in one end near the bottom, and another hole, 2 in. in diameter, is bored in the other end about 6 in. from the top. The smaller opening is connected to the water system, and the larger opening serves as a drain. The water connections to this box should be made through at least 30 ft. of rubber hose, to prevent a ground.

The lengths of iron wire are connected from a common busbar, at one end of the box, to one terminal of

several switches, at the other end, the remaining terminals of the switches being connected to a second busbar. These busbars are to form the termi-

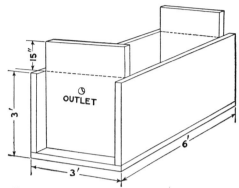

The Box to Hold the Iron Wires, the Ends being Extended for the Busbars

nals of the rheostat, and are mounted on the extensions of the box ends. The number of switches required will depend upon how many divisions of current are desired. The eight wires might be grouped as follows: three in one circuit, two in two circuits, and one in the third. This arrangement would require three switches. The connections from the busbar and the switches to the iron wire should be of copper until they pass under the water. If the rheostat is to be operated on a 110-volt system, the lengths of wire are reduced to one-half of the values given.

### Special Shape for Soldering Iron

In the ordinary soldering iron the copper point is usually shaped like a pyramid with all sides tapering to the tip. In the special shape illustrated, one side is flat, all the other sides tapering to a point on the flat side. This

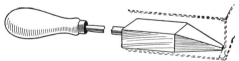

The Point of the Copper is Set to One Side for Use in Close Places

shape permits soldering in confined places, like the edges of long narrow boxes, as the iron can be used when held parallel with the sides.—Contributed by J. W. Ladlow, Globe, Ariz.

## Small Circular Tanks Made from Thin Sheet Iron

Serviceable tanks, up to 1,000-gal. capacity, can be built of thin sheet iron, several widths in height, if the proper

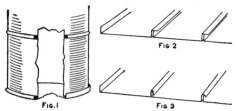

Section of Tank with Upright Edge of Bottom being Peened Over, and Manner of Forming the Metal Sheets

connections are made. In figuring on a certain-size tank the following formulas can be used:

$$G = \frac{22 \times R^2 \times H}{7 \times 231} \text{ or, } R^2 = \frac{G \times 7 \times 231}{22 \times H} \text{ or } H = \frac{G \times 7 \times 231}{22 \times R^2}$$

In which G represents the capacity of the tank in gallons; R, the radius in inches, and H, the height. The radius, as found by the formula, corresponds to the internal dimension of the tank. For the bottom piece an extra amount must be added to form the bead, shown in Fig. 1, connecting it with the side sheet. For every inch of internal diameter of the tank, the side pieces should be $3\frac{1}{7}$ in. long and a further amount added to form the vertical seam. Each side plate, if several are used, should be bent, as shown in Fig. 2, one edge at right angles and the other to a double right angle. The uppermost plate should be formed with a single bend at each edge. The sections can then be put together and the double edges peened over, as shown in Fig. 3, after which the complete side should be rolled to a cylindrical shape. This can be set on the cup-shaped circular bottom, whose upright edge is then peened over. The various connections should be soldered to prevent leaking, and the tank is then complete. A flat or a cone-shaped top may be added if desired.—Contributed by S. C. Shipman, St. Petersburg, Fla.

---

¶Never adjust a machine while it is running.

## Tempering Long and Narrow Pieces of Steel Evenly

Every mechanic knows the difficulty encountered by warping when tempering a long and comparatively narrow piece of steel. One day it fell to my lot to temper a reversible shear blade, 10 in. long, $2\frac{1}{4}$ in. wide, and $\frac{1}{2}$ in. thick, having three $\frac{7}{16}$-in. countersunk holes, 4 in. apart, along its center. The job was accomplished as follows: I procured two straight pieces of common iron, $\frac{1}{2}$ by $1\frac{1}{4}$ in., having a convenient length greater than the blade of steel, and after heating the shear to a bright cherry-red, I laid it parallel with and centrally on one piece, then laid the other piece opposite on top of the shear, and gripping all three pieces firmly with the tongs, plunged the whole in oil. To my surprise, not only was the shear perfectly straight, but the central portion, lying between the two pieces, was toughened to such a point that it could be filed. The cutting edges were nicely tempered.—Contributed by Ralph N. Geffray, Los Angeles, Cal.

---

## Gauge for Indicating Level of Liquid in a Tank

It is frequently necessary to maintain a practically uniform level of the oil, or similar liquid, contained in a tank or engine crank case. A simple

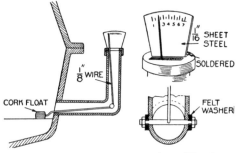

An Indicator and Float Attached to a Pipe for Gauging the Liquid Level of a Receptacle

device for indicating slight variations of level can be made as shown in the illustration. It consists of a piece of $1\frac{1}{2}$-in. tubing, or pipe, bent at right angles, as shown, and threaded at one end for the purpose of screwing it into the tank or crank case. At the top of the tube is placed a cap, provided with a slot for the indicating hand. On a sheet-iron dial, fastened to the cap, can be marked the desired levels and the quantity of oil corresponding to each. A hole is drilled through the tube at the bend to serve as a bearing for the fulcrum pin of the indicating lever. This should be drilled and tapped at the center for two holes, at right angles to each other, to fit the float lever and indicating arm. It is fastened in place with felt washers and nuts, so as to move freely in its bearings while preventing leakage if the liquid should fill the tube. The dial is calibrated by pouring in a definite amount at a time, a mark being made corresponding to each amount added. As can easily be seen, the variations of levels to be indicated must be small, corresponding to the extreme positions of the float lever, as it strikes the top or bottom of the bent tube.—Contributed by Adolph Kline, Newark, N. J.

## Fastening for Segment Ends in Pattern Work

In making wood patterns, it is frequently necessary to have loose pieces in the shape of thin rings, which are always difficult to construct so that they will stand hard usage. The joints commonly made are either feathered or end-lapped. These are difficult to make and unsatisfactory for the purpose.

The illustrations show the manner of using a jig on a circular saw for making a satisfactory joint at a fraction of the cost of the ordinary joint, and one that will hold the parts securely. Cut the segments as shown at A, making them ½ in. longer than a true segment, which allows ¼ in. on each end for the making of the joint.

Saw the segments as shown at B, making the dimension C just the width of a saw cut and ¼ in. deep. Saw the opposite end of the same side as shown at D, making the dimension E the

thickness of C. This brings the work up to where the jig is used on the saw table. Procure a board of any size that is true, and secure it to the saw table

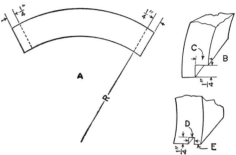

The Segment is Prepared in the Usual Manner and a Kerf and Groove Cut in the End

with screws or clamps so that the saw, when run up through it, will be about 4 in. from the fence. Run the saw up through the board until it projects just ¼ in. Stop the saw and place the kerf D over it, as shown at F, and in this position fasten the strip G as indicated, which must be just the width and thickness of the groove D and about 14 in. long.

To use the jig, place the groove D over the piece G and run the saw through without changing the depth of the cut. The result will be another groove like D at a distance equal to E from it. Proceed in like manner until all ends are completed. The joint thus

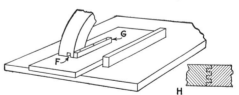

The Jig as It is Placed on the Saw Table for Making All Grooves Uniform and Alike

made appears as shown at H, and when well glued, it is the strongest possible construction.—Contributed by D. D. Gurnee, Hampstead, N. Y.

❡Do not keep a spare casing tied up until the moment it must be used. Substitute it for one in use and take plenty of time to repair small cuts that will permit moisture to reach the fabric.

## A Piston-Head Gauge

The sketch illustrates a device for gauging the head thickness of a gas or gasoline-engine piston. This instrument is very useful in a garage where

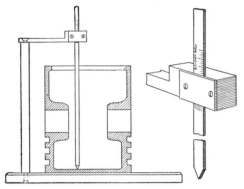

The Thickness of the Metal on a Piston Head can be Easily Measured

new pistons are constantly being made for replacement. It consists of a metal base, planed true on its surface, with a perfectly vertical post carrying a horizontal piece of metal. A metal rod, pointed at the lower end and provided with a scale, slides vertically through the horizontal piece, as shown in the drawing. The length of the post will depend on the largest piston to be measured.

## Graduated Stop for a Lathe Carriage

Where accuracy is required on facing, counterboring holes, and like work on an engine lathe, a graduated stop

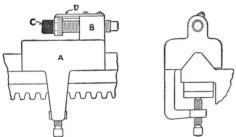

Lathe-Carriage Stop to Aid the Workman in Doing Fine Work on Facing, or Counterboring Holes

for the carriage is desirable. Such a stop can be easily constructed as shown. The body A is preferably made of malleable iron, although gray

iron will do as well, providing the clamp arm which carries the setscrew is large enough to stand the strain.

The boss B, at the top, is bored and threaded to receive a knurled screw, C, which has 40 threads per inch. The large diameter is graduated to make 25 divisions, thus making each graduation .001 in., the readings being easily set by the use of the pointer D. With this stop, it is possible to remove .001 in. from the work, thus doing away with the cut-and-try method.—Contributed by A. Dane, Pottstown, Pa.

## Steel Wasted to Save Time

Several hundred pieces of a certain kind of work were to be made that required a $\frac{1}{16}$-in. pin, $\frac{3}{16}$ in. long, driven into them. After a little trying, it was found almost impossible to handle the pins. The method adopted was to make the pins $\frac{1}{2}$ in. long, and to make a hand punch with a recess, $\frac{5}{16}$ in. 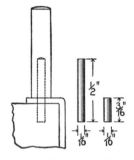 deep and of a size to take the pins. The pins were inserted in the punch and by this means they were started very easily in the hole and driven home. Then they were cut off and the rough end ground level. Over twice the amount of steel wire was required, but the time saved paid for it many times.—Contributed by Donald A. Hampson, Middletown, N. Y.

## Removing Broken Pencil Ends in Telephone "Jacks"

The operators in a telephone exchange persisted in sticking their pencil points in the "jacks" on the switchboard. The points would break off and cause a great deal of trouble. After the switchboard had been almost wrecked one day, I thought of a plan to clean out the jacks without much trouble. I procured a vacuum cleaner and used the round tool on the jacks. This not only removed the pencil points quickly, but also cleaned out all dirt that had accumulated since the board was installed.—Contributed by C. W. Elliott, Toronto, Can.

## An Aid to a Chimney Draft

It is almost impossible at times to get a good draft in a chimney having a square or rectangular hole. The smoke and burned gases pass up in a circular form and a down pull is created in the corners, and it takes a large fire to make an upward draft for the entire area.

To remedy this faulty condition, obtain a number of common stovepipes of a size sufficient to carry the gases from the stove or furnace, and after jointing them up, introduce them into the chimney and connect the lower end to the smoke pipe leading from the stove or furnace. There will then be a circular opening inside of the chimney, out of sight and safe from risk of fire, which will give a better draft than before. It is not difficult to make the connection.

For a similar connection to a grate, it would be necessary to have a funnel-like piece to fit into the chimney just above the fireplace. The opening in the top of this must be circular and of a size to receive the stovepipe. Dampers or other means of control are easy to arrange.—Contributed by Geo. W. Weaver, Standpoint, Idaho.

## Substitute for a Drawing Pen

It is not necessary to use a drawing pen in drawing regular, even ink lines. Use the reverse side of an ordinary steel-pen point, and just as satisfactory results will be obtained. The size pen point to use depends on the width of the line desired. It does away with the time necessary to properly ink a regular drawing pen, as it is only necessary to dip the pen in the usual way.—Contributed by L. E. Turner, New York City.

## Locking an Oil-Tank Pump

A simple means for locking an ordinary tank pump, to prevent its being used, can be easily made from a strip of metal and a padlock. The strip in

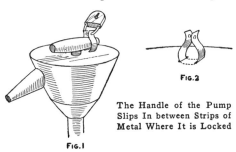

FIG.2

The Handle of the Pump Slips In between Strips of Metal Where It is Locked

FIG.1

Fig. 1 should be of sufficient length to pass around one end of the handle and should have holes at the ends for attaching the padlock. The strip may be attached to the pump head either by soldering it or passing the ends through holes made for them, as shown in Fig. 2.—Contributed by Joseph J. Kolar, Maywood, Ill.

## A Motorcycle Watch Holder

A watch holder for a motorcycle can be easily constructed of a small flat tin can or box of the kind used by druggists for salve or powders. A circular piece, the size of the watch face, is cut from the cover with a circular can cutter. A slot is made in the side to admit the stem of the watch. If the watch does not fit snugly in the  box, paper or cotton may be packed in tightly to fill up the extra space. The cover is put on and soldered in place, and a piece of metal is bent as shown and soldered to the back of the case. The holder is clamped to the handlebar. An inexpensive watch will serve the purpose.

## Setting Compound Rest for Cutting Piston-Rod Taper Fits

The sketch shows a method of turning tapers on a locomotive piston-rod lathe which produces an accurate taper

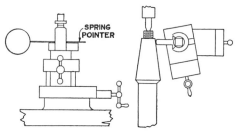

*The Compound Rest is Easily Set to the Proper Taper with the Spring Pointer*

on a rod with the use of the compound rest. The back and front sizes of the taper are cut on the piston rod, the steel pointer is placed in the tool post and tightened, and the compound carriage is set to a correct taper. This can be quickly and easily done, as the spring pointer can be pushed up and over the unfinished portion of the fit while the compound rest is run between the two sizes.

## Self-Truing Pointer for Lathe Work

It is often required to have a point run perfectly true with the shaft of the milling machine or lathe, to locate a hole in a piece of work. In such a case it is generally necessary to chuck a piece of work and true it up with a tool such as a pointer. The device shown does away with this extra work, as it is only necessary to clamp it in the chuck and, by holding something stationary against the point, it will true itself. The spring should have just enough tension against the plun-

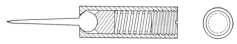

*When Turning in a Chuck the Pointer will True Itself When Something is Held against It*

ger to keep the ball of the pointer firmly seated, the screw in the end being used for adjusting the tension.

## Repairing Burner Base Broken from Blowtorch

It is a common occurrence that a blowtorch is put out of commission by having the blast pipe bent or broken from the head of the gasoline container. Sometimes a slight blow will loosen or cause a leak in the connection. When an accident of this kind occurs, I make a repair by threading the hole in a brass door-knob plate, screwing the pipe into it, and soldering, or riveting, the plate on the top of the container. The edge of the plate extends far enough to make a neat repair.—Contributed by P. D. Merrill, Chicago, Ill.

## Truing Sights on a Rifle

To true the sights on a rifle by the old method a workman is apt to use six or eight cartridges and more than an hour's time. The setting of the sights can be accomplished in 15 minutes with one cartridge, if done as follows:

Fasten a clamp of some kind to a post, or any convenient place, so that it will be rigid and secure. Fasten the loaded rifle in this clamp and set up a wide board in front of the rifle in such a position that the bullet will strike some portion of the target. The distance from the gun to the target must be known, to set the sight. Fire the cartridge and locate the bullet hole, set the sights to target with the hole, and they will be true, provided the gun was not moved.—Contributed by R. D. Benjamin, Cumberland, Md.

## A Substitute Washer

As I needed several washers and none of the proper size was at hand, I made a splendid substitute by wrapping several turns of soft wire on the bolt before putting on the nut. This will work equally well for large bolts as for small ones.—Contributed by H. W. Hilton, Hopington, B. C.

# Proper Construction of Fireplaces

By E. C. KNOPF

After a generation of wood and coal stoves, the open fireplace with its glowing wood fire is again coming into its own, this time taking a permanent place in the home life of those who realize the comfort and enjoyment it lends to a living room or den.

There is a distinct charm about a crackling fire in an open grate, possessed by no other feature of our grandfathers' home life. Colonial furniture, china or architecture are out of place in modern city and suburban life, but the glowing fire of the hearth awakens a spirit that mere age or style of material cannot conjure up. This is nowhere more forcefully seen than in the thousands of homes whose elaborate heating systems, to combat the severe cold of northern winters, are supplemented by the open-grate fire to add cheer to the home. Nor is it out of place among the most modern house furnishings. But the greatest demand for these gloom chasers is in those mild-winter regions where it is desired to heat only one or two rooms.

It has been found, however, that along with some other things which the pioneers did, such as building log houses, the construction of fireplaces which will give satisfactory heating service has become a lost art. Modern masons, with their training based on the demands of modern methods of heating, are not to be censured for their lack of knowledge along this line, any more than the carpenters who do not know how to build a log house.

Out of the large number of fireplaces I have examined, only one—and that one in a mountain camp—was found which possessed the correct principles of construction. In a suburb of a western city, having a district covering a half square mile, 14 fireplaces were found and not one of them was giving satisfaction. Either the smoke came into the room with the heat or both went up the flue together, or it took too much fuel to get the required heat. As a consequence some of these were

closed and stoves installed. If it were not for these disadvantages, there would be three fireplaces to every one now in use.

Having for many years made a study of the principles of fireplace construction, I submit the following plans which have been found to give entire

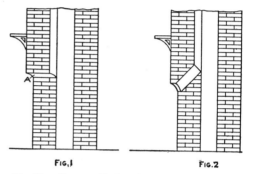

The Most Common Faults of Fireplace Construction Wherein the Heat and Smoke cannot be Controlled

satisfaction. Built on these lines, a fireplace will heat as well as a stove, with the same amount of fuel, and no smoke will enter the room. There are many ways which might be illustrated as the wrong method, but the two most frequently found are shown in Figs. 1 and 2. A cross section of one in which the draft carries all the heat up the flue is shown in Fig. 1. The smoke from the front wood strikes the broad, flat arch A, and some of it goes out into the room. In the one shown in Fig. 2 the heat as well as the smoke will pass up the flue.

A properly constructed fireplace is shown in cross section in Fig. 3. The throat is long and narrow, being gradually shortened as it widens into the flue, as shown by the dotted lines in Fig. 4. For the average-sized fire box, the width of the throat A, Fig. 3, should be about 3 in. at the narrowest part, where the point of the shoulder B comes nearest the apron C. The apron should extend at least 6 in. below the point of the shoulder, so as to catch the smoke. In a large fire box, in which the apron is 5 ft. or more above the hearth, this drop of apron should be at least 1 ft. It may be of arch form, but should not be over 2 or 3 in. thick up to the turn in the throat. Beyond this point it gradually thickens, and the

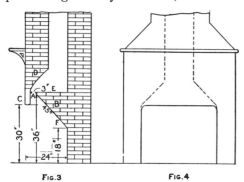

FIG. 3          FIG. 4

Fireplace Construction Where the Heat Enters the Room and the Smoke Goes Up the Chimney

thick wall D, just above the apron, should be built strong enough to support the section of chimney above it. The shelf E is left flat, to stop any down drafts of air from gusty winds. The principle of construction is based on the fact that heat, acting quicker than smoke, strikes the inclined surface F and is deflected into the room while the smoke traveling slower goes up the flue.

The inclined surface, F, of the shoulder, which carries the smoke and heat toward the apron, whether built on a curve or a straight line, should be at an angle of 40 to 45 deg. from the perpendicular. For a fire box 3 ft. wide, the height from the hearth to the apron should be at least 2½ ft. with a 6-in. apron, and the depth should be 2 ft., from the front of the apron to the back of the fire box.

The walls of the throat and flue should be as smooth as possible. If rough stone or broken brick are used, they should be plastered to make a smooth surface. The chimney should extend at least 2 ft. above the ridge of the roof, to insure against down draft in the flue.

---

¶As the weather gets warmer and the automobile bearings run hot, use thick oil, greases and graphite.

## Wax Phonograph Records Used for Insulation

When sealing up some windings, such as magnets, resistance coils, etc., and not having a sufficient quantity of wax or paraffin for the purpose, I made use of a few broken wax phonograph records. I was much surprised at the properties of this wax. In the first place it was very hard compared with paraffin and had a rather high melting point, so that it would not soften and bend as paraffin, that is, it could not be made as flexible. I used this wax in constructing and repairing electrical instruments by coating the outer windings of the magnets, coils, etc., and then shaving down the wax. This looked exactly like hard rubber and had the advantage of being firmly fastened to the wire. I also used it in repairing broken magnet covers, filling the spots chipped out with the wax, with the result that it would take a close examination to detect the repair. Similarly it was used as insulation in constructing a 1-in. coil, and, although I could not test its dielectric properties, I have had no trouble from leakage.

This wax may be used for innumerable other purposes, as it can be melted and the article soaked in it, but it also can be handled in a more convenient manner, similar to soldering, by melting it with a piece of hot iron and applying it where needed, whereupon it is finished with a file and sandpaper, or turned in a lathe.

The wax can be obtained from any dealer in phonographs, especially those keeping record exchanges. Be sure to get the wax records, not the indestructible ones made of vulcanized composition, as these will not melt. Various colors may be had, but black resembles hard rubber and gives a better appearance. The final finish may be done by polishing with a little benzine on a rag. —Contributed by Arthur Worischek, New York City.

---

¶A pneumatic or rubber tire placed on a buoy will prevent it from marring the hull of a boat.

## Cutting Glass Disks

The small shop, not equipped with a circular glass cutter, can cut disks for steam and pressure gauges in the following manner: Fasten a wood disk to the faceplate of the lathe, the disk having a diameter larger than the glass to be cut. Apply a thin coat of glue to both the surface of the wood and of the glass. Place a piece of paper on the glued surface of the glass and then apply both to the glued surface of the wood disk. Rotate the lathe spindle by hand and at the same time hold a common glass cutter on the glass at such distance from the center as to make a disk of the proper size. The glass disk can be removed easily before the glue has time to harden.—Contributed by Arthur Hoem, Butte, Mont.

## Placing Steam-Engine Piston Rings

It is sometimes necessary to put packing rings on a solid head without disconnecting the piston from the crosshead to get the rear rings in place. The rear ring must be sprung over the head and slipped over the first ring groove. It is almost impossible to keep the ring from getting into the first groove and sometimes a number of rings are broken before this is accomplished. The sketch shows how some small pieces of sheet iron can be put under the ring to keep it from dropping into the first groove. The ring can then be easily pushed over the strips of iron to its place in the rear groove.—Contributed by F. W. Bently, Milwaukee, Wis.

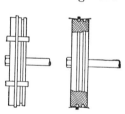

❑When a small pipe connection or a petcock becomes so worn or loose that it leaks, never try to remedy it by soldering the joint, but tin the entire length of the threads, and the wear will be taken up.

## Refuse Holder on a Scraping Knife

When scraping calcimine from a ceiling, the dust, scraps, etc., may be prevented from falling to the floor by using a receptacle shaped like the one

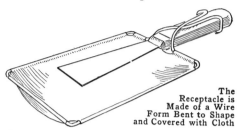

The Receptacle is Made of a Wire Form Bent to Shape and Covered with Cloth

shown in the sketch. The receptacle is made of a wire, about ⅛ in. in diameter, bent in the shape shown. A piece of cloth or canvas is then fastened to the wire frame. When necessary the knife can be released and the contents of the receptacle removed.—Contributed by Chas. J. La Prella, Flushing, L. I.

## Cleaning a Clogged Hopper

Any substance like coal or concrete, in passing through a hopper, is liable to clog the narrow portion and prevent any of the material from passing until it is cleaned out. A very good plan to prevent the clogging is to attach a chain at the upper rim of the hopper and allow it to hang on the inside. If the hopper becomes clogged,

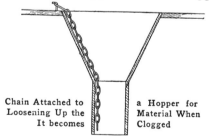

Chain Attached to Loosening Up the It becomes    a Hopper for Material When Clogged

pull on the chain slightly and it will start the material.—Contributed by G. Goodwin, Jr., Ottawa, Can.

❑A scale filed on a bit, beginning at the cutter end, will save the trouble of pulling out the bit every few turns to see if the hole is deep enough.

## An Adjustable Balancing Trestle

The trestle has three legs so that it can be set on any surface, no matter how uneven it may be. The top hori-

The Horizontal Bar on the Trestle Crosspiece can be Easily and Quickly Set Level

zontal piece is provided with a metal bar, hinged at one end and having an adjusting screw at the other. A spirit level is attached to the bar. A pair of these trestles will enable one to do rapid work, as the leveling surfaces can be quickly set level.—Contributed by John E. Elwing, McCleary, Wis.

## Tapering Wood on a Jointer

Many attempts have been made to cut tapers on a jointer, but as the knives cut too deep at the point where the taper starts, a poor job results, says a correspondent of the Wood-Worker.

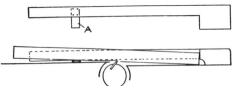

The Form Holds the Work and Starts the Feed, Preventing the Knives from Cutting Too Deep

A form made as shown in the sketch, with a piece of zinc, A, attached will start the feed right and produce nice work.

## To Make a Lusterless Finish on Paint

If it is desired to paint a surface with oil paint and yet have it a lusterless finish, apply a coat of skimmed milk or strained buttermilk over the dry oil paint, or a very thin coat of laundry starch, cooked, which should also be stippled. The advantage is twofold, as it allows the use of oil paint, is easier to apply than flat or turpentine paint, and the protective flat coating can be washed off when it becomes soiled with dust or smoke, leaving the clean oil paint intact, over which another coating of milk or starch can be applied. This is done very often where soft coal is burned. In this way the oil paint may be preserved indefinitely, barring accidents.

## Holding Pipe Threads in a Lathe Dog

In cutting pipe threads in a lathe I could not grip the pipe with a dog without damage to the threads, so I made a little holder to overcome the difficulty. A pipe coupling was pro-

The Coupling Turned on the Pipe Threads Protects Them from the Setscrew of the Lathe Dog

cured and cut to fit in the dog, then a 1/4-in. slot was cut in one side, as shown, and the opposite side filed down thin to allow it to spring slightly. The holder is turned on the threads of the pipe and then the lathe dog is clamped over it.—Contributed by John P. Kolar, Ithaca, N. Y.

## Shank for a Soldering Iron

The sketch shows how I made a very serviceable soldering iron from a discarded extension-bit shank. A large piece of copper was drawn to a point on one end, and the other end was

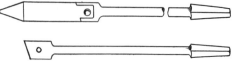

The Shank of an Extension Bit Used as Shank for a Soldering Iron

shaped to fit the shank of the extension bit. A large rivet served to hold the parts together. The square end of the shank was flattened to receive a wood handle.—Contributed by George M. Crawley, Jr., Newark, N. J.

¶In scouring steel cutlery, use a large cork instead of a cloth; it will wear longer and give better results.

## Small Homemade Electric Lifting Magnet

### By J. H. MILLER

IN a large number of shops electromagnets are now being used for lifting and transferring bulky pieces of iron and steel, which otherwise would have to be specially bound with cables and chains or placed in boxes before they could be hoisted by a crane. A magnet of this kind, having a maximum lifting capacity of about 1,000 lb., is shown in the illustration. Its current consumption is about five amperes at 110 volts, causing an operating expense of approximately five to seven cents an hour.

The body of the magnet consists of a circular piece of wrought iron, or steel, 7¾ in. in diameter by $2\frac{9}{16}$ in. thick. Cast iron may be used as well, but its lifting power would not be as great. The bottom face of the body should be machined true, and a circular groove of rectangular cross section turned out in it to fit the magnet coil. The outer end of the groove is counterbored, $\frac{1}{16}$ in. deep by 1¾ in.

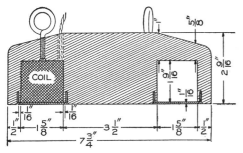

Detail of the Magnet, Giving Dimensions for One That will Lift a Half Ton

wide, to fit a brass ring, which keeps the coil in place. The ring is held in position by eight small flat-head machine screws, equally spaced around the outer and inner edges of

the plate, which is countersunk to fit the sides of the screw heads. When

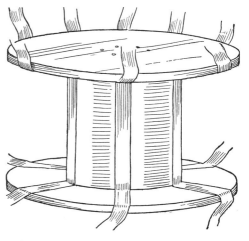

A Temporary Spool for Winding on the Coil of Wire Used in the Magnet

fastened in place, the screws and brass plate should be slightly below the surface of the magnet body.

To support the magnet, three screw eyes, of $\frac{3}{16}$-in. stock, should be provided, and fastened in three tapped holes, equally spaced on a 5-in. diameter circle. The inner ends of the holes are countersunk so the ends of the screw eyes can be riveted over to prevent them from unscrewing.

For winding the wire coil a wooden spool must be provided. It is made with a cylindrical core, 3½ in. in diameter by 1½ in. long, and slightly tapered so the coil may be easily removed when finished. The flanges of the spool are 7⅛-in.-diameter wooden disks, fastened on the cylindrical piece so as to be easily removed. The finished spool is mounted on an axle, or between lathe centers, to allow it to rotate while winding the coil.

Before starting the coil, about a dozen pieces of insulating tape, 7 in. long, should be equally spaced around the spool, and tied or pasted in place, fitting lengthwise with the spool center and up along the inner sides of both flanges. The coil will require about 7 lb. of No. 20 gauge, single cotton-covered copper wire. With a 220-volt circuit, the same amount of No. 23 gauge wire should be used. In starting the coil, about 1 ft. of wire must be allowed for a magnet lead, which is passed through a hole near the center of one of the flanges. The winding should be even and fairly tight, with each layer carefully insulated by a heavy coat of shellac. When the winding is completed, about 1 ft. of wire must be allowed for the outside lead of the coil. The strips of tape can then be brought over and pasted together. To hold the ring in shape more securely, and insulate it from the magnet body, several turns of tape are wound around on the outside. The finished coil should then be baked in a warm oven for a day, to harden the shellac, after which the flanges of the spool may be removed and the center forced out.

The magnet leads can then be spliced to a piece of heavy lamp cord. A ⅜-in. hole should be drilled from the coil groove to the top of the magnet body, and bushed with an insulating tube. In assembling the parts, the lamp cord is passed through the tube, and the coil put in place in the groove. If it has any play, several extra turns of tape should be wound on it. When it is sufficiently tight to stay in the groove of its own accord, the brass plate is fastened in place.

To suspend the magnet from a crane, three equal lengths of chain are attached to one common supporting ring. The loose ends must be fastened to the screw eyes so the magnet will hang level when lifted by the ring. The end of the flexible lamp cord can be attached to a plug to make connection with a convenient lamp socket on a 110-volt electric circuit.

## A Basketwork Boat

A rough and ready, temporary expedient for a river boat is described as follows by a brigadier-general of the U. S. Army in the U. S. Cavalry Journal. The boat is constructed in a reverse position, or upside down. The outline of the boat is marked out on the ground, about 12 ft. long and 6 ft. wide and pointed at both ends. At each end, or bow and stern, drive a tent stake to which the keel is to be attached. At intervals along the sides drive tent pins for attaching the ribs. The material for the ribs and keel is cut from cottonwood, basswood, or willow. Sticks from this material are lashed to the stakes and bent to form the keel and ribs. To prevent them from straightening out, a rope or chain is tied from bow to keel, and thence to

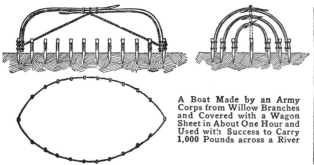

A Boat Made by an Army Corps from Willow Branches and Covered with a Wagon Sheet in About One Hour and Used with Success to Carry 1,000 Pounds across a River

stern, as shown. The gunwale is formed of flexible sticks, lashed along the ends of the ribs inside and out. Smaller sticks of willow are woven in between the ribs to form a basket-work. The shape of the boat is formed upside down. When finished, cut it loose from the tent stakes and cover it with a perfectly good wagon sheet, tying the edges inside of the boat. If the sides tend to spring out, fasten a rope from one side to the other. Such a boat will carry 1,000 lb. and draw but a few inches of water.

## Snow-Shovel Attachment

The snow shovel here illustrated has an addition to it that relieves one of a lot of strain in prying snow loose

which is packed solid. A round-ed piece of wood, about ¾ in. thick, is fastened to the under side of the shovel in the center, as shown. When the shovel is pushed into deep or solidly packed snow, pressure is applied to the ex-treme end of the handle before lifting. Owing to the fact that the shovel rests on the curved piece of wood, the snow will be pried loose easily. If the board is tapered along the edge to a V-shape, it will offer considerably less resistance to the snow.

## Connecting-Rod Balancing Fixture

In assembling multiple-cylinder gas-oline engines, it is essential that the connecting rods have very nearly the same weight. A simple little fixture for weighing the rods can be made as shown in the illustration. It consists of an upright post, provided with a pin freely fitting the small end of the rod. When necessary to weigh the rod, one end is hung on the pin, the crankpin end being supported on a suitable plat-form scale. The supports should re-main the same distance apart, while rods for the same engine are weighed, to have the weighing uniform. The

purpose of weighing by means of hing-ing at one end is to get the same metal

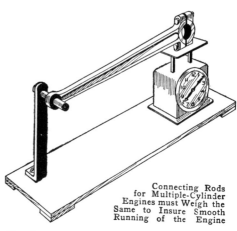

Connecting Rods for Multiple-Cylinder Engines must Weigh the Same to Insure Smooth Running of the Engine

distribution in every rod.—Contributed by Adolph Kline, Newark, N. J.

## Protecting Pulley Sheaves of a Light Chain Block

The pulley sheaves of a light chain block are easily broken through care-lessness, which consequently makes a considerable in-crease in the cost of repair to shop tools. The sketch illustrates a method of pro-tecting the light sheaves. This re-quires a longer pulley pin, but as the sheaves cost more than the pin, a few ac-cidents prevent-ed would make the manufacture

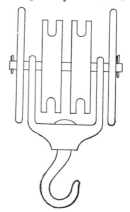

of a new one a paying proposition. The guards can be of $\frac{3}{16}$ or ½-in. iron. They are easy to make and apply.—Contrib-uted by F. W. Bentley, Milwaukee, Wis.

¶In cutting irregular shapes of labels, etc., place the paper on strawboard or bookbinder's board, then, by moving the board carefully, no back gauge will be required.

## Collapsible Stand for Buckets

Decorators and paper hangers usually desire a support for their paste buckets, to raise them off the floor to a suitable height for use. Frequently some convenient box or chair is used for this purpose, but these are not always handy, nor con-

Support for the Paste Pail That can be Folded into a Small Space for Carrying

venient to carry around. In the illustration is represented an easily made collapsible stand, which can be readily unfolded for use or closed up into a small package when carried around.

To make the support, three boards of the same length are necessary, to serve as legs. Near the bottom of each is fastened an ordinary strap hinge, with a hole through the end of the loose half so the three pieces can be rigidly clamped together with a thumb nut and bolt. The hinges should be sufficiently long so that the distance from the bolt to the legs will be several inches longer than the radius of the pail bottom, thereby providing a good base for the stand. Several inches from the upper ends of the legs, three shorter hinges are required, similarly secured with thumb nut and bolt, and acting not only as the upper

braces for the stand, but also as a support for the bucket. By using shorter upper hinges, the legs will slant inward and form a more rigid support. The ends of the legs, extending up on the bucket, hold it in place securely.—Contributed by A. E. Johnson, Frankfort, Ind.

## An Adjustable Parallel Bar

Considerable inconvenience may frequently be caused by not having parallel bars of quite the correct height. Such trouble can be avoided if the bar is made as shown in the sketch, providing not only an adjustable height but one which can be correctly read at all times from a scale marked on the bars. The dimensions given in Fig. 1 allow an adjustment of from 3½ to 4½ in. The two parts, A and B, should be accurately dovetailed and have an easy sliding fit. They are held in place, at any setting, by means of setscrews. The tongue in the upper part A should be machined for a special groove, C, to form a square seat for the setscrews; at the same time avoiding the danger, which might otherwise arise, of marring the fit and surface of the dovetail, were the screws allowed to fit against the inclined surface. The center line, Fig. 2, is drawn across both pieces when they are flush on the

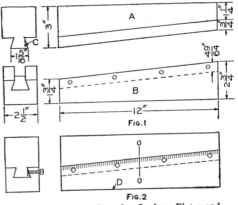

FIG. 1

FIG. 2

Adjustable Taper Bars for Surface Plates and Machine Tables to Obtain Various Heights Perfectly Parallel

ends, the bar then measuring 4 in. in height. On the lower bar, divisions are marked on each side of the center line, perpendicular to the base D, and spaced $\frac{3}{16}$ in. apart, measured along a line parallel with the base. The spacing together with the taper of 1 in. in 12 must be followed strictly, or the scale will not be correct. Every division corresponds to an adjustment of $\frac{1}{64}$ in.; thus, if it is desired to have the bar $4\frac{1}{8}$ in. high, it would be necessary to place the center line of the upper part eight divisions above the center line of the lower piece ($\frac{1}{8}=\frac{8}{64}$; since every division corresponds to a $\frac{1}{64}$-in. adjustment). By dividing the $\frac{3}{16}$-in. divisions into equal parts, each of these will correspond to the same proportion of the $\frac{1}{64}$-in. adjustment, thus enabling extreme accuracy if desired.—Contributed by R McGinnes, Pawtucket, R. I.

## Hitching Ring for Cement Horse Block

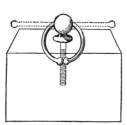

With any scrapped jaw screw from a bench vise a neat and serviceable hitching ring can be made, by first bending the ends of the lever together, as shown, and then sinking the screw into the cement, leaving the ball or head flush with the surface of the block.—Contributed by Wm. J. Tolson, Lyons, Iowa.

## Drilling Holes in Brick Smoothly

When drilling a brick wall with a star drill dampen the brick. This will prevent the chipping of the brick at the surface, and will also make the drill cut faster and hold its edge longer.—Contributed by C. W. Elliott, Toronto, Can.

ⓒCelery can be kept fresh for several days by wrapping it in a wet cloth similar to a turkish towel, which is then covered with paper.

## An Outdoor Fireplace

An old galvanized tub, turned upside down, and with a hole cut in its

An Old Wash Boiler Fitted Up to Make Outdoor Fireplace for Wash Days

bottom to suit the kind of boiler to be used, makes an ideal outdoor fireplace for washdays. A small half circle is cut out, on the upper side, at the back, for the smoke, and another is cut in the lower side, at the front, for putting in fuel, and for draft.—Contributed by Mrs. Julia Bertelsman, San Angelo, Texas.

## Watch Spring to Expand Plunger Leather

To overcome the tendency of a dry plunger leather to shrink away from the cylinder walls of a pump and thereby spoil its action, a piece of flat watch spring may be placed around the inside of the cup. This will keep the leather expanded at all  times. The spring may be secured by weaving it in and through vertical slots in the leather cup.—Contributed by Edward M. Davis, Philadelphia, Pennsylvania.

## Sheet-Metal Worker's Marking Gauge

In marking sheet metal for various widths, considerable time can be saved and greater accuracy attained if a sta-

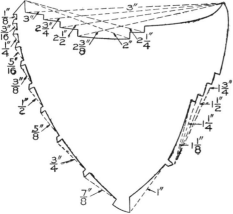

The Points on the Edge Serve Two Purposes, as a Marker and as a Gauge for the Adjoining Length

tionary-point gauge is used, as is shown in the illustration. This should be made of machine-steel plate, about ⅛ in. thick, a section of a broken saw blade being well adapted for the purpose. The various widths desired are marked on the edge of the triangular-shaped piece, in such a way that the gauging distances run from the point of one to the heel of the next, and so on, all around the piece. Where several sizes are used but seldom, one point may be arranged to act as marker for all of them, as there would be but little wear from the small use made of it.—Contributed by David J. More, Peterborough, Ont.

## A Center Square

The body of the center square is shaped from a piece of metal, about ½ in. thick, and a perfect right angle is cut in it, as shown. Exactly in the center of the corner, drill a $\frac{3}{16}$-in. hole for a center punch, which is made of steel and hardened. An L-shaped piece is fitted in one side, so that one of its edges will exactly center the intersection of the angle. The extending L-portion should be carefully turned out at right angles so that its edge will be at exact right angles to the face of the body. The piece is clamped in place with the head of a bolt whose body is drilled to admit the center punch. Both the punch and the L-shaped piece are clamped with the same bolt.

A disk is fastened with a knurled-head screw to one arm of the main part. A level is fastened on this disk at one side of the screw. The disk has four marks evenly spaced, quartering it. The level should be accurately set so that the markings will register level when the angle in the body is perfectly vertical.

It will be readily seen that, when the level bubble registers level, a line can be drawn on the end of the shaft perfectly vertical on its diameter, and that, by giving the disk a quarter turn, a line can be drawn perfectly horizontal, or at right angles to the vertical line across the diameter.

If, for some reason or other, the shaft is taken out of the clamps, and it is then desired to work on it again, clamp it down as before, and set the center square on top of it. The shaft can be

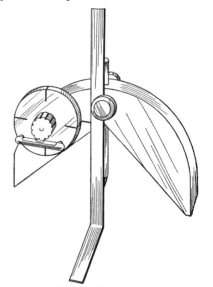

Center Square for Marking Round Stock to Locate the Center and to Lay Out Keyways

set up by letting the center punch touch the line already scratched, and it will bring the shaft up level as before.

## Homemade Measuring Pump

### By A. H. WAYCHOFF

Time and labor can be saved by using an automatic measuring pump. A contrivance of this kind is not so complicated but that it can be made by the average mechanic, from parts obtainable in most places.

The largest and most important part of the homemade machine illustrated is the pump cylinder, which should be a piece of seamless brass or steel tubing, varying in size according to the desired capacity; a cylinder, 6 in. in diameter and 12 in. high, will provide ample storage for a gallon of liquid. The cylinder should be threaded at each end and provided with blank flanges screwed onto the ends. At the lower end it is drilled and tapped for a ¾-in. pipe nipple which connects with the supply tank through a check valve, so placed that it will allow the fluid to enter the cylinder but prevent any escape from it. A similar opening is drilled and tapped at any other convenient place at the bottom, for the outlet, and provided with nipple and check valve as before; in this case, however, the check allows the fluid to leave the cylinder, but prevents its return as well as the admission of air, which would spoil the action of the pump.

The top flange should be drilled and tapped for two pieces of ¾-in. pipe, about 16 in. long and spaced about 4 in. apart. These serve as uprights for the pump head. Two pieces of strap iron, of sufficient length to extend from one pipe to the other, are drilled for bolts which clamp them in place, leaving a space sufficient to allow a rack and pinion to fit in between. The rack should be about 16 in. long and provided with a toe at each end. The pump plunger may consist of two plates of ⅛-in. sheet steel, cut to loosely fit the cylinder, between which is placed a cupped leather washer closely fitting the cylinder. The various parts are held together by the piston rod, which passes through a hole in the center, and is provided with a nut on each side. This rod extends through a hole in the

upper flange, and is fastened to the lower end of the rack.

In order to produce the necessary reciprocating movement for the rack and piston, a pinion, engaging with the rack, is secured to a shaft supported on each side in suitable holes in the iron straps, clamped between the uprights, and provided at the outer end with a

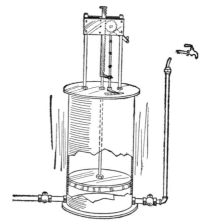

The Size of the Cylinder and the Stroke of the Piston Determine the Measurement of the Gasoline

crank. By turning the crank the rack and plunger will be raised or lowered as required. To prevent the rack slipping away from the pinion, a strip of iron is provided and fastened between the straps so that it will bear against the back side of the rack. If desired, two bolts can be used for the same purpose.

To provide the measuring device, a round rod of sufficient length is pivoted at one end in a countersunk hole in the top flange, in line with the rack and pipe uprights, and, at the other end, in a countersunk block fastened between the iron straps at the top. To this gauge rod, at its lower end, is fastened an indicator, or pointer, which may be shifted to one side or the other, according to the amount desired to be pumped. A scale, over which the indicator passes, is marked on the top flange to some convenient measurements, as, for example, quarts or fractional gallons.

In order to provide the necessary stops for the piston for any particular measurement, gauge stops are drilled to fit the rod and secured to it by means of setscrews. These stops are made with a projecting lug on one side which can be set to strike the toe of the rack, thereby preventing any further upward movement.

In calibrating the tank, the piston is first so adjusted, by means of the upper toe on the rack or washers screwed to the piston rod, that there will always be sufficient liquid in the cylinder producing a level above the check valves when the plunger is at the bottom of its stroke. This will tend to keep the leather in good condition, and give greater accuracy when operating the device. With the cylinder filled up to this lowest or zero mark, the calibration can be continued. The smallest amount indicated on the scale should then be carefully measured and put into the cylinder through the inlet check valve. This will raise the plunger and with it the rack. When the full amount has been added and the plunger has come to rest, the indicator arm is set to the amount corresponding to that let in, and the lowest gauge stop is fastened in position on the rod so as to rest against the lower toe of the rack. This completes the first setting. The second and following positions may be obtained in much the same way. Every time a setting is completed the indicator arm should be moved over to the next point. By so doing, the lug, just set, is swung away from the rack, permitting the plunger to rise on the addition of another quantity of liquid. With the plunger once more at rest, the next corresponding gauge stop is secured in position, locking the rack and plunger against any further movement, and preventing the addition of any more liquid.

In operating the device it is first necessary to place the indicator in the position corresponding to the desired amount. This movement of the indicator brings in place the required stop-gauge. The crank can then be turned and the rack and plunger caused to rise. This will form a vacuum under the plunger which will be filled from the supply tank. With the required amount in the cylinder the crank is turned in the opposite direction, which will cause the plunger to descend, forcing the liquid through the outlet check valve. It is best to have the supply tank above the level of the pump, thereby preventing air from leaking in, which would spoil the vacuum and hinder the operation of the pump.

## Boiler Tubes Fitted with Flanges Substituted for Regular Pipe

Boiler tubes, after their removal, are frequently scrapped for old iron. With but little extra labor and change, however, they can be made to serve as

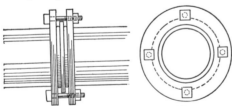

Boiler Tubes Fitted with Companion Flanges to Form a Substitute for Pipe and Couplings

low-pressure pipe. As their diameters do not correspond to standard pipe sizes, they must be fitted with flanges.

These should be sufficiently large and strong to permit their being drawn together by bolts, and clearance space must be figured on for turning the nuts. The flanges should all match in the spacing of holes for clamp bolts, and should be drilled for a loose fit on the boiler tubes. Each length of tubing should be provided with two flanges, and then heated and beaded at the ends, to form a shoulder for the flanges. For high pressure, the ends should be faced off, but with low pressure this is not so necessary, if a good job has been done in the beading. A soft gasket should be placed between the ends of adjacent tubes, and the flanges drawn together, thereby forming a tight joint.—Contributed by John H. Pietgenter.

## To Prevent Poisoning from Lead Paints

Many painters do not realize the danger of lead poisoning from white, black, and red-lead paints. Outside of cuts, the most accessible place for the lead to enter is the flesh around the finger nails. Its entrance there can be prevented by dipping the finger tips into warm paraffin, or beeswax, whereupon gloves are put on and one proceeds with the work. The paraffin can be easily removed when the work is completed, or at the end of the day.—Contributed by Edmond Von Kaenel, Chicago.

---

## Double Lathe Dogs for Heavy Cuts

Slipping can be prevented on work being turned in a lathe, by using an additional dog for driving purposes. The first dog A is clamped to the work in the usual manner with the tail driven by the faceplate B. The second dog C is fastened so the tail bears

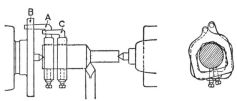

Work on a Lathe Driven by Two Dogs to Provide More Gripping Surface

firmly against that of A. With this arrangement, if the first dog were to slip, the second would still drive the work.

---

## Repair for Broken Automobile Pedal

A simple repair for a broken pedal can be made, as shown, by riveting or bolting the broken section securely in place by means of a suitable - sized angle brace. For the sake of appearance, another brace may be fitted on the unbroken side.

## Supply Cup for Lathe-Center Lubrication

In most tailstocks a hole is drilled in some convenient place for the oil, or white-lead mixture, used to lubricate the center, preventing it from scoring or running hot. This hole is usually small so that, after a few dips, it must be refilled. To avoid this frequent refilling a special oil chamber may be attached, which can be of sufficient capacity to provide a supply for a long time. The usual hole in the tailstock is tapped and the oil cup threaded to fit. A suitable dropper may be attached to the cap, so it may serve the double purpose of not only supplying the lubricant to the center, but also protecting it from dust and dirt.—Contributed by John Harger, Honolulu, Hawaiian Islands.

---

## A Labor-Saving Coal Bucket

The bucket is constructed by cutting a hole the full width in the upper part of one side on a square 1-gal. oil-can, making the cut extend 4 in. down and allowing ¼ in. of the material to turn in all around to prevent injuring the hands. Such a bucket holds more than the usual amount of fuel that is put on a fire at one time, and it will not spill over the edges while pouring the coal into the stove. It does away with carrying and lifting a heavy bucket of fuel—a job that most women dread—when only a few shovelfuls are needed.—Contributed by L. E. Turner, New York City.

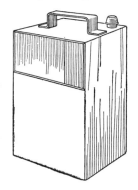

## Lathe Dog for Driving Square Stock

A simple lathe dog for driving square stock can be made from bar iron of the proper width and strength

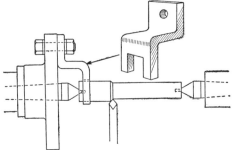

The Dog is Fastened to the Faceplate and the Stock is Slipped into the Square Opening

which is bent to the shape shown in the cut and notched to hold the stock. It is drilled for an ordinary bolt and nut, and clamped in position to the faceplate, but requires no setscrew to hold the stock. One size of dog will drive stock which is not too large to enter the notch nor so small that it will turn around in it.—Contributed by F. H. Mayoli, Pawtucket, R. I.

## Patternmaker's Sandpaper Cone

Turn a piece of maple or close-grained wood to the desired shape of a cone on one end, making the sides as straight as possible, and to form a

A Handy Tool for Smoothing Various-Sized Holes and Curved Parts on Patterns

handle on the other end. Then cut a rectangular groove on the cone end, sufficiently wide and deep to admit the sandpaper ends and a strip of wood, the wood acting as a wedge to hold the paper in place.—Contributed by Carl G. Olson, Chicago, Ill.

⟨To prevent rust, it is a good plan occasionally to oil the hinged joints of an umbrella.

## Tool Chest with Combined Drawer and Cover Lock

Serviceable tool chests can be made out of scrap lumber or box boards which will answer all ordinary requirements. The material necessary for the illustrated chest is as follows:

```
1 cover, ¾ by 15 by 20 in.
2 side pieces, ¾ by 12 by 14 in.
1 back, ½ by 12 by 16½ in.
1 lower rail, ½ by 1½ by 15½ in.
1 center rail, ½ by ¾ by 15½ in.
1 top rail, ½ by 4 by 15½ in.
2 stiles, ½ by 1¼ by 12 in.
2 front finish strips, ½ by 1½ by 19 in.
2 side finish strips, ½ by 1½ by 14½ in.
     For drawers:
2 fronts, ½ by 2⅞ by 15½ in.
2 bottoms, ½ by 11½ by 15½ in.
4 sides, ½ by 2⅞ by 13¼ in.
2 ends, ½ by 2⅞ by 14½ in.
     For drawer slides on chest end pieces:
2 bottom slides, ½ by 1 by 13 in.
2 middle slides, ½ by ¾ by 13 in.
2 top guides, ½ by 1 by 13 in.
2 middle guides, ½ by 1¼ by 12½ in.
2 bottom guides, ½ by 1½ by 12½ in.
2 vertical end strips, ½ by ½ by 12 in.
1 lock bar, ¾ by ¾ by 9 in.
2 cleats, 2 hooks, 1 spring, 1 guide pin, box
     hinges, and chest lock.
```

The side pieces should be carefully squared and finished to 14 in. wide by 12 in. high. To these ends are nailed the drawer guides and slides, so that one becomes the right and the other the left-hand side. The slides extend ½ in. farther back than the guides; both are flush with the front edges of the end pieces. The two vertical end strips are nailed to the end pieces and guides. The two stiles, being carefully squared, can then be attached to the end pieces. All the rails should be exactly the same length and perfectly squared, and can then be fastened in place with finishing nails driven into the drawer slides and through the front stiles. The back can then be added and nailed to both the vertical end strips and chest ends. In putting on the chamfered finish strips, they should be mitered on the corners. After attaching the cover in the usual manner with butt hinges, the frame is completed.

In making the drawers, the fronts should be notched ⅜ in. deep to fit the sides which are nailed in place. The bottom can be nailed in place, flush with the lower edges of the sides and fronts, and the ends added, completing the drawer, except for the drawer pulls, which may be added after the chest is finished.

It will be noticed that a 1-in. clearance space exists between the back of the drawer and the chest back. This is to provide space for the combina-

is their unlocked position. The drawers should be removed and the cleats fastened in place. In order that the bar may not spring up above its unlocked position, the upper strap should be located so the upper cleat will

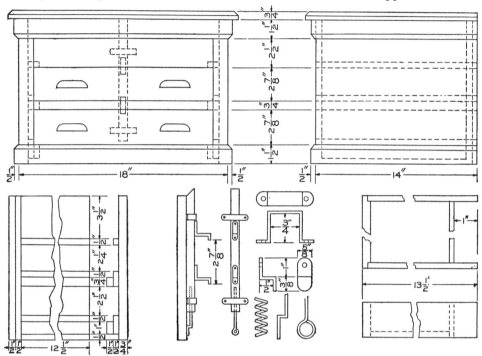

While the Original Chest was Made of Soap Boxes, the Wood Required for Its Construction Would Not be Expensive, and It can be Built of Any Material to Suit, and Finished as Elaborately as Desired

tion locking device. It consists of a ¾-in. square lock bar, about 9 in. long, made of strong wood. At the lower end it is drilled for a guide pin which is fastened to the chest back. A coil spring fits over the pin, supported at one end by the guide pin and butting up against the lock bar at the other. The spring tends to keep the bar in its unlocked or upper position. The bar is held in a vertical position at the center of the chest by two metal straps screwed to the back piece. In locating the position of the cleats, the chest cover should be open. The bar should extend beyond the upper edge of the back about ½ in., and be secured there until the cleats are located. They should be placed and marked so as to clear the upper edge of the drawer backs by about ⅛ in., as this

strike against it, thereby preventing any further movement of the bar; the spring must be set to keep the bar in this position. It is best to round off the upper back edge of the bar, producing an easier closing effect. A good chest lock must be provided and fastened in the usual way. With the drawers pushed in as far as they will go and the cover closed and locked, the cleats hook over the ends of the drawers, preventing them from being withdrawn. When unlocked and the cover opened, the lock bar is pushed up by the spring, thereby releasing the drawers. The chest, after being stained, or painted and varnished, and the handles and drawer pulls fastened in place, will prove a secure receptacle for tools.—Contributed by G. M. Heinroth, Whitstone, S. D.

### A T-Square Substitute

On small work, a 30-deg. triangle can be made to serve the same purpose as a T-square, with accuracy and ease of

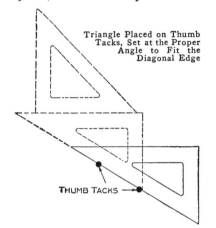

Triangle Placed on Thumb Tacks, Set at the Proper Angle to Fit the Diagonal Edge

THUMB TACKS

manipulation. It is only necessary to place two thumb tacks in the drawing board, a convenient distance apart and in such manner that when the diagonal edge of the triangle rests against the tacks, the other two sides will form the vertical and horizontal lines on the drawing. If desired, another triangle may be used on either of the sides, affording all the advantages of a T-square.—Contributed by G. B. Pollock, Chicago, Ill.

### Block for Tempering Several Tools at Once

A frequently followed method for tempering tools after hardening is to

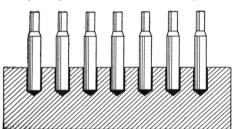

Block to Hold a Number of Tools to be Given a Certain Temper

take one at a time with a pair of tongs, get it to the required heat, and plunge it in a cooling solution. If a large number of similar tools, as punches, are to be tempered, time can be saved and more uniform work produced by using a heated cast-iron or steel block. It is drilled for holes to receive the tools, about $\frac{1}{32}$ in. larger than the diameter of the latter and to a depth corresponding to the length of tempering; in punches, equal to about one-fourth of their length. The tools should be polished for tempering, then placed in the holes of the heated plate and, as they come to the desired color, immersed in water or the cooling solution, as in regular practice.—Contributed by J. F. Tholl, Detroit, Mich.

### Turning a Large Cone

A method of turning a large cone on a lathe is shown in the illustration. A short portion, of the proper slope, is first turned at the apex of the cone with the compound rest set to the required angle. The nut is then taken

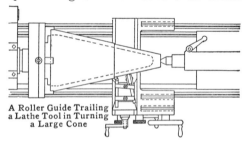

A Roller Guide Trailing a Lathe Tool in Turning a Large Cone

from the cross-feed screw, allowing the slide rest to move freely. The forked holder, carrying the roller, is then secured along with the cutting tool. The action of the roller on the turned surface causes the tool to move in a straight line, but making an angle with the axis of the cone.—Contributed by James H. Rodgers, Hamilton, Ont.

### Marking Steel with Identification Tags

One of the simplest methods of marking steel is to paint it with a colored stripe, a certain color having been assigned to each kind: red, for example, might be used to indicate "Colonial;" white, "Jessop;" yellow, "Ketos," etc.

But if the steel is handled frequently, the color stripes gradually become coated with grease and dirt until they are too dark to be distinguished, or they may even wear off entirely so that the identity of the steel is destroyed. An improvement on this method is to drill a small hole close to the edge of one end of the bar. A metal tag, with the proper identification data on it, can then be wired to the bar. The steel should be used starting with the opposite end so the mark may remain until the last piece is required, when the tag is removed and fastened to the next bar of similar steel.

## Homemade Electric Automobile Horn

In making this horn the two main parts to be considered are the electric buzzer and the homemade horn, or sounding box. The former can be bought at a small cost in any electrical shop or hardware store. The mechanical part of the horn consists of a sounding box attached to a funnel for magnifying the buzzer sound. This funnel can be made from a piece of tin or other thin sheet metal, 10½ in. square and cut to the shape shown in Fig. 1. A ¾-in. strip is marked off at the inner edge and notched to make projections that can be turned up to fasten the horn to the sounding box. In connecting the edges of the funnel to hold it in shape, the ½-in. strips at each end can either be soldered together or, if more convenient, bent up to form a hook, and these interlocked and hammered down, as shown in Fig. 2.

The sounding box consists of three wooden disks held together by a strip of metal fastened around their outside edges. The disk A, Fig. 3, is provided with a 2-in. hole to fit the funnel, which is placed with its small end projecting through the disk, and its ¾-in. notched edge turned up all around, securely holding it in place. To insure its being fastened, nails or screws may be put through the strip into the disk. The sounding board consists of the disk B, to which is attached

the buzzer. The back side of the box is formed by the blank disk C.

In assembling the horn, the metal strip, Fig. 4, is first provided with

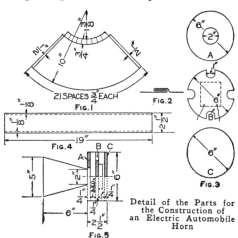

Detail of the Parts for the Construction of an Electric Automobile Horn

suitable holes to fit the screws for attaching it to the wooden frame. It is then bent to form a circle, and the disk C, Fig. 5, is fastened in place. The sounding board B, with buzzer attached, can then be secured in place, precaution being taken to first connect the battery wires to the buzzer, and allowing them to pass out through the end disk C. To complete the horn, the disk A, with the attached funnel, is placed in position, and secured to the shell with screws.

Any convenient method may be used to hold the horn in place on the auto, the simplest being to fasten it with screws into the end disk C, from some part of the frame. For operating the buzzer, a battery and push button must be provided and properly connected.—Contributed by J. J. Flood, Philadelphia, Pa.

## Revolving Stand for Painters

A simple revolving stand, or table, may be made out of a dry-goods box, four sash pulleys, and an iron tire from a wagon wheel. The box should be sufficiently large so that its corners will extend over the tire. The positions for the sash pulleys are located by placing the tire so it will lie an equal distance inside all four corners and scratching lines on the box on each side of the tire. The pulleys are then located and holes drilled to fit

The Revolving Box Used as a Table on a Track Made of a Wagon Tire

them, so the wheels will straddle the marked lines, after which they are fastened in position. The finished stand may be placed in position with the sash pulleys straddling the tire, when any motion given the box will cause it to revolve around the track.— Contributed by William S. Thompson, Hopkinsville, Ky.

### Combination Calipers and Drill Gauge

Considerable time can frequently be saved by using an instrument provided with a combination of gauges, or one

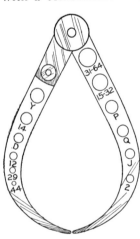

which can be used for several purposes. An ordinary pair of calipers can be so arranged. It may be drilled, reamed, and marked for various sizes of drills, or rods, most frequently made use of. It is then merely necessary to slip the proper-size gauge hole over the round stock, and its size can be read off directly, thereby

avoiding the necessity of first carefully adjusting the calipers and then finding the size on a rule. The calipers would in no way be spoiled for their regular service.

### Arrangement for Adjusting or Leveling Machinery

The following arrangement, while chiefly intended for electric motors, can be applied to other machinery as well. It consists of stud bolts, or plain bolts, threaded their entire length. One end is fastened permanently to a foundation or machine frame, as shown, and the other end is attached to the motor, or other machine, to be held by the bolts. On each bolt, one

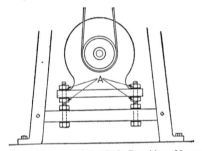

The Long Threads of the Bolt Provide a Means to Adjust the Base of a Machine

nut supports the machine, while a top nut secures it in place. When necessary to make an adjustment, for leveling or for belt tension, the nuts A should be loosened and turned until the desired position is obtained, when they are again screwed up tight.—Contributed by A. P. Connor, Washington, District of Columbia.

### Filtering Tank for Engine Oil

The average small shop, or power plant, frequently cannot afford complicated and expensive oil-filtering devices, nor does it want the cheap affairs which are often no better than ordinary buckets. An efficient and easily constructed filtering tank can be made as shown in the illustration. It consists of a plain tank, A, with a large outlet at the bottom, and is provided with a cover, B. This has three openings: one for a receiving funnel, C; another, in the center, for a plunger rod, D, having a handle at the upper end and a perforated plunger at the lower end; and a third for a siphon, or drain pipe, E, which conducts the filtered oil from the tank to an outside can. At the inner end, the siphon E is U-shaped so it may remove the top or purest oil without disturbing the remainder. The siphon is fastened in place by means of the bracket F and the thumbscrew G. The valve H regulates or shuts off the flow of oil from the tank. When operating the filter, the impure oil is poured into A, until it fills the tank about three-eighths full; then warm water of from 90 to 100-deg. temperature is turned in with the oil and the two thoroughly mixed by means of the reciprocating plunger, after which the mixture should be allowed to settle for several hours.

The oil will come to the top, leaving the impurities with the water at the bottom where they may be drained off. A sight-glass, K, should be placed in the side so the settling process can be observed and the siphon intake ad-

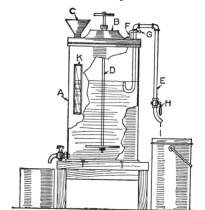

**A Filter Tank for Separating Engine Oil from All Its Impurities**

justed. In order to get the best results, it is advisable to wash out the tank thoroughly and frequently.— Contributed by F. W. Bentley, Jr., Milwaukee, Wis.

⊄An abrasive wheel will glaze over if it is too hard or run at a high speed.

## A Collapsible Contact Maker

The collapsible contact maker shown in the sketch is very serviceable to linemen making frequent tests on tele-

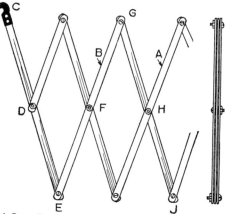

**A Lazy-Tong Contact Maker for Linemen to Use Instead of Climbing a Pole**

phone and power lines that require electrical connection with the wires, as the desired connection can be made without climbing a pole.

The device consists of a number of pieces of dried hickory, about 3½ ft. long, 1¼ in. wide, and ⅜ in. thick, fastened together with bolts to make it similar to lazy tongs. The number of pieces required will depend on the desired length of the extended device. Alternate pieces, such as A and B, are in duplicate, which places a uniform strain on both ends of all the bolts, thus lessening the tendency of the pieces to split out at the ends and also increasing the ease of operation. It is best to put locknuts on all the bolts, so that their tension may be adjusted and locked. Washers are placed between the ends and centers of the various pieces, so that they will move past each other without rubbing. Suitable handles are fastened to the outside ends of the bottom pieces.

A metal hook, C, is attached to the free end of the uppermost piece, to be used in making electrical connection with the wire. The electrical circuit may be carried to the ground by means of a flexible conductor attached to the hook C, and run through the openings in small screw eyes turned in the pieces at the points D, E, F, G, H, J, etc., which prevents the wire from becoming tangled when the device is closed without interfering with the free operation of the device at any time.

## A Radial Rule

In locating center lines of tie rods, or other radial lines, along a curve whose center is not on the drawing, the

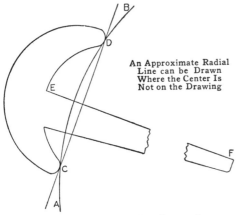

An Approximate Radial Line can be Drawn Where the Center Is Not on the Drawing

radial rule offers a simple and convenient method when the approximate location is wanted.

To find the approximate radius of the curve AB, for instance, points C and D of the radial rule are placed on the curve, and the line, or edge, EF of the rule indicates the radial line.—Contributed by H. A. Thompson, Johnstown, Pennsylvania.

## Fastening Split Patterns for Turning

It is frequently necessary to make patterns split, or in halves, in a lathe in order to be easily drawn from the mold, and it is also desirable to have the split, or joint, exactly in the center of the turned piece. One of the simplest and probably one of the best ways of fastening the two pieces together for turning is to glue the ends for about ¾ in., allowing 1¼ in. of material on each end to be cut off; but if it is a job that must be removed from the lathe and taken apart to fit a flange or something of the kind, this method is not suitable.

In this case it is customary to use a screw in each end, countersinking them so that they will not come in contact with the turning tools, or to depend on dogs driven into the ends, which, however, is to be avoided, as the dogs are apt to loosen, permitting the pieces to leave the lathe centers.

Another method, sometimes used on pieces that are not doweled together, is to make a center mark on one piece with the divider point, and place a small bird shot on the point or center mark, whereupon the other half is placed on this and struck sharply with the hand or a hammer, the shot transferring the center to the upper half. Holes are drilled in both center marks to take the screw part of an ordinary wood screw, after removing the head and shank. The upper, or larger, part of the threads are filed slightly tapering and screwed into one of the pieces with the use of a pair of pliers. The pointed end of the screw is started in the hole in the second piece and the two screwed tightly together by turning the second piece as if it were a nut.

Center plates are ordinarily used on large pieces for centering and holding the joints together while being turned. They are usually made of metal, from ¼ in. to ½ in. in thickness, and vary in shape and form, some being round and others square or oblong. The round kind is the best, but they should be finished all over and have three screw holes each side of the center line; and after the center recesses are turned in them, the hole should be continued through the plates with a small drill, preferably one that will be a fit for a 1½-in. brad. It is only necessary then to locate the center on the stock and drive the brad in about 1¼ in. It is then withdrawn and slipped through the small hole in the center of the plate where it serves as a pin for centering the plate on the piece to be turned.

Center plates cannot be used very well on small pieces, and it becomes necessary to drive a spur and dead center exactly on the joint—a very difficult thing to do—and to correct the variations by tapping the ends of the piece with a hammer to force the piece to one side of the center or the other as the case may demand. To determine how much a piece is off center and which way to tap it in order to correct the mistake, scribe three or four circles about $\frac{1}{16}$ in. apart on the ends of the pieces. These lines should be made from the joint on each end of the pieces before fastening them together, locating the outer line close to what will be the periphery of the piece. Turn the ends down first, and if the turned part coincides with the first line each side of the joint, the piece is central. If the line is turned away on one side and still shows on the other, it is off center, and must be tapped on the side where the line is turned off. After it has been forced over as far as may be considered enough to bring it central, turn down to the second line and note the result. The reason for having three or four sets of parallel lines is obvious. Three or four concentric circles drawn on each end with a pair of dividers will answer the same purpose, or the piece may be stepped off with a pair of dividers after a spot on each end has been turned up, but the use of gauged lines will be found more accurate than either of these methods.—Contributed by J. A. Shelley, Brooklyn, N. Y.

---

## Motorcycle Carrier for a Traveling Bag

While touring on a motorcycle I had considerable trouble in keeping the traveling bag, which I take along, fastened to the luggage carrier. Finally I made a simple device which overcame all this trouble. It was simply a tray made of wood and fastened to the luggage carrier with U-bolts. The inside dimensions of the tray were the same as the dimensions of the bottom of the bag, and the sides were about $1\frac{1}{2}$ in. high. To attach the bag, it is set in the tray and fastened down with one strap.—Contributed by Abner B. Shaw, N. Dartmouth, Mass.

## Mailing Bag for Parcel Post

A mailing bag that can be used to inclose a great variety of goods is made as illustrated. An ordinary sack is procured, such as a salt sack, and a strip of cardboard, about 1 in. wide and equal in length to the width of the bag, is placed in the bottom. The bag is then stitched on a machine just above the strip of cardboard. This keeps a space of 1 in. at the bottom stiff enough 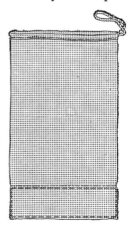 to write upon where it is easily seen. The remaining space of the bag is used for the goods.—Contributed by J. J. Kolar, Maywood, Ill.

---

## Cleaning Out Blast Holes After Explosion

In order that lack of water during a dry season should not injure trees grown on sand rock only slightly covered with soil, it was decided to form storage pockets in the rock, in which the water could collect. Holes were drilled and the bottom blasted out with dynamite, but considerable loose sand still remained. To remove this, the device shown in the sketch was made. It consists of a handle somewhat longer than the total depth of the drilled hole, to which are  fastened two cutting blades, on opposite sides, and a wide clock spring, or spring band. When necessary to clean out a hole the spring was compressed so it would enter at the top, and the entire device shoved to the bottom. The handle is then turned which causes the knives and spring to cut out the sand. In drawing out the tool, part of the sand will be brought up by being wedged in between the spring and the cutters; this must be done several times before the hole is all cleaned out.—Contributed by F. E. Dougan, Pawnee, Okla.

## Forming Leather Cups for Air Pumps

Leather cups for replacing worn ones on air pumps can be easily formed from bits of leather with the use of the de-

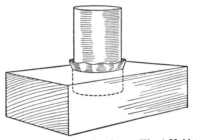

Driving a Piece of Leather into a Wood Mold to Form a Pump Cup

vice illustrated. The mold consists of a block of hard wood, bored to make a hole of the same diameter as the pump barrel. The depth of the hole should be the same as the width of the flange on the leather. A plunger is cut from another piece of hard wood and turned to a diameter to make a drive fit when a piece of leather is placed under it.

The leather is thoroughly soaked, then driven into the hole and allowed to remain until it dries out. The edge is trimmed before removing the cup from the mold.—Contributed by Wm. A. Robinson, Waynesboro, Pa.

## Tool for Testing Irregularities on a Circular Surface

It is frequently necessary to test revolving work for projecting pins, teeth, or outlines, so they may all be finished

Revolving the Wheel with an Irregular Periphery Causes the Pointer to Indicate the Outline

alike. A simple device for this purpose can be made as illustrated. On a suitable base is attached a round pin to fit the bore of the wheel, or part, to be tested. An indicator arm is pinned in place near one end, so as to have a free circular movement when pressed against the irregular surface of the test piece. The outer end of the indicator travels over a graduated scale fastened to the base. A spring is attached to the indicator, to keep it in contact with the face of the part tested, so that when this is rotated, its irregularities will be indicated on the graduated scale.—Contributed by George Jaques, Chicago, Illinois.

## Detachable Hook for a Steel Tape

Steel tapes are not provided with any kind of arrangement for holding the end so that one person can use the tape in making a measurement. The cut illustrates a one-piece hook which is small enough to be carried in the vest pocket and can be attached to or detached from a tape in an instant. It will not slip, or let go, when in use. The groove shown should be bent slightly rounding, with the slot on the

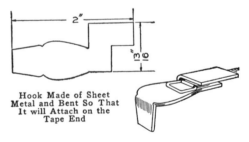

Hook Made of Sheet Metal and Bent So That It will Attach on the Tape End

near side just wide enough to allow free entrance of the tape end. Insert the tape into the slot and draw it back against the ring; the rivet heads at the splice will wedge it tightly in position.—Contributed by E. O. Ritter, San Francisco, Cal.

¶It is false economy to purchase cheap inner tubes, for they will quickly put an expensive casing in the scrap pile.

## Homemade Thread-Cutting Machine

By J. B. MURPHY

One of the most frequent difficulties experienced by the home mechanic, or machine operator in an out-of-the-way place, is to provide an inexpensive means for threading bolts, pipes, and machine parts. For such purposes a thread-cutting machine, as shown in Fig. 1, can be made, which will cut all intermediate sizes up to the largest. By using one head, all threads cut will be exactly the same. No other driving power is required than that applied with a pipe wrench.

The machine consists of a cutter head, and a vise for holding the stock. Three main parts constitute the cutter head. They are: a stationary head; a pipe or tube, attached to it and threaded with the desired master thread; and a rotating tool holder. The pipe should be of such size as to allow the largest diameter of stock to be threaded to enter freely. One end must have sufficient threads for a coupling to screw on to it completely. Two holes are drilled through the center of the pipe, at the unthreaded end, for bolting it to a wooden frame, or headstock, which, when completely assembled, is fastened to a workbench. The block is provided with a semicircular, or V-shaped, groove, to hold the pipe, and should be sufficiently high, so that the threading tools will have ample clearance above the bench.

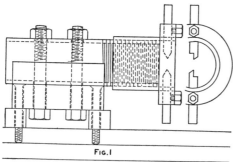

Fig. 1

An Inexpensive Machine for the Small or Home Shop to Thread Pipe or Bolts

The bolt holes in the block are countersunk in the base, to admit the bolt heads.

The rotating tool holder consists of a coupling, threaded to match the pipe thread, and having a tool-holder ring

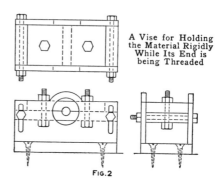

A Vise for Holding the Material Rigidly While Its End is being Threaded

Fig. 2

shrunk on at one end. Two slots, on directly opposite sides, are cut through the ring and coupling, to admit the threading tools. Their distances from the outside face of the ring must differ by one-half the thread pitch, so the tools will track when ground exactly alike. To clamp the cutters in place, holes are drilled and tapped in the slots for setscrews.

To clamp the stock in position for threading it, any portable vise will answer, which, when bolted in place, will hold the stock so its center lines up with the center of the cutter head.

If no suitable vise is at hand, a substitute can be made, as shown in Fig. 2, which will answer as well. For this purpose a strong, three-sided wooden frame is made. The intermediate piece serves as the base for the vise, and should space the two parallel sides about 2 in. apart. These should have sufficient width at the center, so that a circular hole may be cut through, having a diameter slightly greater than the largest-size stock to be threaded. The distance of the center of the hole from the workbench must be exactly the same as that of the center of the cutter head from the same base.

The clamping device consists of two iron bars, 1 in. thick by 2 in. wide. These are drilled and clamped together with two bolts and nuts, which are spaced sufficiently far apart so that the largest stock will easily fit between them, when clamped in place. A hole is drilled through the 2-in. width

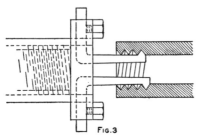

Fig.3

Cutters Used in the Head for Making Threads on the Inside Surface of a Hole

of the clamp, midway between the bolts and with one half in each bar. This must correspond to the smallest size of stock to be held; the larger sizes will be gripped on the four edges of the circular opening. The upper bar is only long enough to provide a bearing for the clamping nuts; the lower bar must extend out farther, so that it can be drilled at each end for adjusting bolts, which fit in slots in the wooden uprights. The completed vise is fastened in position so that it lines up as closely as possible with the cutter head, allowing sufficient space between to permit removing of the coupling.

In using the machine, the tool holder is first turned on the pipe as far as it will go, and the stock is then set. It is clamped in the vise, with the end to be threaded extending to within a short distance of the tools. To adjust the stock centrally with the cutter head, a pair of inside calipers, or a common rule, may be used. The distances from the stock to the edge of the holes in the vise frame, should be measured, and when these are all alike, the stock is in proper alinement with the cutter head, and is fastened in that position by the adjusting bolts.

In setting the tools, the one nearest the outside face of the tool holder is adjusted first for a suitable cut in the metal. The holder is then given a half turn, and the other tool set so it will track in the cut made with the first setting, but sufficiently deep to remove an additional amount of metal. If the tools have been ground alike, not only with respect to shape but also as to length, the cuts can be determined by measuring the distances the tools project from the ring.

When all parts have been adjusted and fastened, the tool holder may be turned with a small pipe wrench, the tools meanwhile cutting and advancing along the stock with the rotated coupling. When the required length of thread has been cut, or the limit of the machine has been reached, the coupling is turned back to the starting point, the setscrews are slightly loosened, and the tools are driven in and fastened for another cut, and so on, until the thread is completed.

When cutting pipe threads, if the setscrews are loosened slightly near the end of the cut, the tools will be forced out, thereby producing the taper necessary for a tight joint.

To cut inside threads for nuts and pipe couplings, the tools shown in Fig. 3 may be used. As before, they should be alike. The cuts are produced by forcing the tools away from the center into the stock.

---

## Building Up Current in Generator with Dry Batteries

When starting up electric generators, difficulty is frequently experienced in building up the current. The brush-holder ring may be fastened in position corresponding to the greatest efficiency at full load, but interfering with the shifting of brushes when starting up. This difficulty can be avoided by the use of a battery. The carbon of the battery should be connected to the armature terminal of the generator; the zinc, to the field terminal, and a push-button switch put into the battery circuit. In using the battery, the current should be switched on only long enough to start the pilot lamp glowing.—Contributed by M. R. Jenkins, Red Creek, N. Y.

## Fire Caused by an Unclean Automobile Sod Pan

Some automobile fires are caused by neglect to clean the machine carefully. In one instance, what might have been a disastrous fire was caused by not keeping the sod pan clean. While cranking the motor, a backfire ignited the oil in the sod pan, and great damage was avoided only by the quick action of the garage owners. It was apparent that the owner had not cleaned the sod pan for several months, and the accumulation was so great that it easily produced a large flame. It is well to clean out the oil dripping frequently.

## Small Crane for a Wagon

Occasionally heavy objects must be lifted into a wagon bed, which calls for two or more men to do the work. Not always having sufficient help at hand, one farmer made a light crane that can be readily attached to a wagon, which aids him in hoisting all loads too heavy for one man to lift.

The crane consists of a 2 or 3-in. gas pipe, about 12 ft. long, and two brackets, also a block and tackle. One of the brackets, A, is forged to fit over the rear axle of the wagon and provided with a vertical bearing on which to set the end of the pipe. The other bracket, B, is shaped to form a ring around the pipe, and is attached to the wagon bed in front of the standard. The pipe has about 2 ft. of one end bent over, as shown, which is drilled to receive a ring that can be used to fasten the tackle. A double tackle will be sufficient for all purposes.

The pipe can be easily taken out when not in use. The bend in the pipe will allow the object being hoisted to

clear the rear end of the wagon box, whereupon the crane can be swung

Wagon Crane Made of a Length of Gas Pipe with a Block and Tackle Attached

around and the object lowered.—Contributed by C. E. Carmack, Louisville, Ky.

## Repairing a Broken Stag Handle on a Knife

The staghorn on my pocketknife split, allowing a part, for about one-half the length of the handle, to slip away from the rivets. I quickly repaired it by filing a groove in the broken part of the horn, as shown in the sketch, and slightly beveling the edge as in countersinking a hole. The broken piece was replaced and pressed firmly under the rivet heads. After cleaning the brass lining of the handle

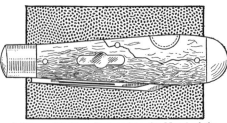

A Piece of Solder, Fastened to the Metal of the Knife, Holds the Broken-Off Horn in Place

and applying flux, I filled the groove full of solder, then dressed it down to the proper shape. In a longer break two or more grooves could be used with success.—Contributed by C. E. Stewart, Jr., Edgeworth, Pa.

## Protractor Attached to Lathe Spindle

Considerable time and labor can be saved and greater accuracy assured, by using a graduated ring as protractor attached to the lathe spindle, for laying out work held on the lathe. The ring should be sufficiently large so it may be counterbored to fit the spindle shoulder, which projects out slightly from the headstock housing. The front end of the housing, being faced off, affords a good surface over which the ring may revolve. Center lines, at exact right angles with each other through the spindle center, should be marked on the end of the housing, for obtaining settings with the protractor. The face of the ring opposite the counterbore is beveled

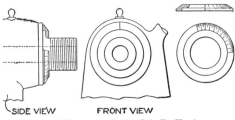

SIDE VIEW　　　FRONT VIEW

Graduated Ring on a Lathe Spindle Used as a Protractor for Laying Out Work

off, to provide a larger space for the protractor divisions.

In graduating the ring for degrees and fractions of a degree, the utmost care must be taken, since the value of the instrument as an accurate protrac- tor will depend mainly on the correct- ness of the divisions. If a regular pro- tractor is available which closely cor- responds in size to the outside diameter of the ring, the necessary divisions can be transferred direct. In case no suit- able instrument can be had, a prelim- inary graduation should first be made on a piece of paper. For this purpose a circle may be drawn, as large as the compass will permit. Without chang- ing the setting, the compass will step around the circle exactly six times. If these divisions are further divided into six parts, each part will equal 10 deg. It is not necessary to subdivide more than one of the 10-deg. divisions into degrees and half degrees. A smaller circle may then be drawn from the same center used for the divided circle, but corresponding in size to the out- side diameter of the ring. Radial di- vision lines may be drawn across the smaller circle, by using a straightedge as a guide, placed over the center and in line with the successive divisions of the large circle. The ring should then be placed over the smaller circle— pasted on, if preferred, to fasten it more securely—and the divisions trans- ferred carefully all around. To form the finer divisions, the ring may be shifted 10 deg. each time, and the marks on the paper carefully trans- ferred as before. The completed pro- tractor can then be fastened to the spindle with pins or countersunk screws. No harm will result from the faceplate or chuck fitting up against the ring, as this takes the place of the spindle shoulder.—Contributed by D. H. Moss, Washington, D. C.

## To Aid the Cooling of an Automobile Engine

The overheating of an automobile engine can sometimes be remedied by changing the pitch of the fan blades, so that an increased amount of air will be thrown against the radiator. A little twist to the blades will help considera- bly in keeping the engine cool.

## Assembling Piston Rings Properly

Faulty compression on a gasoline engine is due in many cases to the lining up of the piston rings; that is, all slots are located so that they are in line with the length of the piston. This forms a path for the gas to escape. Trouble of this nature can be easily avoided if care is taken when the engine is overhauled and reassembled. The slots of the rings should be staggered, and in addition, the right and left slots should be alternated. Then, even if the slots should happen to line up, the path of the escaping gas is broken up more or less, and very little compression is lost.

---

## Thawing Pipes by Electricity

The gasworks in a city used a 2-in. pipe line, run under a street, to carry oil from car tanks on a railroad. During a cold snap, water from condensation was frozen at the lowest point in the pipe under the street. To take up the pavement and dig down to the pipe in the frozen soil would have been an expensive job. An electrician was consulted, and by way of an experiment, electricity was tried out with success to thaw out the frozen part. Two transformers were placed in a line wagon and connected together so as to reduce the voltage and increase the amperage. The wagon was located at a pole on the street and connection made to the overhead wires, using the pipe under the ground as a part of the

## Muffler for a Stationary Gas Engine

Where it is desired to muffle the noise of an exhaust to a minimum, use a barrel set in the earth and filled with

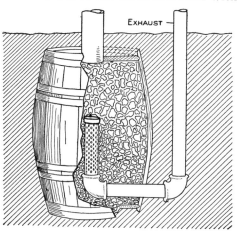

A Barrel Filled with Cobblestones and Set in the Earth to Make a Muffler

small stones about the size of cobblestones. Dig a hole and set the barrel —an oil or sugar barrel—below the surface, then run the exhaust into it from the bottom. A short piece of pipe at the end is capped and the body drilled full of small holes. A large opening should be provided at the top for the discharge of the burnt gases.

---

## Shaping a Log Canoe

To give a permanent form to a log canoe, such as described in a recent issue of this magazine, follow out the method described herewith. When the

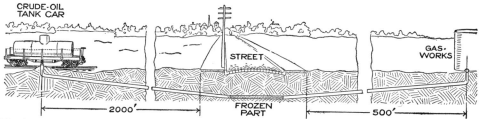

Heating a Long Underground Pipe Line with Electricity to Melt Out Ice Frozen at the Lowest Point under a Street Where It Was Impossible to Get At without Considerable Expense

line. About 600 amperes were used to sufficiently heat the pipe to melt the ice. It took four minutes to remove the ice and start the flow of oil.

canoe is finished, block it up properly and fill it with water. Build a good fire to one side, and place a collection of small boulders in the coals.

When the stones are well heated, place them in the water. This will quickly raise it to a boiling heat. In a few hours, the wood will be thoroughly softened. Then sticks are placed at proper intervals to bend the sides out to the proper curve given to gunwales. The water and stones are then removed, and the canoe is left to dry. This will give the canoe a good shape which it will retain without blocks of any kind.—Contributed by H. L. Whited, Ashland, Ore.

## Repair for Automobile Steering Lever

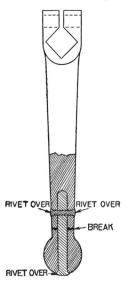

RIVET OVER   RIVET OVER

BREAK

RIVET OVER

A quick, yet efficient, road repair of a broken steering lever on an automobile can be made as shown in the illustration. The lever broke near the ball end. The parts were put together and drilled for a suitable-size rod. This was pressed into the pin end of the lever, and a hole drilled through both, after which a rivet was driven in place, uniting the two. The ball end of the lever was then pressed over the projecting rod, which was then securely peened into a countersunk hole in the ball, completing the repair.

## Hard and Soft Lathe Centers

Lathe centers for metal working are made of tool steel and finished hard or soft according to the work. For the tailstock, the center is hardened after turning it up to the proper taper, and finished smooth. It is drawn to a light-brown color on the point. There is never need for a soft center for the tailstock.

For the headstock, both hard and soft centers are advisable. When a lathe has a hollow spindle, and rods are run through the hole, the center is frequently removed and replaced. Even though the center and its hole are kept clean, a replaced center rarely runs perfectly true on the point. When a job requires accuracy, this center must be turned up true each time it is set in the headstock spindle; consequently the life of such centers are very short.

If a lathe-center grinder is available, the center can be made hard and ground true instead of turning it. It is economy to keep a hard center for the headstock and use it on jobs that do not require great accuracy.

## Marking Fluid for Stenciling

Procure a light, neutral spindle oil and some lampblack in oil. Add enough of the black paste to the oil to produce a black ink, allowing the oil to be as thin as water. Use sparingly, as a very little goes a long way. This makes a good impression, as it is absorbed into the wood and no pigment will remain on the surface to smut; it dries satisfactorily, and does not gum up the brush and pot. It can be used in a fountain brush.—Contributed by E. P. Schafer, Cleveland, O.

## Notches in a Typewriter Eraser

The circular typewriter eraser will prove more efficient if teeth are cut in its circumference, as shown in the sketch. The common type of an eraser becomes hard with use and will make a blotch when erasing words on a carbon print.

The teeth have a tendency to clean themselves, consequently make a neater erasure.

## Boiler and Heater Connections for a Range Boiler

### By J. J. O'CONNER

As a gas stove took the place of a coal range, we had no way to heat the water in the range boiler, therefore a small tank heater was installed for the the tank-heater system could be changed from the range boiler to the heating system, or vice versa, by turning valves. The small heater is suffi-

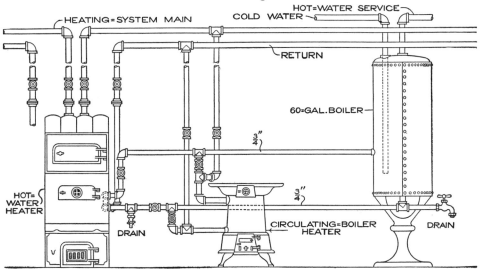

Hot-Water Heating System and Its Connections with a Small Tank Heater and Range-Boiler Heating System So That the Tank Heater can be Used in Mild Winter Weather to Remove the Chill from the Rooms

purpose, which was used during the summer, and in winter the water was heated with a coil made of 1-in. pipe and placed in the fire box of the boiler for the heating system. In making the connections I thought of a way to connect the pipes from the tank heater to the range boiler with the trunk lines of the heating system so that the tank heater could be used to take the chill from the rooms in the early fall and late spring.

The connections were so made that cient in mild winter weather and is a great saving of coal. Another good feature is that the large boiler heats up the system too hot for mild weather and the little tank heater keeps the rooms in a moderate temperature for such weather. The illustration shows the connections. Care must be taken always to close the valves that are open before opening other valves. This precaution will prevent the overflow of the expansion tank from the pressure of the water main.

## A Speed and Voltage Regulator for a Dynamo

The speed of a shunt motor decreases if the voltage of the circuit to which it is connected decreases, or if the load it is operating increases. If the strength of the magnetic field of the motor be weakened a proper amount, when there is a decrease of speed due to either of the above causes, the speed may be restored to the original value and the operation will continue until there is another change in load or supply voltage.

A somewhat similar condition exists in the operation of a generator; that is, if the speed of the machine increases, there will be an increase in the generated voltage, and there will be a decrease in the available voltage at the terminals, if the load increases. With an increase in the speed of the machine the strength of the magnetic field must be weakened in order that the voltage

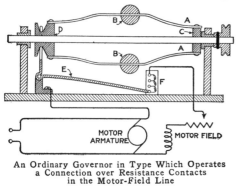

An Ordinary Governor in Type Which Operates a Connection over Resistance Contacts in the Motor-Field Line

may remain constant, and with an increase in load, the magnetic field must be strengthened in order to maintain a constant terminal voltage.

Some of these conditions may be greatly reduced and in some cases almost entirely eliminated by the use of a simple device similar to the one shown in the illustration. Briefly, the device is nothing more nor less than a centrifugal governor, the operation of which controls the position of a movable contact on a resistance. The device may be either belt or direct-connected to the machine with which it is to operate.

The flat steel springs A carry weights, B, fastened at their center. The right ends of the springs are attached to a small disk, C, which in turn is fastened rigidly to the shaft of the device, while the left ends are fastened to the disk D, which is free to move along the shaft, as the weights move out or in, due to a change in their speed. A lever, E, has a U-shaped end that fits in a groove in the disk D, and its other end moves along the resistance F as the disk is caused to move along the shaft. The weights are thrown outward and all the resistance in F is in the circuit. The connection to the resistance F may be changed from the upper to the lower terminal, in which case the resistance will all be out of the circuit when the weights are thrown out.

The operation of the device in controlling the voltage of a generator is as follows: If the speed of the generator is decreased, the field must be strengthened in order to raise the voltage, and this means that there must be a decrease in field resistance as the speed goes down, or the connection should be made to the upper end of the resistance F. The value of the resistance in the different sections of F will depend on the required change in field current.

In the case of a motor, the connection to the resistance F should be made at the bottom, so that the field current will be decreased with a decrease in speed, and as a result the motor tends to speed up, due to the weakening of the field. The speed, of course, will not be restored to its original value, as the operation of the device depends upon there being a change in speed, but the speed will be nearer constant with the device in circuit than it is without it.

----

## An Automobile Pedal Pad

A handy device to incorporate on the pedal of an automobile is a rubber covering for the ordinary pedal pad, which is especially useful in the winter when the shoe soles are more or less covered with snow, which makes them slip off the pad.

The rubber covering shown is made of ordinary rubber matting, 3/8 in. thick, and fastened to the pedal pad by means

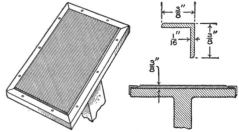

Rubber Pad Held in Place on the Face of a Pedal with Brass Molding

of some angle brass molding, held in position with small brass screws. When polished, the pad will present a very neat appearance.

## Making a Perfect Register in Printing Circulars

In printing the forms for circulars or booklets that have borders or cuts alike on both sides, such as a rule border in color to be printed the same on all pages, use the following method to get a perfect register. Be sure to have a smooth, hard tympan, and after the job is made ready, make alternate impressions on the tympan. The offset will be as good as the original print.—Contributed by M. F. Labrum, Los Angeles, Cal.

## Suspended Frame for Transferring Canoe into Locker or Boathouse

Difficulty is frequently experienced in transferring a canoe from the water to the canoe locker or boathouse, but by means of the arrangement shown, the operation can be done quicker and eas-

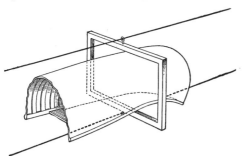

The Frame Guides the Canoe into the Locker and Makes It Easily Handled

ier, besides avoiding the wear and tear otherwise produced in storing the canoe. For this purpose a wooden frame should be provided to fit the canoe, and a screw eye, or pulley, fastened in the center of the top and bottom pieces. The frame must be guided and suspended by two wire cables, securely fastened in the locker.

In using the device, the frame is first pulled to the front of the locker. The canoe is turned upside down, and one end slid into the frame; then, by supporting the other end, the canoe may be easily pushed into the locker, or as easily withdrawn when required. —Contributed by H. A. Weddell, Chicago, Ill.

## Gas-Plate Attachment for a Coal Range

In the place of the shelf which came attached to the range stove I fastened a two-burner gas plate. The legs on

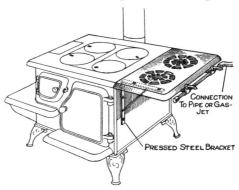

Gas Plate Attached with Two Sheet-Metal Brackets on a Coal Range

the gas plate were removed, and the burner part was attached with two small pressed-steel brackets, purchased from a local hardware dealer. With this arrangement the gas plate not only answers all the purposes of the original shelf, but it converts the range into a first-class combination gas and coal stove.—Contributed by W. R. Humelbaugh, New York City.

## To Make a Long Rope Short without Cutting

Double the rope in the center or at a point where it will not strike obstacles, such as pulley blocks, to get the required length; then put a half hitch in the rope near each end of the doubled part. Adjust the half hitches

A Part of the Rope Doubled and Half Hitches Made over the Looped Ends

over the looped ends as shown. The rope will stand any strain up to its limit.—Contributed by W. J. Tolson, Lyons, Ia.

¶ To prevent scoring rule from cutting the ink rollers, place a small heavy-faced rule at each end.

## Preventing Waste in Filling Oilcans

In stock rooms, or places where oil is supplied to men through a window, a considerable amount is usually

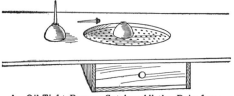

An Oil-Tight Drawer Catches All the Drip from Cans being Filled at the Window

spilled or dripped from the cans being filled. In wiping this up a dangerous accumulation of oily rags, or waste, results. This can easily be avoided and an appreciable oil saving effected by the means illustrated. A portion of the window sill is cut out, and covered with a perforated plate or wire screen. Under this is placed an oil-tight drawer, or receptacle, for catching the oil as it drips from the cans, which may be removed as desired or necessary.—Contributed by George Jaques, Chicago, Ill.

## Turning a Long Cylindrical Pattern

One of the chief difficulties in turning long cylinder patterns is the tendency of the joints to open. Pinch

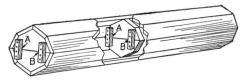

A Long Cylinder Pattern Held Together Temporarily with Blocks While Turning the Staves

dogs, ordinarily used to hold the two halves together, require resetting as the turning progresses and also frequently work loose. These difficulties may be overcome by joining the halves of the heads by means of blocks, A and B, as shown in the sketch. The head pieces are first fitted for dowel pins in the usual way, after which one half of the cylinder may be formed. Then the heads should be put together and the strips A and B

nailed or screwed to them; the end heads should have the pieces on the outside so they may be easily removed when the pattern is turned up. After having assembled and turned the cylinder, it may be separated into halves by first removing the pieces A and B from the outside heads. Then wedge the halves of the cylinder apart slightly so as to allow a thin saw or hacksaw blade to enter, with which the strips on the center head may be cut in two.

## Removing a Broken Knuckle Pin on a Railway Car

Some makes of drawbars are equipped with lugs directly below the knuckle-pin hole, to keep the lower part of a broken pin from dropping out, and if a pin is broken without it being quickly noticed, the lower end is liable to become battered and bruised to such an extent that it cannot be easily removed.

In cases of emergency, remove the top part of the broken pin, take a pin of the same size, or one a little smaller, and drop it into the hole as far as possible, then force it through with a heavy hammer. This will force out the broken part as well as the lugs on the lower side of the drawbar, and replace the new pin.—Contributed by D. C. Lautz, Centralia, Wash.

## Preventing Gear-Box Trouble

When making repairs on the gear box of an automobile, be sure to keep the opening covered to prevent anything falling into the box. One owner had to pay the price of two new gears because a careless workman allowed the box to remain open and a nut dropped in without his knowledge. The nut got in the gears while traveling on the road and ruined them. A thorough examination should be made of the box prior to pouring the grease in, to make sure that it is freed from anything that may have accidentally dropped into it.

# Stopping-Off Pump-Yoke Pattern for New Design

By J. A. SHELLY

It frequently occurs in figuring on new designs, that an old pattern can be changed, by additions and stop-off pieces, to serve the purpose for the new design without spoiling the former. In shops where castings of one kind are made in great numbers, it is not advisable to use patterns with stop-off parts, but where a large pattern is used only occasionally, and with slight changes will answer for a new design, stopping off is economical and practical. In complicated work of this nature, it is usually necessary that the molder understand drawings, and have them at hand to avoid mistakes.

Figure 1 represents, by the full lines, a design for a steam-pump yoke,

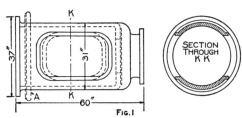

Full Lines Represent the Yoke Pattern and the Dotted Ones Indicate the New Design Wanted

which it is desired to change as indicated by the dotted lines. The side opening on the pattern, Fig. 2, can be reduced by filling in with the proper thickness of wall and adding a new flange. If the flange on the original pattern is loose, it may be removed, otherwise it will be necessary to fill in that part of the mold as shown in Fig. 3. In shortening the yoke, two new end flanges are necessary. At one end, A, Fig. 1, the change can be made by adding the new flange to the original pattern. It will be further necessary to change either core box or mold; if the core box is changed, it should be enlarged, as shown by the dotted outline B, Fig. 4. It may be simpler for the molder to make the necessary change in the mold, which can be done by leaving the new flange in position,

then filling in with molding sand that part, C, Fig. 3, formed by the cut-off portion of the original flange and yoke.

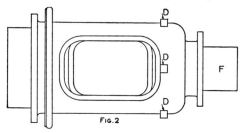

The Exterior Appearance of the Combined Old and New Patterns with Core Prints

To form the new flange at the other end, three prints, D, Fig. 2, should be placed on each half of the yoke pattern; these being necessary for locating the stop-off piece shown in Fig. 5. This should correspond to the desired exterior shape of the new design. It should be provided with prints, E, corresponding to the prints D, Fig. 2, and with a core print matching the original print F, of Fig. 2. If it is desirable to shorten the dry-sand body core, it may be done in the core box by stopping off with circular pieces. If the end F, Fig. 3, is thus removed, it will be necessary to fasten a batten, G, Fig. 5, on the piece H, also shown in Fig. 5, so this

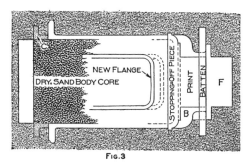

Fig.3

Plan of Mold Showing Method of Stopping Off the Unused Flanges of the Original Pattern

may be held in proper position in the mold, the batten resting on each side. With the piece H in the mold, the spaces formed by the original pattern should be filled in with molding sand, thereby forming the exterior shape for the new design. The body core box

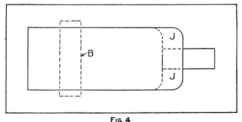

FIG. 4

Plan of Body Core Box with Changes for New Design Indicated by Dotted Lines

must be provided with a loose piece, J, Fig. 4, corresponding to the inner side of the new flange. With the changes made as described, considerable time and money is saved, which

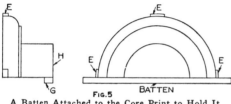

FIG. 5

A Batten Attached to the Core Print to Hold It in Position in the Mold

would have been necessary for an entirely new pattern producing the same results.

## Reclaiming Old Gold

To sell scrap gold to the United States Mint, it must be reduced to almost pure gold or about 24 carat, says the Keystone. Melt the junk and roll it into very thin sheets. Place them in a bowl, so that the pieces will not lie together, and pour chemically pure nitric acid over them. This will separate the gold from the base metal, the latter being dissolved and the gold forming a powder on the bottom of the vessel. After this powder has formed, pour off the acid, put water into the vessel, and shake well, after which allow it to settle, then pour off the water. Repeat this washing several times to clean the powder of acid. Allow the powder to dry, and put it in a crucible with some flux—pearlash or

bicarbonate of soda. Melt it into a lump in the bottom of the crucible. This will be almost fine gold, but not absolutely pure. While melting, be careful not to inhale the fumes, as the remaining acid that cannot be washed out is very injurious to the lungs.

## Turning Cams on a Lathe

There are many different ways of turning rough cam blanks on a lathe, to match master cams, but one of the simplest is that shown in the illustration. The master cam for this purpose should be somewhat wider than the regular finished blank, so that the guide roller may have a continuous bearing even though the cam-cutting tool is not in contact with the cam. The regular cam blanks should first be bored, faced, and keyseated, as required, and then machined for the desired outline. To do this, the master cam and work blank should be put on the same arbor, alined with a key, and fastened in place. In case no key fastening is to be used, the master cam may be drilled and tapped for a suitable stud, and a hole correspondingly drilled in the work blank to fit the stud. When alined and fastened on the arbor, no slipping will occur unless both cams slip together.

On the tool rest, to one side of the tool post, can be bolted the guide-roller bracket. This consists of an iron block provided with a horizontal pin at one side, on which the guide roller is held. The pin can be made separate if desired. In that case, the block should be drilled to fit the roller pin, and a groove cut through on one side, to clamp the pin in place. A hole is drilled through the bracket so that it may be bolted to the tool rest with a T-bolt and nut. This not only holds the bracket in place, but also securely clamps the roller shaft.

In order that the roller bracket may slide back and forth, corresponding to the outline of the master cam, the slide-rest screw should be removed, and a smaller, loosely fitting rod put in its place. This should have sufficient length and be threaded on each end, so that two locknuts can be screwed on the front end, while, on the opposite side, must be a compression spring, with a washer at each end, all held in place with locknuts. The compres-

## Homemade Engine-Driven Tire Pump

The long and laborious operation of pumping up tires with a hand pump can be easily and cheaply replaced by

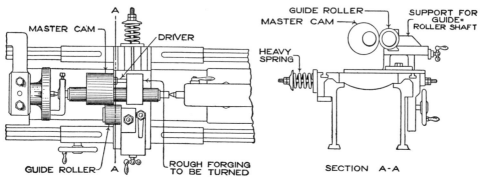

A Master Cam is Fastened on the Shaft with the Part to be Turned and It Controls the Tool Post of the Lathe, Thereby Causing the Cutting Tool to Turn the Blank into a Cam

sion spring must allow the guide roller to travel from one extreme point of the master cam to the other, and as the lathe tool is fastened to the same slide rest, an outline will be cut on the work blank exactly corresponding to that of the master cam. To obtain successive cuts across the work, the tool must be reset for each cut.—Contributed by J. V. Romig, Allentown, Pa.

## Restoring Faded Writing on Old Manuscript

To restore faded or effaced ink writing in old manuscripts, moisten the writing with freshly made "sulph-hydrate of ammonia" (SH, NH$_3$), and in a few moments the letters become plainly visible. A fresh solution in water is colorless, but turns yellow quickly when exposed to air. The surplus chemical is removed by washing with cold water, and the paper is then dried by slight heating or with blotting paper. If the writing again fades after this treatment, a tannin solution should be applied. This process is only useful for restoring ink made with gallic acid.

¶When printing gummed paper dampen the floor about the press thoroughly.

the homemade, pistonless pump illustrated. The parts necessary for its construction are as follows:

One spark plug.
One ⅜-in. close nipple.
Two 2-in. pipe caps.
One 2-in. pipe nipple, about 3 in. long.
One motorcycle-engine inlet valve.
Three ⅛-in. pipe nipples.
One ⅛-in. globe valve.
One pressure gauge.
Sufficient length of hose to reach all tires from the engine.

One of the pipe caps should be drilled and tapped in the center for the ⅜-in. close nipple, the other is drilled and machined to fit the motorcycle inlet valve, and provided with two ⅛-in. pipe openings, leading to the outlet valve and pressure gauge, through the ⅛-in. nipples. The two caps are screwed on the 2-in. nipple. The spark-plug nut, or that part which screws into the cylinder head, is drilled and tapped for a ⅜-in. pipe thread, and connected to the lower 2-in. flange

with the ⅜-in. close nipple, completing the pump.

When it is necessary to pump up the tires, one of the engine spark plugs should be removed and the pump screwed into its place. The engine is then run free. The compression in the attached cylinder will force the air, which has been sucked in through the pump inlet valve, out through the regulating valve and through the hose into the tire connected to it. The time required to change from spark plug to pump and back again amounts to very little, while the labor saved and satisfaction gained by its use, if figured in dollars and cents, would pay for it in short order. Its compactness permits easy storing in the tool box.—Contributed by A. H. Waychoff, Koenig, Col.

## Indicator for Testing Centering of Work on a Lathe

When work is attached to a lathe faceplate, or in a chuck, it is frequently necessary to test the setting with an

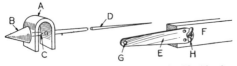

Test Indicator for Setting Parts to be Machined
True on the Faceplate of a Lathe

indicator in order to obtain accurate results. The sketch represents a simple design of indicator that can be easily made; answering the purpose as well as an expensive instrument. It will be necessary to provide a bent strap of metal, A, carefully drilled through the two ends so the holes line up accurately. On one side is fitted a pin machined to pointed centers at each end; one end, B, pointing toward the outside, and the other, C, projecting into the space formed by the bar A. In the opposite hole is fastened a metal bar, D, about 5 in. long, carefully ground to a point on the outer end, corresponding to the center of the rod.

In order to hold the indicator in position a strip of spring steel, several

inches long, should be provided and fastened to a bar, F, suitable for being held in the tool post. A slot, H, is cut into the fastened end of strip E, for adjusting it, and a small hole, G, drilled through the outer end for holding the indicator.

When necessary to use the indicator, the bar F is fastened in the tool post, and the strip E adjusted so the hole G will line up exactly with the lathe centers. When this has been done, no further adjustment should be made that will in any way throw the hole out of line. The indicator can then be held in position, with the center B fitting in the center prickpunch mark of the work, and the end C fitting in the hole G of the spring strip. When the work is rotated the end D will describe a circle, if the setting is off center, until perfect alinement is obtained, when the point D remains stationary, as the three centers D, C and B, as well as the work center, are then in line with the lathe centers.—Contributed by J. J. Kolar, Maywood, Ill.

## Lead-Pencil Sharpener

The illustrated lead-pencil sharpener was made of No. 24 gauge sheet metal, forming a cone open at both ends with flat edges flanged out on the sides. A suitable piece of sandpaper can be cut out and fitted to the inside of the cone, with sufficient length to allow the two ends to pass out through the opening on the side. All surplus stock is cut off from the ends of the cone, and the remaining part trimmed and held in place under the bent-over edges of the

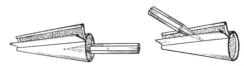

Two Positions of the Sharpener in Making a Round
and a Flat Point on a Pencil

flanged sides. When sharpening the pencil for a round point, the inside of the cone is used; for a chisel point, use the flat sides.

## Preventing Rats from Gnawing Insulation from Wires

A telephone line that had been "fished" under a floor gave considerable trouble and had to be connected with new wires from time to time, owing to the rats gnawing the insulation and causing a ground. Several remedies were suggested and tried out, but all failed until a pair of lines was coated with white shellac as it was drawn in place. This ended the trouble, and the line has been in use for more than a year.—Contributed by C. W. Elliott, Toronto, Can.

## Holding Broken Hacksaw Blades in a Frame

A method of holding broken blades in a hacksaw frame is shown in the sketch. The arrangement consists of a bent-over strip of sheet iron provided

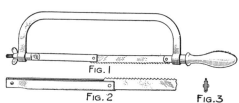

A Piece of Sheet Metal is Used to Hold the Broken End of the Blade

with a hole in each end. The end that hooks over the pin on the saw frame is hammered flat, and the other end is placed over the saw blade and fastened with a rivet, or small bolt. The temper must be drawn from the blade before a hole can be drilled in it.—Contributed by Wm. A. Robinson, Waynesboro, Pa.

## Alarm for Filling Cans with Thick-Flowing Fluids

During cold weather we had trouble with the cylinder oil running slow, and many a can was run over for the reason it was allowed to fill without attention. For an alarm to warn us when the can was about full, we constructed the device shown in the sketch.

It was made of an ordinary wood

packing box with a V-shaped piece of flat iron, ⅛ in. thick, to guide the stem, which was a ½-in. rod surrounded by

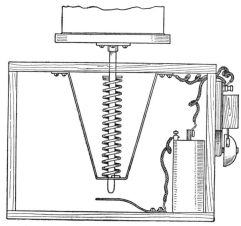

The Electric Circuit is Closed When the Weight of the Liquid is Correctly Measured

a spiral spring. A flat spring at the lower end serves to make contact when the proper weight has been reached. The device can be adjusted by filling the measure or can, and setting the spring to the proper tension after which it will need no attention. The bell will ring when the can fills to the level it is set to measure.—Contributed by C. C. Heyder, Hansford, W. Va.

## Method for Finding Lift of Valve without Instruments

A simple means of determining the available lift or rise of a valve without the use of instruments, is by compressing a piece of lead or similar soft material between the top of the seated valve and the inner side of the chamber cap. Having

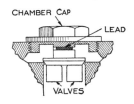

turned the cap to its usual position, it may be unscrewed and the lead measured for thickness, this representing the distance of available lift.

❡It is always best to hang belt shifters vertically when the belt is on the loose pulley.

### Turntable for a Cash Register

By the use of a turntable, as shown in the illustration, it is possible to have a cash register on a counter for use

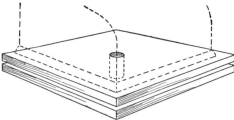

A Pivoted Table That will Permit the Use of a Cash Register from Both Sides of a Counter

from either side. The device simply consists of two symmetrical boards, centrally pivoted by a large pin of sufficient length to keep the boards slightly separated. The register is placed on the platform, balancing the top board as closely as possible, and can then be turned in any direction.—Contributed by A. B. Shaw, N. Dartmouth, Mass.

### Window Cleaner for the Railroad Engineer

In the winter time the damp snow often clings to the little narrow window in front of the engineer and ob-

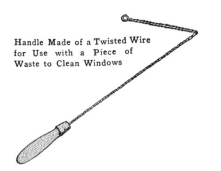

Handle Made of a Twisted Wire for Use with a Piece of Waste to Clean Windows

structs his view. As it is not pleasant or safe to crawl out on the running board to clean the window, some person devised the cleaner shown. It is made of a heavy wire twisted and bent to make a loop at the outer end.

In use, a piece of waste is pulled through the loop; the engineer then opens the window at his side and,

reaching around the outside corner of the cab, swabs off the front window. The dimensions of the cleaner will be determined by size of the cab.—Contributed by Clyde L. Adams, La Grange, Ill.

### Protecting Sleeve for a Tailstock Center

Great accuracy is usually required in grinding machine work. The centers of the machine and the center holes of the work must therefore be carefully guarded in order not to nick or bruise them in any way. By means of the protecting sleeve illustrated this difficulty is overcome.

The sleeve is made to fit the machine center nicely, and turned out to fit the work to be ground approximately, allowing a slight clearance all around the

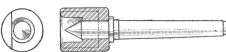

Protecting Sleeve for the Tailstock Center to Prevent the Grinding Wheel from Striking It

circumference. In order to secure easy centering, the inner edges of the sleeve are made slightly rounded. This guides the work to its running position safely and rapidly, avoiding the painstaking centering operation otherwise necessary. One side of the sleeve must be cut away sufficiently to allow the grinding wheel to pass when running off of the work.

### Restoring White Shellac to Its Original Color

If kept in tin cans, white shellac will often lose its color and turn a rusty brown. It can be restored in the following manner: Pour it into a wooden pail and stir with a long stick reaching to the bottom of the pail, at the same time adding dry oxalic acid, until the whiteness returns; then strain through cheesecloth into another can. White shellac, if kept in glass, stone, or wooden jars, will not lose its color readily.—Contributed by G. P. O'Brien, New York, N. Y.

# To Determine the Resistance of Two Coils in Parallel

By A. E. ANDREWS

The combined resistance of two or more coils, or resistances, connected in series is obtained by merely adding the resistances of the respective coils, and the sum total is the resistance of the combination. Thus, if three resistances of 15, 25 and 18 ohms, respectively, are connected in series, their combined resistance will be 58 ohms.

When resistances are connected in parallel, the procedure in determining their combined resistance is more tedious than in the case of the series connection, and for this reason the following graphical method will be found a great time saver and at the same time sufficiently accurate for almost all commercial purposes. The chart to be used in making the graphical solution should be constructed as follows:

Obtain a sheet of cross-section paper used in all engineering offices, having at least 100 vertical lines and 100 horizontal lines. The number of vertical lines is not so important as that of the horizontal ones. On each vertical edge of the paper lay off the scale of resistances, allowing at least 10 horizontal lines per ohm, which gives a total of 10 ohms on each side if there are 100 horizontal lines.

To use the chart proceed as follows: Suppose it is desired to find the combined resistance of a four-ohm coil and a six-ohm coil when they are connected in parallel. Draw a line from the lower left corner of the paper over to the four or six-ohm point on the right vertical edge; in the instance shown, to the six-ohm point. Draw a line from the lower right corner over to the four-ohm point on the left vertical edge. Trace along the horizontal line that passes through the point where the two lines just drawn intersect until it touches the right or left vertical scale. The value at the point where this line passes through the scale represents the combined resistances of both coils in parallel. The intersection point in this instance is on

line 24, not counting the lower line, and represents 2.4 ohms.

Resistances higher than 10 ohms may be handled by increasing the value of the vertical scale in ohms. Thus each scale may be multiplied by 10, and resistances up to 100 ohms may

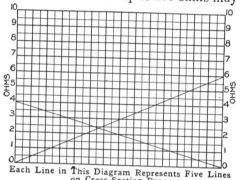

Each Line in This Diagram Represents Five Lines on Cross-Section Paper

be handled. If 60 and 40 ohms were added the result would be 24.0 ohms, or just 10 times what it was with the four and six-ohm coils. In adding resistances above 100, both scales may be increased by multiples of 10 to meet the requirements. The value of one scale cannot be increased alone, but both must be increased together, and the result is determined on the basis of the increased scale.

The accuracy of the results may be increased by using a much larger sheet of paper with more lines on it, say, 1,000 each way, and laying off the scale with 100 lines per ohm.

The following simple method may be used in determining the point of intersection of the two lines without actually drawing them. Mount the sheet of paper on a smooth board that may be placed or hung vertically in a convenient position. Obtain two pieces of fine thread considerably longer than the horizontal dimension of the paper, and attach one end of each piece to a small needle placed in the lower corners of the paper. Attach small weights to the other ends of the threads, and hang them over two other needles placed on the points of the vertical scale. When the last two needles are placed on the scales properly, at the points corresponding to the resistances to be added in parallel, the two threads will intersect at a point corresponding to the intersection of the two lines, and the combined resistance is determined as before. In order to correct for errors due to the thickness of the thread where it passes over the needles, these should be placed a trifle below their proper positions, the center of the thread then passing through the proper resistance point.

## Bolt Rack

If bolts, nuts, and washers are not kept in special racks, they are very apt to be mixed up, and considerable time

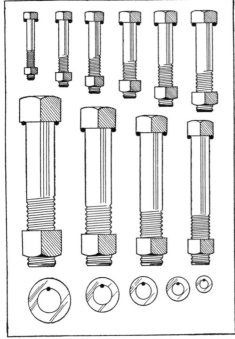

Bolts, That are Used to Clamp Work on Machine Beds, Kept on a Rack

is lost in sorting out those required. The simple rack shown can be used to take all sizes and lengths. Any convenient-sized board is selected, and the bolts are arranged on it in successive lengths, starting with the smallest at one side of the board and increasing in size toward the opposite side. Directly under the longest bolt of the first row, the second row should start with the next size of bolt, and successively increasing sizes should be placed under

correspondingly decreasing sizes of the upper row. Any number of rows may be thus arranged, and space economized. The bolts are hung up by finishing nails driven into the board. Under the bottom row of bolts, the various sizes of washers may be hung up on nails, and arranged in succession. If several boards are used, it would be best to have only one diameter of bolt with all the desired lengths on each board.—Contributed by J. P. Kolar, Ithaca, New York.

## House Number Cut in Window Shade

Before putting up the window shades for the front windows of a house, cut the house number in the shade, near the roller at the top when the shade is drawn out full length for the window. This will provide a means for visitors to find the house on the darkest night, as the light from the lighted rooms will show plainly through the stencil when the shade is drawn.—Contributed by O. M. Southworth, Benton Harbor, Michigan.

## To Hold a Cap Screw

Machine designers usually call for the use of through bolts instead of cap screws wherever possible. The ordinary cap screw, or tap bolt, has a habit of working loose which is often disastrous in its results. There is no chance to put a nut on the "far" side to lock it, and if used in cast iron, the average tapped hole is of such size that it makes a loose fit for the screw which soon jars out. If it is set up tightly, the screw is strained beyond the safe point, or it is twisted off.

Various methods have been employed to keep tap bolts in place, but one that can be worked without preparation or expense is as follows: A split washer, now so familiar to the automobile trade, is put under the head before screwing it down. These washers are made of special spring steel, split and given a twist, then tempered. The twist, when flattened out, puts a constant tension on the cap screw, and in many cases will be the means of keeping a screw tight, just as it keeps a nut tight. Its cheapness and general availability make it a valuable aid.

## An Electric Steam-Pressure Alarm

In a small manufacturing plant three boilers are used to supply the power and are carrying a full load in running the machinery of the establishment. At times during the day, and quite frequently at that, portions of the machinery is stopped, and the pressure rises to the blowing-off point. The superintendent was in the habit of becoming very excited when the safety valves of the boilers would open up, as he considered this a needless waste of fuel. The engineer consequently experienced a little irritation, as he had no way of knowing, unless informed immediately

by some one from the plant, that portions of the machinery would be shut down and the load lightened. The boilers, being forced to maintain the full load, would soon raise enough pressure to "blow off," before they could be cooled down a little by regulating the draft and the application of injectors, which were only used to safeguard the boilers in case of trouble with the feed-water line.

There were two large pumps used for filling a reservoir which were run with the boilers after the plant was closed for the day. The engineer could

at times catch the rise in steam pressure by opening the pumps, but sometimes the safety valves were forced to operate before he could drop other mat-

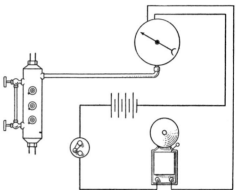

Diagram Showing the Connections of the Gauge with Steam and with the Bell Circuit

ters in the engine room and get to the pumps, located in a building some distance away.

The simple homemade electric alarm shown in the sketch was tried out with success. An old gauge was used to make it. Two small swinging contact strips of thin sheet copper were suspended from the frame of the gauge. The hand was set by another gauge so that it would push the strips together at a pressure a few pounds lower than the amount set to open the safety valves. The contact closed the circuit, which would ring a small alarm bell in the engine room that could be heard in any part of it. The pressure tap for the alarm gauge was taken from the column and led to the gauge, located on a small shelf near it.

Usually an old gauge can be found in almost any engine room, and it need not register all pressures accurately, as any gauge can be set to show correctly at one point, although its adjustment may be in error for other pressures. The batteries and wire are inexpensive, and the arrangement in cases of this kind will relieve the engineer's mind to a great extent.—Contributed by F. W. Bentley, Missouri Valley, Iowa.

❡Paint is not always an insulator, and it should not be used on installed telephone apparatus.

## Removing Drill Chuck Quickly from Miller Spindle

In the making of jigs and fixtures, it is often necessary to do drilling on the milling machine, and in so doing 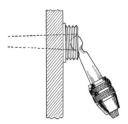 the chuck must be removed and replaced a number of times to substitute special boring or facing tools. After the work is properly located, it is very inconvenient to lower the table out of the way to drive out the drill chuck.

If a part of the drill-chuck shank is cut off, and the end formed as shown, it will not be necessary to move the work out of the way, as the chuck can be taken out and replaced in a very small space.—Contributed by Henry J. Marion, Pontiac, Mich.

## Securing a Wheel in Place with a Threaded Key

In cases where an easy and frequent removal is required for a wheel, secured in a definite position on a straight shaft— 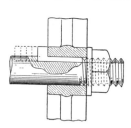 not provided with a shoulder —a simple solution of the difficulty is to provide a threaded key, as illustrated. The key has a shoulder at one end, against which the wheel is held. The other end is threaded at the same time the shaft thread is cut, so the two match when a nut is screwed on it. This key need not have the tight fit the usual drive keys must have in order to hold the wheel in position. When necessary to secure the wheel in place, it can be slid on the shaft together with the key, or this put on first, if desired, and the wheel slipped on afterward. The key is then placed so

that its threads and those of the shaft match, when the wheel fits in the desired position and against the key gib head. Then, by slipping on a loose collar and screwing on a nut, the wheel will be held rigidly on the shaft between the gib head and the collar. No sliding motion can result when fastened, and an easy removal can at any time be obtained by simply unscrewing the nut.—Contributed by F. P. Reidhaar, Connersville, Ind.

## To Muffle Loud Noises in Telephone Receiver

On private exchanges, where the operator is liable to slam the receiver on the hook and make a noise that may injure the ear of the one listening at the end of the line, hold the receiver in the following manner:

Answer in the usual way and at the same time press the tragus of the ear close to the concha with the flange of the receiver, as if pressing the fingers in the ear to shut out any undesirable sound. The sound waves cannot enter the ear, as the tragus deadens the noise. —Contributed by H. W. Potter, Oakland, Cal.

## Homemade Lift Pump

It is frequently desired to have a pump for emergency service where a tedious, slow bailing out with a pail would otherwise have to be resorted to. The pump illustrated can be cheaply and easily made, and will serve the purpose as well as an expensive manufactured article.

For the pump barrel, or cylinder, A, Fig. 1, a 2-in. piece of pipe, about 12 in. long, should be provided, and threaded at each end for standard pipe threads. The inside surface should be carefully filed and smoothed, to remove all irregularities. Three circular washers are required for the pump plunger: two of leather, or rubber, corresponding in size to the inside diameter of the pipe; the third, B, of hard wood, or metal, slightly smaller than the pipe, and smoothed up on both sides, to form a water-tight joint for the plunger. This washer forms the seat of the plunger valve, and is provided with a 1-in. hole for the passage of water when pumping. In the upper washer C, Fig. 2, a narrow slot is cut so that the 1⅛-in. center piece, or flap, is attached only through a short strip, which acts as a hinge, allowing the flap to swing up or down, corresponding to the open or closed position of the plunger valve. To assist the flap in closing readily, a weight should be fastened to its upper side. The bottom washer simply acts as an additional plunger packing.

In order to attach the plunger to its rod, D, a bail, E, must be provided. This may consist of a piece of round bar, threaded at each end for standard nuts, and bent to the shape shown in Fig. 1. The three washers should be clamped together, and drilled to fit the parallel ends of the bail, after which the various parts can be assembled and fastened with the nuts, the upper ones acting as a shoulder against which the washers are drawn up by the lower nuts. If it is not convenient to thread the ends of the bail, a simpler construction would be to provide suitable metal washers, and solder them in the place otherwise occupied by the upper nuts. With the plunger disks in place, a small metal washer should be slipped over the projecting ends of the bail, and these riveted over to form a head. A suitable iron rod should be provided for the plunger rod, and one end securely bent around the bail, and soldered in place to prevent slipping.

For the discharge of the pump a 2-in. elbow will answer. In this should be drilled a hole providing a loose fit for the plunger rod to pass through. In assembling the pump, the discharge elbow is screwed onto the pipe A, and the plunger put in position with one end of the rod passing through the hole in the elbow, whereupon a suitable handle is bent on the plunger rod. Water can then be pumped, but it will be necessary to have the lower end

submerged all the time in order to draw up any water. It may not always be convenient to be so near the water, in which case a foot valve must be made

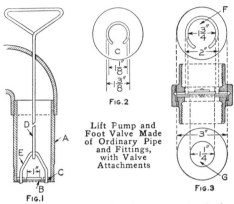

FIG.2

FIG.1

Lift Pump and Foot Valve Made of Ordinary Pipe and Fittings, with Valve Attachments

FIG.3

and attached to the lower end of the pump cylinder, with the necessary water line and fittings. In operating with a foot valve, the greatest vertical distance the pump can work at, will be 10 to 15 ft., depending on the water-tightness of the plunger in the pump cylinder.

The foot valve consists of a 2-in. pipe union provided with a flap valve similar to that in the plunger. Two leather washers should be made, as shown at F and G, Fig. 3. The upper washer F is provided with a hinged flap, acting as a valve. A 3-in. metal, or wooden, disk, with a 1¼-in. hole through the center and both sides smoothly finished, can be used as valve seat for the flap to close against. A weight fastened to the flap will assist it in closing rapidly. In assembling the union, the usual rubber washer between the ends is omitted, and the three disks are inserted in its place, with the metal valve seat in the center, the flap disk at the top, and the plain washer at the bottom, to prevent any leakage through the union except through the main passage of the valve. The completed foot valve may then be attached to the pump, either with a length of plain pipe and coupling, as in a straight lift, or with a hose and necessary fittings, for places which can be reached only by a crooked suction line.—Contributed by G. M. Heimroth, Whitestone, L. I.

## How to Make an Adjustable Sprocket and Gear Puller

Removing tightly fitting gears or sprockets from their shafts frequently requires considerable skill and patience,

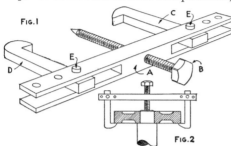

Gears Tightly Fitting a Shaft can be Easily Drawn with the Puller and Spanner Wrench

but with the simple adjustable device illustrated, the job can be easily accomplished. The gear puller consists of: a crosspiece, A, Fig. 1; a forcing screw, B; pull jaws, C and D, and two bolts, E. The piece A may be of convenient length and proper thickness to suit the jobs it is most likely to be used on; for automobile-repair work, a ¾-in. square piece, 7 in. long, would probably answer all purposes. The ends of the rod are slotted to fit the jaw pieces C and D, being ⅜ in. wide in this case. Holes should be drilled, at varying distances from the center on each side, to fit the bolts E, so that the jaws C and D can be set at the places best suited for grasping the gear. The jaws consist of flat, L-shaped pieces, about 3 in. long. The piece A should be drilled and tapped through the center to fit the forcing screw B, which can be an ordinary standard bolt—½ in. in diameter in the case mentioned—tapered at one end to fit the shaft centers, and threaded all the way up to the head. In using this device, first fasten the pieces C and D in the holes best suited for gripping the gear; then, by catching it on the under side, as in Fig. 2, and turning the screw B, it can be easily removed.—Contributed by Adolph Kline, Newark, N. J.

---

❦A small, sharp spade with a folding handle is a handy tool to carry on a touring trip.

## Horsehair Used to Remove Particles from the Eye

The illustration shows a device for removing particles from the eye which I have found quite handy. The particles may be sometimes removed by pulling down on the upper lid until it laps over the lower one, then allowing it to draw back in place, but this method is not always successful.

The instrument for this purpose is made of a piece of wood, cut in the shape of a penholder for a handle, the small end being about ⅛ in. in diameter. This end is cut, or split, and a horsehair inserted so that it makes a loop about ¼ in. in diameter. The hair can be fastened with wax or mucilage.

To remove a bit of dust, or the like, lift the upper lid, and move the horse-

The Horsehair, Being Smooth, will Not Injure the Eye as It is Moved over the Surface

hair around the ball of the eye. This will always get the intruder.—Contributed by Alfred R. Wagstaff, Lake Forest, Ill.

---

## Pouring Liquid from a Large Can

Nearly all 5 and 10-gal. cans containing oils have only the regular handle for carrying purposes, and to pour the contents from such a can is not an agreeable thing to do, as one

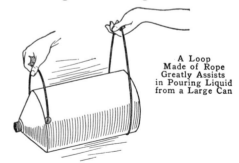

A Loop Made of Rope Greatly Assists in Pouring Liquid from a Large Can

hand must be used to grasp the bottom, which is usually covered with oil and dirt. A loop of rope placed about the lower end of the can will prevent soiling the hands and also aid in the lifting.

## Homemade Concrete Mixer

### By H. B. STRALEY

TO mix small portions of concrete for odd jobs with a shovel or a hoe becomes a tedious task, and to have a large mixer would be entirely too expensive for the amount of work required of it. One farmer, with the outlay of only a few dollars, made a small mixer that will do as good work as any power-driven machine, yet it is small and uses very little material for one charge.

An ordinary oil barrel was procured and mounted on a framework of 2 by 4-in. material. A square frame was constructed around the center part of the barrel, which had a steel band without any rough joint fitted on. In the lower corners of this frame two brackets were fastened, each made of two pieces, between which a flat-faced wheel was placed on a shaft run through the pieces. The main portion of the barrel is supported on these wheels, their faces running on the steel band. A little to one side of the center of

this frame two pieces were rigidly attached at right angles so that their ends extended a couple of feet beyond the bottom of the barrel when it was in its place.

Across the diameter of the barrel bottom a piece of metal, or timber, was placed and solidly fastened with bolts. Exactly in the center of the barrel bottom and crosspiece, a hole was bored and a shaft fastened, which was long enough to run through the bearing set in the frame, and to have sufficient end to attach a bevel gear. A cross shaft was provided and supported in a bearing fastened to the extending pieces attached to the square frame.

The square frame was mounted on bearings, centrally located in its sides and connected with brackets, as shown, to the upper ends of vertical pieces, braced and connected to pieces sloping toward the rear, forming a triangular framework for the machine. A band wheel and a sprocket wheel were

In Making Silos, Foundations, Feeding Floors, Fence Posts, and the Like, It Is Necessary to Have a Mixer for the Concrete, and the One Shown will Serve the Purpose Where There Is No Large Amount of Work

mounted on one shaft that was attached to the outside surface of one upright. A chain connected the two sprocket wheels.

A long lever, fastened to the crosspiece on the upper part of the square frame and wired to the ends of the

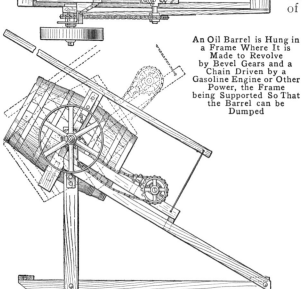

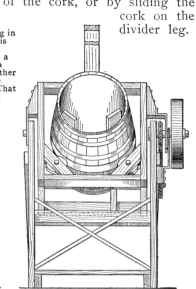

An Oil Barrel is Hung in a Frame Where It is Made to Revolve by Bevel Gears and a Chain Driven by a Gasoline Engine or Other Power, the Frame being Supported So That the Barrel can be Dumped

## Dividers Used as a Bow Pen and Pencil

Instead of carrying a complete drawing set about in making sketches, a pair of dividers, a 6-in. scale, and a small cork will answer for all purposes.

In one end of the cork, insert one of the divider points, in the other end cut a small, deep slit. Place a pencil lead in the slit, and use it as a bow pencil. To use as a bow pen, remove the lead and place an ordinary pen in its place. The adjustment up and down can be had by moving the lead or pen point in or out of the cork, or by sliding the cork on the divider leg.

pieces that extend to the rear of the barrel, provided a means of tilting it, to pour out the contents when the mixture was completed.

On the inside surface of the barrel several pieces were attached, so that they projected and furnished obstructions to catch and spill the aggregate as the barrel revolved. The machine may be driven from any power with a belt.

---

❡A bag made of soft flannel is best to keep inner tubes in, and the mouth should be tied around the projecting stem.

## The Use of Waste in an Oil Cup

The general impression that a pad of waste stuffed in an oil cup, or oil recess, will feed out the oil a little at a time and save a lot of attention is absurd, as what oil gets to the bearing will run there in spite of the waste.

In considering the facts, it will be found that in but very few cases does the waste come in contact with the revolving shaft. If it did the shaft would be lubricated as long as that part of the waste was saturated. Suspend the wad of waste above the shaft, and the only oil that will drop is the excess that filters through by its own weight. The waste may be well saturated, but there is little capillary attraction in the mass, and, contrary to the general idea, it does not act like a wick.

In cases where the bearing does get oil, it is because the waste is sufficiently porous to permit some of the oil to pass through every time any is squirted into the cup. To prove these facts, pour a tablespoonful of oil into an empty ink bottle, and lead a small wick out from it so that the drip will be caught in another vessel. In a couple of hours the bottle will be dry, only a portion of the oil remaining in the wick. Contrast this with the waste. Roll up a ball of the waste, about the size of an ink bottle, saturate it with oil to the same degree as the wick, and suspend it by a wire over a vessel and note the result. A dozen drops will fall in a day's time. Pour on a teaspoonful of oil, and a small percentage of oil drops off. Repeat it, and only a little more falls. If the intervals between the application of oil are long enough and the amount is small, the oil simply dries up in the waste.

Any case in which waste is depended upon to do self-feeding should be carefully investigated. The slow speeds at which the shaft revolves, the loose fits, and the generally oily condition of some machinery on which the waste pad is used, have given credence to its wonderful properties. Liberal quantities of oil will pass through almost any body not solid, but such liberality is not economy. Waste in an oil cellar in contact with a revolving journal will lubricate under the worst of conditions, as is easily shown by the large amount used on car journals, but a wad of it in an oil cup is of no assistance whatever in oiling a bearing.

---

⟨When riding over sand roads with a motorcycle, let some air out of the tires, especially the front one, which should flatten quite a little. Use just enough pressure to keep the rims from striking the ground.

## Eliminating Gas Fumes from a Gas Stove

To eliminate the fumes from a gas stove, make a closed tank, the size of the stove top, and run the pipe into

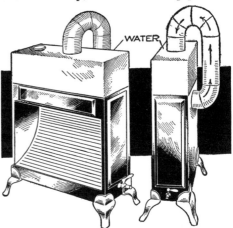

The Fumes of the Gas are Discharged into the Tank of Water on the Stove

it as shown. Fill the tank with water through a hole in the top, which should be provided with a screw-cap cover. With this arrangement, the stove can be taken wherever required, as a chimney is not necessary for a vent.—Contributed by David H. Brook, Dayton, O.

---

## Holding Odd-Shaped Pieces in a Pipe While Drilling Them

In drilling odd-shaped pieces on a drill press, it frequently is necessary to hold them in a vise or some special jig. A piece of suitable-sized pipe can often be used to serve the purpose as well. One end, which should be square with the sides, rests on the drill-press table. 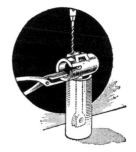 The other may be square or suitably cut to fit the irregular piece to be drilled.—Contributed by D. C. Goff, Knoxville, Tenn.

## Bookcase for Itinerants

When moving the ordinary bookcase, all books must first be taken out, and moved independently of the case. This

Fig. 1—The Packing Boxes When Assembled Give the Appearance of an Ordinary Sectional Bookcase

not only means much extra work in unpacking, repacking, and final rearranging when destination is reached, but also requires special boxes for the books and a crate for the bookcase—if this is to be shipped from one city to another. The illustration, Fig. 1, shows a new type of case in which the sections form the packing cases for shipment, and Fig. 2 the manner in which they are made up to stack in a case.

The outside frame, made and finished in any suitable manner, consists of four parts: a base, A; top, B, and two sides, C. The various sections for the books consist of open boxes, all of one length. Their height may vary according to the size of books stored in them. Their width must be such that when the doors F, are fastened in place they will come flush with the edges of the sides C. Molding strips, D, are fastened to A, with the two end pieces so located that the section boxes and sides C will fit in between them snugly; the molding

pieces E, on the top B, are likewise so spaced as to hold all parts securely. The glass doors F are made to fit the boxes and completely cover the open side. They are attached by hinges to metal strips, G—or strong wooden molding, if preferred—which are fastened in position to each side by means of thumbscrews H. When opening any particular section, its door is swung down. The bottom and top box should have several strips, K, fastened to the sides facing the bottom A and the top B, corresponding in length to the width of the boxes, and of such a thickness that the edges of those boxes come in line with the edge of the molding. In this way, the top and bottom doors may be fastened like the rest. If the top and bottom boards are of sufficient thickness, they may be mortised to receive the sides C, in which case it would not be necessary to use the molding strips E and F, nor the lining-up strips K.

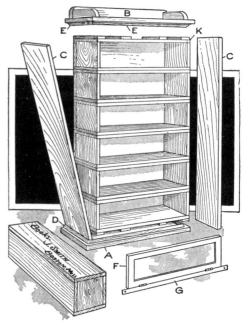

Fig. 2—Case in Sections Ready for Assembling, and a Section Box Closed Ready for Shipment

When necessary to move the case, the doors should first be unscrewed, and then the sides C and top B taken off. Each box section, with books in it, is then taken off and closed up with an ordinary board cover, after which it is ready to be shipped. The case and doors may be put up in a convenient bundle, or crated. On arriving at the destination, the covers can be readily removed from the boxes and the case assembled as already described. The books being in place, much time and labor is thus saved.—Contributed by E. H. Witman, Danville, Pa.

## Protecting the Bed Hammock

Owing to the size and weight of a bed hammock it is generally left outside in all kinds of weather. A good plan is to fasten two awning pulleys to the ceiling of the porch over the hammock so that a rope may be run through them, then attach hooks to the ends of the rope for hooking into the lower part of the hammock. The hammock can then be pulled up close to the ceiling, when not in use, so that it will be out of the sun and rain.

## Blocking Attachment for a Shop Truck

In loading heavy pieces on the bed of a common shop truck, it is often necessary to block the wheels to prevent them from rolling back on the floor and spilling or tipping the load as the weight is raised by the front of the truck. I have seen quite a few accidents occur while workmen were attempting to swing the load on the truck without properly blocking the truck wheels. This is often foolishly attempted when there happens to be nothing immediately at hand suitable for use as a block. The sketch shows an arrangement which can be attached to the truck. Just before tipping the truck the blocking piece, or bar, can be kicked out of its hooks with the foot and replaced quickly, when the load is swung up and balanced on the truck. With this arrangement attached, there is no need to look around for a block. The piece of iron with its

chains is so light and so located that it will not interfere with the use of the truck. As a safety device it is hard

Bar Attached with Chains to the Under Side of a Truck to Block the Wheels

to beat, and will prevent a number of accidents to workmen handling heavy material.—Contributed by F. W. Bentley, Jr., Missouri Valley, Iowa.

## Hopper for Measuring Sand Unloaded from Freight Cars

In unloading sand from gondola cars into wagons, it was necessary not only to measure the amount in cubic yards accurately, but also to avoid spilling the sand on the ground. The arrangement shown in the sketch successfully overcame the difficulties. It consists of a hopper, A, of 1-cu.-yd. capacity, with a hinged bottom, B, held shut by means of a catch, C, fastened to the side. Wrought-iron braces, D and E, attach it to the side of the car so it can be slid along as the unloading advances. The hauling wagons can be

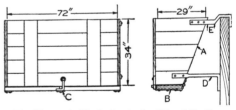

The Hopper is Hooked onto the Side of the Car Where It is Loaded with Shovels

driven under the hopper, and the known amount dumped entirely into them.

## Fastening Molding to Automobile Doors

The usual method of attaching a molding on an automobile door is to  drill holes and put in screws from the top. A better method is to rabbet the door top as well as the molding so they fit together, and fasten with round-head screws from the inside. Plates can be formed and fastened on either side, with their upper portions bent and placed under the molding, as shown. With this method no screw heads will show on top of the door molding.—Contributed by Frank P. Reidhaar, Connersville, Ind.

## To Prevent Down Draft in Chimneys

Procure a 5-gal. can and perforate the sides near the bottom with holes, ½ in. in diameter. The can is then 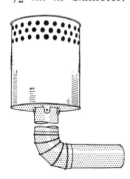 set over the end of the chimney pipe and fastened with brackets. The chimney pipe should extend into the can a short distance. The holes will let out the burnt gases, but a sudden gust of wind will not affect it in the least.—Contributed by P. D. Merrill, Saugatuck, Michigan.

## Roach Makes Ground in a Telephone Relay

Being sent out recently by the wire chief to clear up a line which was grounded, I finally located the trouble in the instrument, and when I told the chief the cause he would at first not believe it. A roach had wedged itself between the frame and the magnet of the relay, thus causing a contact between the springs. The telephone being one of the four-party type, it easily caused a ground.—Contributed by C. W. Elliott, Toronto, Can.

## Liquid Spattering Avoided with Fixed Corkscrew

When it is necessary to remove a cork from a bottle it frequently occurs that the corkscrew has been misplaced, and when found and used in the usual manner, part of the contents are often spattered over one's clothing. To 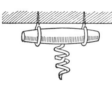 avoid these troubles, the corkscrew can be attached to a wall, or shelf, in a convenient place, where it can always be found when needed. In using it, the bottle is screwed onto the puller and gripped with both hands to remove the cork, thereby providing not only a better grip, but also avoiding the otherwise necessary position in line with the contents as they flow or spatter out of the bottle.—Contributed by L. E. Turner, New York, N. Y.

## Locating Centers of Pipe Fittings

To locate the center of pipe fittings, such as elbows, tees, and crosses, I made a tool in the shape of a triangle  to use in connection with an ordinary pocket rule. The fitting is placed on a bench, or board, and the triangle inserted in the opening of the tee. The rule is then placed against the edge of the triangle. The center line on the triangle gives the dimension wanted. The material required to make the device is a piece of board, ⅜ in. thick.—Contributed by A. L. Kerbaugh, Allentown, Pa.

# The Making of Distilled Water for Laboratories

By W. M. MILLS

IT is so necessary to have plenty of distilled water on hand in large laboratories, or in buildings where chemical or technical investigations are carried on, that it is imperative to have an arrangement that will give satisfaction along this line. The illustrations show two installations. In the first, distilled water is the main thing sought, and in the second it comes as a by-product from the steam coils of the building or steam otherwise condensed.

In the first sketch the water is distilled from an ordinary laboratory still, thence it is conveyed to a carboy below, from which the water, being protected from dust by a cotton filter, is again drained off through pipes into 1-gal. bottles, as needed. For use in a laboratory where it is made, it is forced from the carboy to the covered jar above by a force pump attached to a tube below. A pipe is fitted from the

The Arrangement of a Still and Carboy to Produce Distilled Water Free from Contaminations

carboy to the jar above and the water passes up easily till the jar is filled, which is enough to last a large class

in analysis for a few days. The bottles filled from below are for other

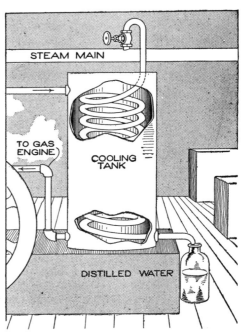

Distilled Water can be Produced from a Steam Main with a Connection and Coil in a Tank

classes in other laboratories about the buildings.

The second method of preparing distilled water is by the condensation of live steam through a copper coil attached to one of the mains of the plant in the building. A hole of the proper size is drilled through the upper side of the main, or if that is impracticable, well up on the side of the main, in order that when the steam or water issues from it there will be no sediment carried with it to contaminate the water. Thread the hole and connect a pipe to it by a threaded connection and globe valve. Lead the copper pipe downward through a water jacket, such as shown in the illustration—in this case the cooling tank of a small gasoline engine. After making several coils in the tank, it is led out through a waste nut fitted at the bottom, and the end is turned down so that 1-gal. bottles can be set under it. After running some time the valve can be so adjusted that the live steam will all be condensed. This apparatus is well adapted for all northern states where steam is employed in heating, while the first one is best adapted for the southern states.

## Flat-Bottom Fire Bucket Fitted with Curved Base

When ordinary flat-bottomed pails are set aside to be used in case of fire only, they are frequently taken —as they are usually found in convenient places—and employed for other uses. If an iron strap be riveted to opposite sides of the pail with the center portion forming an arc, it cannot, without difficulty, be set up straight, and consequently is spoiled for other purposes than fire.—Contributed by George Jaques, Chicago, Ill.

## Automatic Valve for Water-Glass Fittings

To make a safety water-glass fitting, provide a ball valve for the valve part that attaches to the boiler, as shown. If the valve end has a very small hole, ream this out tapering, so that a cavity will be made for a steel ball. The large end of the opening is then fitted with a disk, to keep the ball in place. The holes in the disk and into the valve part should be somewhat smaller than the diameter of the ball.

In action, when the gauge glass breaks, the force of the steam or water will drive the ball into the conical-shaped seat, made by reaming the hole tapering. This will close the hole and prevent the steam, or hot water, from escaping until the valves can be closed. The ball will then drop back into the cavity and allow the steam and water pressure to balance each other in the new glass gauge when it is in place.

## Fastening for Rope Ends of Extension Ladders

Painters, and others, using rope extension ladders can very easily save themselves the annoyance of having the end of the extra rope underfoot, as follows: Tie the free end of the rope to the bottom rung of the top section, so that, when it is extended, it will take up the slack automatically, thus doing away with the bother of having it underfoot.—Contributed by C. H. Lockwood, Masonville, N. Y.

## Valve-Lifting Tool for Automobile Engines

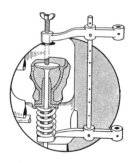

The simple device illustrated is one that a repairman should have in his kit of tools, or an automobile owner in his tool box. It compresses the spring so that the washer and key can be easily removed or put in place. It is simple to make and consists of two arms joined together with a rod made adjustable by drilling a number of holes through its diameter. The arms can be forged and swaged to suit the maker. One arm has a fork on its end to fit over the valve stem under the spring, and the end of the other arm has a tapped hole to receive a wing-head screw. Its application is obvious.

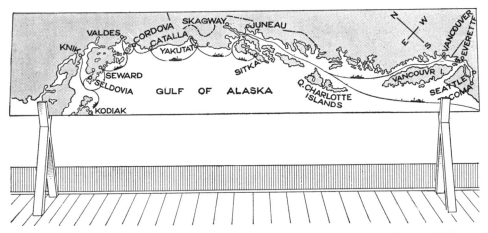

Model Boats are Set in Grooves on the Chart and Placed Each Day According to Wireless So That a Glance will Tell the Movements of All Vessels Entering One Port

## Steamship Chart for a Hotel Lobby

As there is always great interest in the shipping in and out of a port in Alaska, I had a frame made, 8 ft. long and 20 in. wide, of material 2 in. square. The frame was then covered with galvanized iron with a small tin groove soldered on it in the channel to hold pieces of wood shaped like boats. The chart was then colored, and the boats were painted in the colors of their respective lines operating in the port. The name of each boat was written on paper with a typewriter and the paper pasted to the boat's bow.

The position of each boat is changed on the chart every day, according to wireless advice received on their location from the time they leave Seattle until they return.—Contributed by Harry F. Cain, Juneau, Alaska.

## Multiple-Size Punch

The illustrations show a punch for cutting four different-size holes. The general idea of the tool can be applied for a greater or less number of cutters, as desired and practical. The largest diameter of cutter becomes at the same time the body, or holder, A, Fig. 1. It is bored out to a size slightly larger than the outside diameter of the second largest punch, which, in turn, is

bored out slightly larger than the next size, and so on, down to the last, which is drilled to the size of punch diameter required. The body A is drilled for a pin, B, at such a distance from the cutting edge as to cause the remaining cutters, when resting on B, to assume the positions shown in Fig. 2, each projecting out a little farther than the next larger size. In this way each cutter is held rigidly in place, being braced by those of larger size, and the thrust comes on the pin B. To prevent the cutters from slipping out

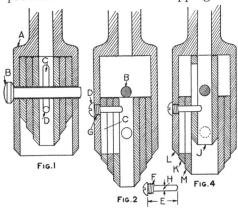

FIG.1
FIG.2 |←E→|
FIG.3

Three Positions of Punch for Using the Largest, Smallest, and Second Cutters, Respectively

when in their extreme position, they are provided with a long slot, C, through which passes a pin, D, securely held in one position in the body

A. This pin, Fig. 3, is of sufficient length, E, to pass through all the cutters on one side. The pin is threaded at the end F, to fit a correspondingly threaded hole, G, in the holder A. The body of the pin is of a diameter, H, slightly smaller than the width of slot in the cutters.

Whenever it is desired to use the largest punch, the pin B is withdrawn, allowing the cutters to drop to the bottom of the holder. In this position, each cutter—having been drilled with a hole slightly larger than pin B—is held in place by putting the pin through the holes. If the smallest cutter is to be used, all the cutters should be put in their extreme outer position, and the pin B put in place as in Fig. 2, the desired cutter being

thereby braced and held on all sides. Supposing it is required to use the second smallest punch, it is necessary to allow the smallest cutter to drop into the holder, after which the pin B is replaced, holding all cutters in the set position. This is shown in Fig. 4, the second cutter M being drawn out, leaving the smallest J in the holder, and the larger cutters K and L supporting the second. Any other combination—within the limits of the tool—can be made, first allowing all cutters larger than the required size to come out in cutting position with the desired cutter; all smaller cutters must remain in the holder. The hole in the body A is for inserting a rod for removing the punching scraps.—Contributed by John Harger, Honolulu, H. I.

## A Hand-Power Bench Shaper

### By J. B. MURPHY

There is no tool that can take the place of a shaper for certain kinds of work, but the owner of a home workshop usually cannot afford a machine of this kind, so that when it is necessary to do this class of work, it takes hours of time to obtain the results with a file. To provide a tool that can be worked by hand power and take the place of an expensive machine, the one illustrated was designed and most of the parts made of white oak.

The shaper is built on the workbench, where it is attached by means of the bolts A. The general dimensions are omitted, as the machine can be made in length and width to suit the class of work required of it. The lever B—made of hickory, 24 in. long and 2 in. thick—for operating the ram C, is tapering and slotted for the driving stud D.

The ram C is made of a piece of oak, 6 in. square and 40 in. long, and is beveled, as shown in the cross section EE. Adjustment for wear is made by the piece F, which is controlled by the screws G, tapped directly through the wood gib. The ram moves upon a three-piece bed, the center piece being

a little smaller than the two outer pieces that form the ways. This gives the ram proper clearance and avoids unnecessary friction.

In the front, or working, end of the ram, a piece of heavy 1½-in. tubing is driven into a hole bored in the end of the wood, and a pin H is inserted in a hole drilled through both ram and tubing to prevent the latter from turning. In the outer end of the tubing and close to the end of the ram, a ½-in. hole is drilled for the tool J. The tubing tool post is located centrally in the end of the ram, as shown in the cross-section sketch.

The tool can be made of a discarded round file, ground properly and tempered to cut metal. One side of the file is ground flat to make a seat for the setscrew. The setscrew is fitted to the end of the tubing by locating it centrally and pouring babbitt metal around it. A large or coarse thread is necessary, and its bearing should be about 2 in. long.

In the detail of the cross feed, the nut K is recessed in the under side of the platen. The bolt L is turned by hand with the pin M. The bolt, when turned

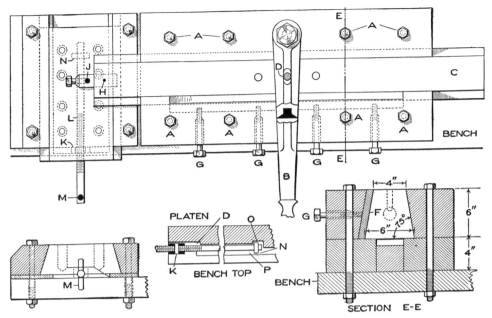

Details Showing Well-Proportioned Parts of a Shaper That will Produce as Good a Grade of Work as an Expensive Machine, Most of Its Parts being Made of Hard Wood

in or out through the fixed nut K, causes the head N to draw the platen either way as the cut is taken. The head N fits into a recess, O, cut in the under side of the platen. A clearance groove, P, is cut in the bench top for the lower part of the bolt head as it travels from end to end.

A good lubricant for the surfaces that slide together is oil and graphite. A cut, $\frac{1}{32}$ in. deep, can be taken with a feed of $\frac{1}{64}$ in. All light planing for experimental work can be done with this planer.

### A Gas Water Radiator

The illustration shows a gas water radiator that I constructed from pipe and fittings, using an ordinary gas water heater. Enough 1¼-in. pipe and return bends were used to give about 25 sq. ft. of radiation. The manner of connecting the pipe to the heater is clearly shown. The upright pipe accommodates the rise of the water level due to expansion. A safety valve is placed at the upper end of this pipe. A small pressure gauge is shown,

but this is not necessary. A pressure of from 1 to 5 lb. makes the radiator much more effective, especially in cold weather. This heater was intended to be used for chilly weather in the spring and fall, but it has been in use every day and night during the entire winter, and keeps an ordinary-sized dining

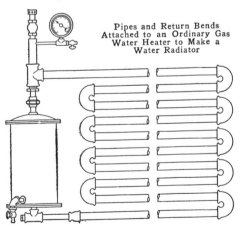

Pipes and Return Bends Attached to an Ordinary Gas Water Heater to Make a Water Radiator

room at a very comfortable temperature with a very small consumption of gas.—Contributed by Claude Swaim, Indianapolis, Ind.

# Determining Generator Efficiency by Stray-Power Method

By A. E. ANDREWS

ALL the losses in a direct-current generator or motor may be grouped under one of two main heads, namely, electrical losses and stray-power losses. The electrical losses (I²R) include all losses in armature winding, commutator segments, brush resistance, resistance of leads to terminals of the machine, and the series and shunt-field windings. The stray-power losses include all friction losses, such as bearing and brush friction, windage, which is the loss due to the fan action of the revolving portion of the machine, and the hysteresis and eddy-current losses, which occur in the armature core, armature inductors, and pole shoes.

The sum of these two groups of losses represents the difference between the input to a machine and its output. The commercial efficiency of a machine is equal to its output expressed as a percentage of its input, so that if it were possible to determine the losses, the commercial efficiency could be determined when the output of the machine is known.

The electrical losses in a machine can be determined by first measuring the resistance of the various circuits after they have reached a temperature corresponding to operating conditions, and then multiplying this resistance by the square of the current the circuit is carrying. The electrical losses in watts will vary directly as the square of the current and resistance to the first power.

When a motor is running without load, all the mechanical power developed in the armature is used in overcoming the stray-power losses, and the value of the mechanical power developed, in electrical units, is equal to the product of the counter electromotive force and the armature current. The stray-power losses in the machine will be practically constant for all loads, since there is a very small change in the field strength, or induction density; speed, friction, and windage losses are also practically constant for all loads.

To determine the stray-power loss of a machine that is operating as a motor is to determine its counter electromotive force, which is equal to the difference between the impressed voltage and the copper drop (current times armature resistance), multiplied by the armature current, when the machine is operating without load, the speed being the same as when loaded.

Example: Suppose a 20-hp., 110-volt motor has an armature resistance of .004 ohm; a shunt-field resistance of 55 ohms, and takes a current of 7 amperes when running without load, and it is desired to determine the commercial efficiency, when the armature current is 120 amperes. The counter electromotive force of the motor, running light, will be

$$110—7\times.004=109.972 \text{ volts},$$

and the stray-power loss will be

$$109.972\times7=769.804 \text{ watts}.$$

The electrical loss in the field will be equal to the field current times the voltage:

$$(110\div55)\times110=220 \text{ watts}.$$

The electrical loss in the armature will be equal to I²R, or

$$120^2\times.004=57.6 \text{ watts};$$

total electrical loss:

$$220+57.6=277.6 \text{ watts};$$

and total losses:

$$277.6+769.8=1047.4 \text{ watts}.$$

The total current taken by the machine would be $120+2=122$ amperes, and the watt output would be

$$122\times110=13,420 \text{ watts}.$$

The input minus the losses represents the output, which, therefore, is

$$13,420—1,047.4=12,372.6 \text{ watts}.$$

The commercial efficiency, or the output expressed as a percentage of the input, will thus be found to be

$$\frac{12,372.6}{13,420}\times100=92.2 \text{ per cent}.$$

More exact results may be obtained by operating the machine as a motor with a series of impressed voltages corresponding to the counter electromotive force generated in the machine when operating on various loads as a motor, and then computing the product of the counter electromotive force and armature current for each particular impressed voltage. The speeds should be the same in both cases. This will give the value of the stray-power loss for each load, but it will be found practically constant for most cases.

In the case of a generator, the stray-power losses are determined by operating the machine as a motor, with impressed voltages corresponding to the generated voltage for various loads when operating as a generator. The speeds should be the same in both cases.

The great advantage of this method of determining the commercial efficiency is the small cost of energy to make the test, and the possibility of testing a large machine with a small generator, or battery, as only the losses need be supplied.

## Repairing a Broken Bearing Cap

The following describes a neat repair on the crankshaft bearing cap of an automobile engine. The engine was a very old type, and a new part could not be obtained. The break occurred at the point indicated in the drawing. Two strips, A, of ⅛-in. cold-rolled steel were cut in 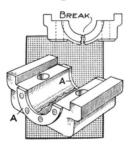 the shape of semicircles. The bearing cap was then planed off ⅛ in. on each side. The plates were then riveted to the cap by means of $\frac{3}{16}$-in. rivets. These rivets were of the flat-head type, set into countersunk holes. The heads were finished off flush on the sides. The repair made a neat job and at the same time was inexpensive.—Contributed by Adolph Kline, New York City.

¶It is quite necessary to examine the oil pump on an automobile engine frequently, as clogging is one of the causes for an overheated motor.

## A Cottage Candlestick

A very simple camp and cottage candlestick, that cannot be extinguished in a draft, can be constructed from an ordinary candlestick and lamp chimney. The candle pillar is removed and in its stead a block of wood, 3 by 3 by ⅞ in., stained with a suitable color, is nailed to the base from underneath. On the four sides of the block pieces of metal are  nailed to form clips for holding a No. 2 lamp chimney. Four small finishing nails, driven part way into the upper surface of the block, serve as a candle pillar, or holder.

The candles used are the short kind, or "twelves," with a small wick. These are less apt to smoke up the chimney. Such a candlestick produces a steady flame; can be used on a porch; is safe in passing near portières or curtains, and readily takes the place of an oil lamp on a writing table.

## Ventilating Inclosed Automobile Bodies

When an automobile becomes uncomfortably warm for its occupants, one good way of ventilating it is by means of the doors. A hook made of an iron rod can be fastened in holes made in the body and door, as shown, which will cause sufficient draft to  readily cool off the car, without danger of the door flying open and being caught or wrenched off.—Contributed by Abner B. Shaw, N. Dartmouth, Massachusetts.

## Cam-Cutting Fixture for a Bench Lathe

When it is necessary to cut a large number of cams to the same pattern, quite a little time can be saved, and greater accuracy gained, by using a cam-cutting attachment, one form of which is shown in the sketch. It consists of a base, A, clamped to the bed of the lathe, or milling machine, whichever is used. It is provided with two standards, B and C, bored to fit a cam spindle, D, at a height corresponding to the center of the cam-cutting tool. The spindle D is turned with a shoulder to fit against the work cam blank E, which is secured in a position by the nut F, and screw, at the end of the spindle. The master cam G is fastened to the spindle between the standards, and caused to bear against a guide roller, H—which is fastened to the base A—by means of a compression spring, fitting the spindle between the standard C and the hub of the master cam. If the spring is not desired, a weight can be used, by fastening it to one end of a cord, or wire cable, which passes over a pulley, I, and is attached to the spindle. The cams may be rotated by a handwheel attached to the spindle. This, although the simplest method, is not very practical where slow feeds are necessary. A better way is to drive the spindle by means of a worm and gear. The gear J is attached to the outer end of the spindle. The worm K is fitted in bearings cast on a bracket, L. This bracket, at its upper end, fits in between the worm gear and a shoulder on the spindle, so that any lengthwise motion of the spindle will carry the bracket with it, thereby keeping the worm and gear in mesh constantly. The bracket is prevented from turning on its bearing by the stud M, fastened to it and made a sliding fit in the base A. The cam outline is cut by an end mill cutter fastened in the headstock spindle. In order to provide for end feed, an adjusting screw, N, and bracket are bolted to the lathe bed and, after slightly loosening the headstock bolts, the screw can be turned, causing the cutter to move for end feed, as required. If the cam-cutting attachment is fastened to the compound rest of the lathe, or on the table of a milling machine, no special adjusting screw is necessary.

In order to dispense with the weight or compression spring for keeping the master cam firmly pressed against the guide roller H, it will be necessary to have a double-faced cam. In this case another roller, O, must be provided which is fastened to the standard C, at a place directly opposite the roller H, the distance between the rollers corresponding to the width of face of the master

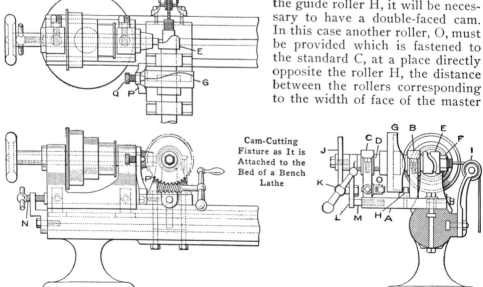

Cam-Cutting Fixture as It is Attached to the Bed of a Bench Lathe

cam. As the two rollers are fixed in place, the cam, fitting between them, should have a radius corresponding approximately to the distance the rollers are from the center of the spindle. If a smaller cam has been developed for the desired motion, its outline must be developed on a blank of the required size, and this formed by the cutter in the usual way. In transferring the outline to the large blank, the small trial cam is put on at the cutter end of the spindle, and rests against a round rod fitted in the tailstock spindle. The master blank is fastened to the spindle in its regular position, the guide rollers being removed to permit the blank to enter. The outline is marked by a scriber attachment, which consists of a bracket, P, fastened to the base A. At a height corresponding to the center of the cam spindle, a hole is drilled and threaded for a tool-steel scriber, Q, adjustable for slightly different diameters of blanks by screwing it in or out. As the master blank slides back and forth, the scriber marks an outline corresponding to that of the small trial cam. If desirable to have a double-faced cam, the scriber bracket should be sufficiently wide so the scriber can be set over a distance corresponding to that between the rollers H and O.—Contributed by E. P. Fickes, Dayton, O.

## Cutting Attachment for an Oxyacetylene Welding Torch

For cutting metal with an oxyacetylene welding torch, it is necessary to have a higher pressure of oxygen, at least 40 lb. A separate tank must be provided to produce this pressure, or the gas bought in a high-pressure tube. To make the cutting attachment for the torch, procure a piece of $\frac{1}{8}$-in. pipe and bend it as shown. Make a tip, or if desired, several of them, with openings from the size of a pin point to $\frac{1}{32}$ in. in diameter. Attach a lever valve just in front of the torch handle, as shown, so that it can be operated with the thumb. Attach the auxiliary pipe to the lower pipe of the torch with

clamps, so that the point of the tip will be within $\frac{1}{4}$ in. of the regular welding tip.

To use, heat the article to be cut with the welding tip, then turn on the

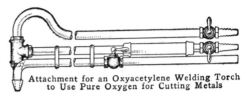

Attachment for an Oxyacetylene Welding Torch to Use Pure Oxygen for Cutting Metals

oxygen through the cutting attachment. With this attachment any kind of metal may be cut quickly and accurately. No changes are made on the welding torch to use this attachment.

## A Gambrel Hook

Farmers use a pole to hang the hogs on at slaughtering time in winter. On this pole a grambrel stick is placed, the ends being inserted in the hock of the animal's leg. It is always a hard job to do the hanging and place the gambrel stick at the same time. A better way is to provide a double hook of metal, heavy enough to support the animal, and hang the gambrel stick on this hook, as shown. The metal may be square or round, bent into a U-shape of such dimensions that it will fit over the timber used in hanging the hogs and with a hook formed on each end. It is an easy matter to insert the gambrel while the hog is lying on the work

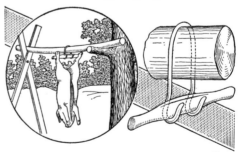

The Hook Provides an Easy Way to Hang a Hog after the Gambrel Is in Place

table, then lift it by the gambrel and place the latter on the hooks.—Contributed by Leslie R. Sutter, Towanda, Illinois.

## Gas-Engine Exhaust Water Heater

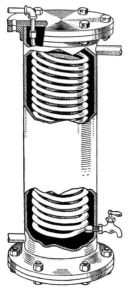

The heater illustrated utilizes the heat from the exhaust of a gasoline engine, and can be used for heating a small shop, or for washing purposes. To make it, procure a piece of pipe, 12 in. in diameter and 36 in. long. Both ends are closed with caps, or plates. Two openings, one at each end of the pipe, are made for the exhaust to pass through, and a coil of pipe is inserted inside, its ends passing out at the top and bottom. Connect the heater as close to the engine as possible.

## Cracking Prevented in Bending Lead Tubes

When small lead tubing is bent with sharp turns it will frequently crack or break, unless special precautions are used to prevent it. One of the cheapest and simplest methods to overcome the difficulty is to wind the place with several layers of fine flexible wire before trying to make the bend.

## Furnace for Metals of Low Fusion Temperatures

Experimenters desiring to make small castings of zinc, brass, copper, and other metals of low fusion point, will find the simple furnace illustrated suitable to their requirements. The body of the furnace was made of an old 10-gal. milk, or cream, can, which was lined on the inside with fire brick, whereupon a base, about 4 in. high, was built up with the brick in the bottom for the crucible. A crucible, 6 in. in diameter and 8 in. high, was purchased and set on the built-up base, then two walls of fire brick were built up on each side of the crucible to within 4 in. of the top of the shell. These walls should fit snugly against the crucible and the sides of the brick lining of the can. The cover for the top is lined with fire clay which is made to lie on top of the can so that it will form a tight fit.

A hole, 3 in. in diameter, was cut in the shell, on one side, and a 4-in. hole on the other. These holes should be located so that the smaller one enters the side at the center of one compartment formed by the walls and crucible, and the other makes an outlet in the other division, both holes being near the bottom of the can. The flame from a Bunsen burner, A, is directed through the smaller hole against the crucible, and by the walls deflected upward along the side of the crucible and over the top, thence down the opposite side and out. This method utilizes all the heat from the fire and will melt brass, copper, or aluminum in a very short time.

The type of burner and fuel tank used was the kind used by bicycle repair men in brazing small parts. — Contributed by A. H. Waychoff, Koenig, Col.

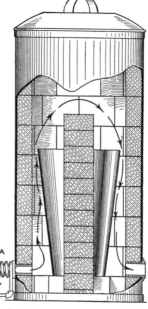

Milk Can Lined with Fire Brick Used as a Furnace to Melt Metals of Low Fusion Temperatures

❡A deep-red stain for woods is made of ½ oz. alkanet root to two fluid ounces of turpentine.

## Silencer for a Rifle

The silencer is made of a piece of steel tubing, having walls about $\frac{1}{64}$ in. thick, about 5 in. long, and of an inside diameter to fit snugly over the end of the gun barrel. The tube should have a number of holes, ¼ in. in diameter, drilled through it.

Another tube, about twice the diameter of the first one and 8 in. long, is drilled with a ⅛-in. drill to make it well perforated on the under side. Two pieces of sheet steel are cut or turned to fit the inside diameter of the large tube and holes are drilled in them, off center, the size of the outside diameter of the smaller tube. They are then placed in the ends of the larger tube so that the holes will coincide. The smaller tube is fastened in one end

Rifle Silencer Made of Two Pieces of Perforated Steel Tubing of Different Sizes

only, and at such a place that a small portion of its end will project out of the end of the large tube. After the parts are in place, they are brazed at all joints. A setscrew is placed in the projecting end of the small tube to hold the silencer on the end of the gun barrel.

## An Electric Fence Rider

To do away with the necessity of walking or riding around a farm fence to see if it is in repair, the simple device illustrated may be used. A piece of 8-in. board is fitted, as shown in Fig. 1, with battery, push button, call bell, and binding posts, designated by the letters A, B, C, D, E, F, and G. The method of connecting the fence wires is shown in Fig. 2, the letters designating the binding posts to which the end of the wires are attached. Obviously, none of these wires must come in contact with any other wire, and it would, therefore, be better to use insulated wires from the board to the fence. In making a break for

a gate or opening in the fence, the wires must be connected by an underground cable and each one insulated from the others.

To make the test, connect the binding

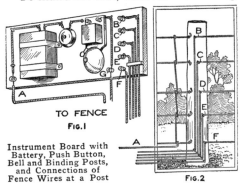

TO FENCE
FIG.1

Instrument Board with Battery, Push Button, Bell and Binding Posts, and Connections of Fence Wires at a Post

FIG.2

post G to any one of the other binding posts, B, C, D, E, or F, and press the button. The resulting ring, or silence, of the bell will tell if the strand in the fence is continuous or broken. Reversing the connections to the wires will eliminate, to a great extent, a circuit caused by the fallen end of a broken wire, as it is not often a wire breaks so that both ends will come in contact with the other wires.—Contributed by R. H. Tuttle, Minneapolis, Minnesota.

## Oil-Level Gauge for Automobile Crank Case

A smoky exhaust on an automobile can usually be attributed to an excessive amount of oil in the crank case. Oil gauges on the crank cases are frequently omitted, especially in the older types of engines, but simple homemade devices can be made to serve the purpose very well. A hole should be drilled and tapped in the lowest corner of the crank case for ⅛-in. pipe thread. Into this is screwed a petcock, having a male thread at one end and a female thread at the other. A piece of ⅛-in. pipe is then threaded at one end and bent so one side will be vertical when the pipe is screwed in position in the petcock. The amount of oil required in the crank case should then be determined, and the vertical pipe cut off at that level. The opening may be flared out to show the oil level more easily. All threaded connections should be white-leaded to insure tight joints. In bending the pipe, hot rosin should first be put in, thereby preventing dents or splits. The petcock should only be open when testing for the oil level or when desirable to add more.

## A Distance-Marking Gauge

For gauging lines on a plane surface the ordinary marking gauge answers very well, but if it is necessary to gauge a line parallel with an edge, with a raised portion between the gauging point and the point where the line is desired, the ordinary gauge is useless. It was to overcome this difficulty that the distance-marking gauge was designed, and with it a line may be gauged on the inside of the bottom of a box or drawer, parallel with any of its sides. The scriber bar, being round, can be swung to the right or left and clamped in either position, so that the scriber point can reach places that could not be conveniently reached in any other way.

The head, or stock, is made of hard

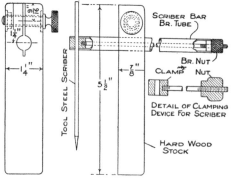

This Gauge will Scribe a Line on Uneven Surfaces over High Parts, as a Drawer Side

wood, and is bored to receive the scriber bar, which is made of brass tubing. This piece of tubing, in the gauge

illustrated, is $\frac{7}{16}$ in. in outside diameter and $\frac{5}{16}$ in. on the inside. The head-clamping device is made as shown, all parts being of brass. The knurled thumbscrew, running completely through the head, is threaded to turn in a plate, let into the side and fastened with two small screws; the same method being used for the plate under the shoulder of the thumbscrew.

The scriber is made of $\frac{1}{8}$-in. tool steel, hardened at the point. The clamping device for the scriber consists of the knurled nut, turned with a shoulder to fit the inside of the scriber bar and tapped to receive the threaded end of a $\frac{1}{8}$-in. brass rod that is screwed into the scriber clamp at the opposite end of the bar. This clamp is a short piece of brass rod turned to a sliding fit inside of the tube. The clamping device should be fitted to the tube, and the hole for the scriber drilled through the tube and clamp at the same time.— Contributed by J. A. Shelley, Brooklyn, New York.

## Riveting Head for Thin Tubing

The sketch illustrates a very simple, cheap, and effective device for riveting joints in thin tubing, such as rain pipes, stovepipes, furnace pipes, and the like. Instead of merely telescoping them together, making a very insecure and unmechanical connection, this tool will enable all joints to be securely riveted where they cannot be soldered.

The head, Fig. 1, is made of machine steel with slightly countersunk holes drilled in the periphery and then casehardened. For convenience, the holes are drilled all around and spaced about $\frac{1}{16}$ in. apart, so that the walls will not break out in use. This will make it easy to locate the holes, much more so than if there were only a few.

In construction, a number of disks, about 6 or 8, of varying diameters are turned up and countersunk, and a $\frac{3}{4}$-in. hole is drilled through their centers, whereupon all are casehardened. The different diameters are necessary for the different-sized tubes. The disks must be about $\frac{1}{16}$ in. smaller than the tube diameter, but not more than ⅛ in. smaller.

A piece of ⅝-in. gas pipe, A, is threaded on one end for 2 in.; the remainder is turned down to ¾-in. outside diameter, and a collar, B, is fitted to turn on the pipe threads at the end and fastened there with a rivet, C. The desired head for the size of work at hand is slipped on the pipe against the collar B, and a fixed washer, D, is placed outside on the pipe and held with a hexagon nut.

When in use, the head is inserted in the pipe, and by tapping the outside of the pipe the location of the head can be determined and the holes punched with a tool similar to a belt punch. Place a rivet in the hole, head up, and drive it down. The countersink of the hole in the head will form the rivet head on the inside. The head must be smaller than the tubing in order to clear the rivet head, yet not so small but that the tube will spring back to its original shape when the riveting is finished.

The head can be placed in a straight or curved pipe, around inside of elbows, and all standard angles, with the use of a length of wire-wrapped garden hose attached with a clamp to the free

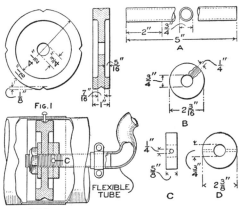

**FIG. 1**

**FIG. 2**
Head to Insert in a Pipe to Serve as an Anvil in Riveting the Joints

end of the gas pipe, as shown in Fig. 2. This also provides a means of keeping the head straight when it is used in a long pipe.—Contributed by J. B. Murphy, Plainfield, N. J.

## Injecting Puncture-Sealing Compound into Tires

The body of the injector consists of a piece of 2-in. pipe, 8 in. long, with a cap screwed on the upper end, and a

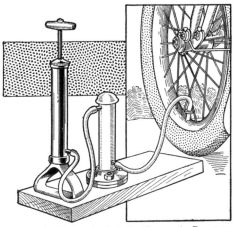

Pressure Applied to the Cylinder Forces the Puncture-Sealing Fluid into the Injured Tire

flange on the lower. A tire valve is soldered into a hole drilled in the pipe near the upper end, and a piece of ⅛-in. pipe screwed into a tapped hole at the bottom. The cylinder is mounted on a base of hard wood that is large enough for a foot pump also. To fill the cylinder, the upper cap is unscrewed. When the cap is replaced, a pressure is put on the fluid, after attaching a hose between the small outlet pipe and the tire valve.

## To Prevent Rust Forming on Tools

Those who desire to use a rust preventive will find that if the tools are wiped with a cloth slightly saturated in mercurial ointment, they will obtain the best results possible. It is not necessary to leave more than a trace of the ointment on the steel. A cloth so impregnated that it will smear a pair of spectacles a little will answer.

This ointment is the very best possible to use on guns, to prevent them from rusting. It will also prevent the barrels from leading and will remove lead from the rifles. It has no action whatever on the metal of the barrel.

## Finger Rest for an Oilcan

In places where an oilcan is used very frequently, and especially where it may be covered with oil, making it  hard to hold, a finger rest can be provided which will serve several purposes. A thin double-winged washer is made and provided with a hole, giving it a tight fit when slipped over the spout to the threaded end. It can then be soldered in place, and the projecting ends bent to conform closely to the finger positions when using the can. This attachment not only prevents slipping of the can when covered with oil or grease, but also provides a good grip for unscrewing the spout.—Contributed by J. J. Kolar, Maywood, Ill.

## Holding Collar with a Torn Buttonhole

In the laundry I find a great many collars with the rear buttonhole so badly torn that it is impossible for the  collar button to hold it in place. Otherwise the collar is good and can be worn a number of times, but is usually thrown away. To make use of such a collar, take a piece of linen or cardboard and make a hole or slot with a knife point like a buttonhole, and place it in the pocket of the collar over the torn buttonhole. This will aid the button in holding the collar in place.—Contributed by John T. Morrison, Philadelphia, Pa.

¶When an inner tube is immersed in water to discover a leak, make a mark around the hole with an indelible pencil.

## Removing Globes from Flash Lamps

Small electric globes in flash lights are very difficult to remove from the socket when it becomes necessary to put in a new one. When in the socket, the outside surface is so smooth that the fingers will not turn it. I have found a very good method which consists in using a piece of rubber tube about $\frac{3}{8}$ in. in diameter and $1\frac{1}{4}$ in. long, and pressing its end against the globe, then turning it. In this manner a globe can be easily removed or replaced. A good place to keep the piece of rubber tubing is in the coil-spring space in the rear of the cap on the flash-lamp casing.

## Plugging a Petcock on a Gasoline Tank

If the valve is lost from the petcock on the lower part of the crank case,  or gasoline tank, or similar place, do not plug the hole, A, where the valve came out, but unscrew the petcock and fit a wood plug in the upper end. Then there is no danger of the plug losing its hold and causing further leakage.

## Erasing Shield for Typewriter Rolls

When erasing a word or letter while the paper is in the typewriter, a much neater job can be done if the shield  here illustrated is used. It consists of a piece of thin metal, about $\frac{3}{4}$ in. wide and 2 in. long, with a number of holes cut in it, as shown. The metal plate is then bent to conform to the shape of the roller. In erasing, the plate is laid over the paper on the roller, and the word or letter to be erased is brought under one of the openings. It can then be erased without danger of marring the adjoining letter.

## Difficult Weld by the Chemical Process

### By F. W. BENTLEY, JR.

THE efficiency of chemical welding as a restorer of broken machinery parts has long been widely recognized and put into practice. The use of it in repairing heavy casting parts, where the necessity of extreme accuracy is not a paramount factor, makes the process to some extent a simple one. However, in a great many instances where such welding is attempted the operation calls for considerable skill and knowledge of the many points which go to make the work a success.

Shafting and other journal pieces of moderate diameter present a phase of welding that is covered to some extent with varying results. The illustrations represent a piece of work successfully executed in a small railway shop. The shaft was from an alternating-current generator, belonging to a plant on the railway line at some distance from the railway shop. The shaft was 14 ft. 8 in. long, and 8½ in. in diameter at the largest part. The break occurred about 4 in. from a fillet on the larger portion of the shaft. It was successfully repaired at a safe margin of cost under one-fifth the price of a new one. The operation of welding covered a period of less than one day, and when placed in the lathe for trial, the shaft did not run out of alinement more than ¼₄ inch.

To those not familiar with the process, a brief description of the operation may be of interest. A number of large V-blocks are shaped from a block of iron bars bolted together on the bed of a slotter. The V-blocks, each of exactly the same size, are then stood up on the bed of a large planer,

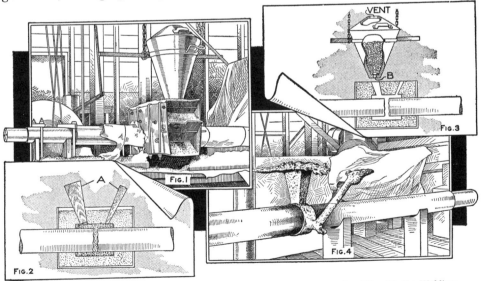

The Mold as It is Built Up around the Broken Ends of the Shaft, the Crucible with the Welding Compound Suspended over It, and the Weld after Removing the Mold

and the shaft pieces laid horizontally in them, as shown in Fig. 1. The shafting is then lined up, the faces of the break being set about 1 in. apart. Softened paraffin is next placed, shaped, and filled in around the broken ends of the shaft, as shown in Fig. 2. This forms the body mold of the welding mass. The sand, or mold, box is then built in sections and bolted around the shaft, and the sand pounded firmly around the paraffin filling over the break. Through the sand and touching the paraffin extend two triangular, or circular, pieces of wood, A, which make the pouring opening, or gate, and overflow, or vent, in the mold. A gasoline blowtorch is then applied to the mold and the whole arrangement heated, causing the paraffin to run out through a small hole made for it in the bottom of the mold. This hole is plugged with sand when all the paraffin has run out. The application of the torch is continued until the ends of the shaft are heated to almost a melting point. This leaves a coring space to be filled by the welding com-

pound when it is allowed to run from the crucible into the sand, or pattern, boxes.

The funnel-shaped arrangement over the sand box, or mold, holds the powderlike chemical, freely mixed with small special-steel billets. The funnel is nothing more than a special crucible, made of sheet metal and lined with fire clay. This is shown in section in Fig. 3. When the combination is lighted, the burning of the thermit, or welding, compound melts the steel, which at the right moment is let down into the mold through the hole B. This hole is stoppered the same as a cupola. The shape of the welding mass, after removing the mold, is shown in Fig. 4. The protruding parts are then drilled and cut off, leaving the weld complete.

The chemical compound most commonly and successfully used is known as the thermit welding compound, a mixture the nature of which is but little known, but the oxidization caused by it heats the crucible of welding steel in from 10 to 15 seconds.

---

### Folding Rule Used as Marking Gauge

An ordinary 2-ft. folding rule and a lead pencil can be readily used in place of a regular marking gauge.

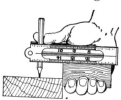

Place the pencil between the folds of the rule so its short wire pins will be forced into the wood of the pencil, firmly holding it in position. With the aid of a small block pressed tight against the bottom of the rule and held against the board to be marked, any desired gauge line may be drawn. The block may be omitted if no fear is felt of running splinters into the hand, in which case the gauging must be done with the forefinger of the hand sliding along the board, the thumb resting on top of the rule as before.—Contributed by Abner B. Shaw.

### A Painter's Air Brush

In painting complicated machinery, or irregular surfaces, spraying may often be resorted to, which will result in covering every part neatly, and in considerably less time than required to do it with a hand brush. To make the illustrated air brush, or spraying device, a glass jar should be obtained, having a metal screw top. In this cover, two holes should be made as far apart as possible; one, for connecting with the angle valve A, and the other with an air-pressure regulating needle valve, B. The handwheel and stem of the valve A should be removed. From the inner, or valve, end of the stem, a $\frac{1}{16}$-in. hole should be drilled lengthwise through the center to within $\frac{1}{4}$ in. of the outer end. If the stem is longer than convenient, part of its outer end may be cut off, but the precaution should still be observed not to drill all the way through with the $\frac{1}{16}$-in. size.

An outlet is provided by a $\frac{1}{64}$-in. hole continued through the undrilled $\frac{1}{4}$-in. section. In order to make a connection between the drilled stem and the contents of the glass jar, a piece of copper tubing, C,—such as is used on gas-engine carburetors—should be threaded at one end to fit a drilled and tapped hole in the hollow valve stem, so that, when the valve is in position on the jar and the stem tightly fitted to its seat, the tube can pass into the jar and reach to within $\frac{1}{4}$ in. of the bottom.

With the spraying head finished, the necessary piping can be cut and fitted, connecting the regulating valve B and stop valve D with the head A. It is necessary to have all joints tight, and the valves A and B so spaced that they will fit the holes made for them in the cover. A nipple fitted with a hose coupling must be attached to the stop valve to connect it with the air-pressure tank. All the necessary piping being completed, the screw cover should be soldered to the valves A and B. With the jar filled with paint, the cover may be screwed on and the sprayer is ready for operation.

The air necessary for spraying may be supplied by a small tank and hand pump, capable of furnishing a pressure up to about 15 lb., depending on the kind of paint to be sprayed. In operating the sprayer, the valve D is first

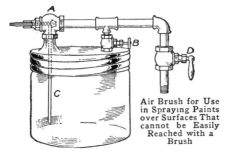

Air Brush for Use in Spraying Paints over Surfaces That cannot be Easily Reached with a Brush

turned open. The pressure inside the jar, regulating the flow of paint, is adjusted by the needle valve B.—Contributed by A. H. Waychoff, Koenig, Col.

❧ Cover the exposed parts of a damp clay runner with oil—preferably kerosene—before pouring in melted babbitt.

## Umbrella Equipped with Celluloid Window

If a piece of about 2 by 6-in. transparent celluloid, such as is used on

A Small Celluloid Window in the Umbrella Top Is Convenient in a Driving Rain

automobile tops, be sewed over a prepared opening in an umbrella, the difficulty of looking ahead in a driving rain can be overcome, without the necessity of raising the umbrella and thereby running the risk of getting wet, or having the umbrella turned inside out. —Contributed by H. W. Hahn, Chicago, Ill.

## Solid Object in a Barrel Kept Away from Opening

A bung, plug, or cork pushed into a barrel will cause trouble when tapping until the entire contents are removed. It will push its way into the outlet as the liquid flows and obstruct the opening. An excellent way to keep the trouble maker away from the opening is to drive four small nails in the end of the faucet around the hole before inserting it in the barrel bung. The nails are only driven in far enough to hold, allowing most of their lengths to project. The nails will keep away any floating object from the opening.—Contributed by A. H. Woodyard, Ada, Oklahoma.

## Reducing Traction Power by Filling Space between Wagon-Wheel Spokes

Considerable power can be saved, when pulling a heavy load, by filling in the space between the spokes of the  wheels on a wagon or truck, as illustrated. This method was devised by a driver after observing how the sand would fill in between the spokes, and be lifted almost level with the hub as the wheels revolved, before it spilled out. The added weight of the sand was considerable, and a load on the wagon formerly requiring six horses, could be easily pulled with four horses after the spaces had been filled.

## Safety Chain for a Door

Timid women frequently dread to open a door if they suspect that  strangers are on the outside. Security can be assured if the door is provided with a chain and hook as shown in the illustration. It is necessary to have two strong screw eyes, 6 or 8 in. of strong chain, and a hook with a loop 3 or 4 in. long. One of the screw eyes is opened up sufficiently to allow an end link of the chain to enter, after which it is again closed up tight. The long hook should be attached to the other end of the chain in the same manner. The screw eye, with the chain attached to it, should be screwed into a convenient place in the door casing a little above the door knob. The second screw eye should be so placed in the door that it would be necessary to have this nearly closed before the hook could be put on or taken off the screw eye. This precaution will prevent the possibility of an intruder unhooking the chain from the outside. When in position, the chain will allow the door to be opened merely sufficient to see the stranger or carry on a conversation; it would be impossible for anyone to enter.—Contributed by L. R. Buzzell, Malden, Mass.

## A Pocket Bath Spray

The pocket bath spray consists of a nickelplated copper tube bent in the shape of a fishhook with a ½-in. opening or slit in the  curved end, the body being flattened out so as to produce the spray when the water is forced through it. The other end of the tube is inserted through the center of a cork, cut tapering to fit various-sized faucets, and has a round plate soldered to the upper end to prevent it from slipping through the cork. The attachment can be carried in the vest pocket and is instantly fitted to any bathtub or lavatory faucet, or it can be used outdoors on a hydrant for removing the salt water after a dip in the ocean.—Contributed by D. S. Rockwell, Ocean Beach, Cal.

## Metal Lining for Clothes Pocket

To safely carry articles in a pocket where they would be easily broken or crushed, metal linings can be provided. For this purpose a very thin, hard sheet brass is used. A strip is cut having a width equal to that of the pocket, and a length corresponding to  twice the depth, with an additional amount of approximately ⅜ in. to form the bottom of the pocket and a small strip, ¼ in. wide by ⅜ in. long, at the center of one end for securing the lining in place. The metal is folded, as shown, to form a pocket, the top having a tendency to spring shut. The extra lap A, on the one end, is bent over the outer side of the pocket, securely clamping the lining in place. —Contributed by J. E. Noble, West Toronto, Ont.

## To Prevent Dust When Removing Ashes from Furnaces

In removing ashes from furnaces, there is always a considerable amount of dust created that makes the task disagreeable, besides covering everything near by. One resident eliminated the dust with a homemade device, as illustrated. A piece of pipe was procured that would reach to the rear part of the ash pit in the furnace and project far enough to make a handhold. The pipe was capped on one end and fitted with a hose connection on the other end. The part that extends into

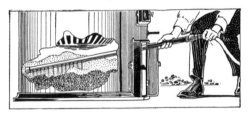

A Pipe with Numerous Holes is Fastened to a Hose for Wetting Ashes to Prevent Dust

the pit was drilled to make a number of small holes evenly spaced throughout its length. The pipe was then connected to a hose running from the laundry tubs.

In removing the ashes, the pipe is connected up and run into the ash pit, the water turned on, and by swinging the pipe about, the ashes are well wetted down so that in removing them no dust will be raised.

⸿A 2-in. paperhanger's roller, covered with soft plush and inked on glass in the same manner as a printer's roller, makes an excellent device for inking over stencils.

## A Singletree for Use in an Orchard

In getting in around apple trees in an orchard with a cart drawn by a horse, many trees are skinned by the

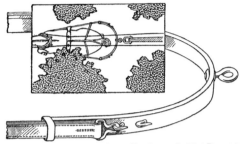

The Rounding Ends of the Singletree do Not Present Any Projection That will Bark a Tree

ends of the singletree. Sometimes a bunch of rags tied on the ends will prevent the skinning, but a much better way is to have a special singletree made in a semicircle, as shown. It can be bent to shape from a piece of heavy tire iron, a leather loop being attached to each end for passing the traces through, and hooks to engage the traces riveted on. The location of the hooks should be far enough back so that they will not be exposed. No part of the singletree, nor the hooks, will then touch a tree, and the leather traces will slip past easily.

## Pole to Loosen Window Catches

The height of some window sash brings the catch out of reach, and to open a window means to climb a chair and loosen the catch. To overcome this difficulty, I made a device as follows: A stick, long enough to reach the catch, was procured, and a coat hook attached close to one end. In use,

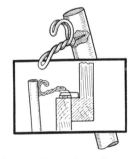

put the hook on the catch and push up or pull down, and, for catches that turn sideways, give the stick a twist.—Contributed by Maurice Baudier, New Orleans, La.

## Coat and Hat Hanger for Shops

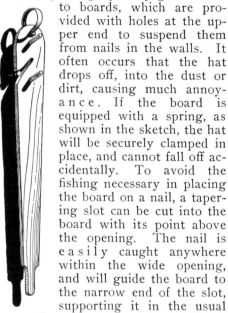

In many shops coats and hats are frequently hung up on pegs fastened to boards, which are provided with holes at the upper end to suspend them from nails in the walls. It often occurs that the hat drops off, into the dust or dirt, causing much annoyance. If the board is equipped with a spring, as shown in the sketch, the hat will be securely clamped in place, and cannot fall off accidentally. To avoid the fishing necessary in placing the board on a nail, a tapering slot can be cut into the board with its point above the opening. The nail is easily caught anywhere within the wide opening, and will guide the board to the narrow end of the slot, supporting it in the usual way.—Contributed by John J. Kolar, Maywood, Ill.

## Gasoline Can with Combination Whistle and Vent

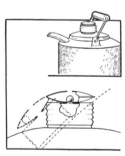

Even though gasoline cans are distinctively colored, usually being painted red, dangerous mistakes are very apt to occur if the can happens to be in a dark place, or otherwise so situated that its contents are not readily detected. A better safety device is to provide a whistle which automatically blows every time the can is tipped.

To make this device, a small oval whistle is required which will fit within the screw cap of the can. Inside of the whistle is placed a steel ball, sufficiently large to cover the whistle hole, but free to roll around inside when the can is tilted. A hole is made in the screw cap and the whistle, on the inside, so that the hole in the cap will line up with the one in the whistle.

When the can is tilted for pouring out oil, the ball will roll away from the hole, allowing air to pass through which will serve two purposes: it will blow the whistle, thereby giving an alarm which will probably result in an examination as to the contents of the can; and it will also act as a vent, enabling a freer flow of oil from the can.—Contributed by W. C. Loy, Rochester, Ind.

## To Stop Noise of a Valve Push Rod

VALVE STEM

A common fault of a gasoline engine is its noisy operation when the valve is lifted. This is usually caused by the steel-to-steel contact of the valve stem proper and the lifter-adjusting screw A. Bore a hole, $\frac{3}{8}$ in. in diameter, in the screw to a depth of about $\frac{5}{8}$ in., countersinking it slightly, as shown. A piece of hard-fiber rod, $\frac{3}{8}$ in. in diameter and approximately $\frac{13}{16}$ in. in length, is pressed securely into the hole and hammered down until the countersunk portion is completely filled. The extending portion of the fiber is filed flush with the top surface of the screw. All the screws are fixed in a like manner. This will make an engine almost noiseless.

## Starting Motorcycle Engine in Cold Weather

In starting a cold motorcycle engine, close the air shutter on the main jet, and then, by quickly opening and shutting the throttle while cranking, the motor will draw a rich mixture and start quite easily. The auxiliary jet will usually pick it up, and the air shutter can be again adjusted where it runs best.—Contributed by F. L. Prescott, Starke, Fla.

## Rack for Storing Chain or Rope Tackle

In order to store rope or chain tackle conveniently, a rack can be provided, as shown in the illustration. It consists of two frames, one for the tackle and the other for the hoisting gear. The first consists of two angle irons connected by a rod on which to suspend the tackle. The ends of the rod are threaded sufficiently so they can be fastened to the angle irons, with a nut on each side of the webs. The frame for the hoisting gear is similarly made but further provided with a loose sheave on its connecting rod, which should be free to slide back or forth, or revolve. The angle irons should be shorter than in the former case so that the sheave rod will be above the tackle support.

To rigidly fasten the frame, each of the angle irons should be cut at its upper end, with one web of each bent at right angles to its length, as shown at A, and each end drilled to fit a supporting bolt. The frames can then be placed and fastened to a convenient support overhead, so the sheave rope—used for raising or lowering the tackle—will tend to pull the tackle hook over the supporting rod when, by slightly lowering the hook, it will catch on the rod and be suspended from it. In taking down any tackle, the looped rope is first placed so as to catch under

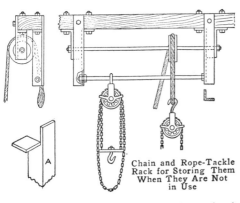

Chain and Rope-Tackle Rack for Storing Them When They Are Not in Use

the hook, which can then be raised off the rod, and the tackle lowered to the floor.—Contributed by John Harger, Honolulu, H. I.

## A Lock for a Theater Emergency Exit

A good panic-proof emergency-door latch for theaters that is always locked

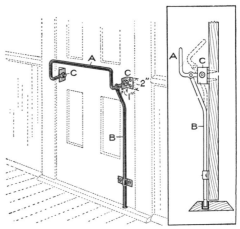

The First Person in a Rush for the Emergency Door Releases the Latch Automatically

from the outside, but which complies with any fire ordinances, can be made at small cost in the following manner. The latch is formed of a rod, about $\frac{1}{2}$ in. in diameter. The piece A is bent as shown in the sketch and one end is flattened for $\frac{3}{4}$ in., through which a $\frac{1}{4}$-in. hole is drilled, while the other end is flattened for 2 in. and provided with two $\frac{1}{4}$-in. holes, one near the end, and the other $1\frac{1}{4}$ in. from the first hole.

The rod B is flattened on one end only, and a $\frac{1}{4}$-in. hole drilled through this end. It is then bent, as shown, so that it will clear the door about $\frac{1}{2}$ in. The angles C are made of iron, 2 in. square and $\frac{1}{4}$ in. thick. These are bent at right angles, so that each part extends 1 in. Two holes are drilled in one end for screws, and a $\frac{1}{4}$-in. hole is drilled in the other end, to admit a bolt to hinge the rod A. The parts are assembled with stove bolts having double nuts, so that the rods A and B will swing easily. The rod B engages in a hole in the floor, or preferably, in a small iron plate screwed to the floor. A light pressure on the bar A will raise the rod B from its keeper, and allow the door to swing open. On theater doors all other locks should be removed. A rush for the door causes the latch to be released by pushing against it.—Contributed by R. R. Cantrell, Red Oak, Iowa.

## Homemade Steam Trap

It is frequently desirable to have a trap for draining water from steam mains, but the purchase price for the manufactured article may not be on

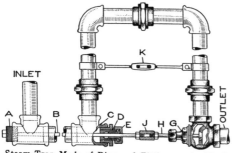

Steam Trap Made of Pipe and Fittings to be Used with the Bend Lying on Its Side

hand. In most places sufficient odds and ends are lying around to construct one as shown in the figure. The necessary fittings are: two tees, two ells, one angle valve, six pipe nipples, three unions, one plug, one reducing bushing, one packing box, gland and nut, two bronze, or brass, valve stems, and a threaded coupling for the same.

The side outlet of one tee forms the inlet of the trap. One end of this tee is closed with a plug, A, which is drilled and tapped for a suitable brass, or bronze, rod, B, of sufficient length to extend about halfway between the uprights of the U-bend trap. The second tee, C, is fitted with a reducing bushing, D. Into this is screwed a packing box, E, which should be made to fit a gland and nut from a discarded valve. The angle valve G requires a few slight changes before it can be used for the trap. The valve stem should be turned down to the diameter of its projecting end, thereby permitting it to move back and forth without the necessity of rotating it. The valve stem H and the rod B are threaded and connected by means of a coupling, J. Lock nuts should be used to keep the valve in the set posi-

tion. Adjustment may be made by turning the stem H. Three unions are used in the pipes forming the U-part so that the trap may easily be assembled or removed without breaking the main line. Should the trap vibrate excessively, it will be necessary to bind the sides of the U-bend by means of a tie rod, K. Whenever the pipe line is full of water, the valve G should be open, allowing the water to leave at the outlet. When the pipe is drained and steam starts to flow, the steam, being hotter than the water, will cause the stem B to expand. This in turn forces the stem H and valve against the seat, thereby shutting off further escape of water or steam.—Contributed by H. L. Hauptmann, Cleveland, Ohio.

## A Weed Remover

Having a hand cultivator which broke up the soil well but did not remove very many weeds, I tried the following plan with success: Some strong but rather small wire was stretched tightly between the teeth and fastened at such a height that the wire just cleared the surface of the ground. When in use the teeth break up the soil and the wire pulls out the weeds as it is drawn along close to the ground.—Contributed by Abner B. Shaw, N. Dartmouth, Mass.

## Sign Painter's Palette

The conical tin caps of varnish and other similar cans come in very handy when one has to use small quantities

of various colors on one job. The caps can be inserted in holes bored in a piece of board, or fastened to a tin plate with a bit of solder. The tin plate can be turned up at the edges.—Contributed by James M. Kane, Doylestown, Pa.

# Core Boxes for Square and Rectangular Cores

### By J. A. SHELLY

IT is not the purpose of this article to describe all devices used for making the kind of cores under this subject, but a number of the most common forms will be mentioned.

It is always best to have the core-box part at opposite corners, unless they are very shallow or have plenty of draft, in which case they can be safely fastened at all four corners. There are cases where it is necessary to have the box part at all four corners, as, for example, when there are small projections on the four sides of the core, that cut into the sides of the core box and make it necessary to draw the sides of the box away in lines at right angles to the sides of the core.

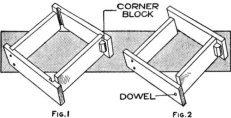

FIG.1      FIG.2

Two Ways of Forming the Joints to Make the Core-Box Part on Opposite Corners

The most common kind, and probably the best corner joint, is the housed joint, shown in Fig. 1. By its construction, it effectually prevents the ramming out of the ends of the box. It is the standard form for first-class work.

Where a cheaper job is required, the box shown in Fig. 2 is frequently used. It is of butt-joint construction

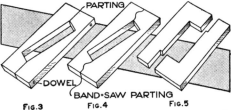

FIG.3      FIG.4      FIG.5

Small and Thin Cores are Made in Boxes Formed of Two Pieces of Wood

and depends on dowel pins in the loose corners to withstand the end strain of ramming. This form is not to be compared with the one shown in Fig. 1, but where only a few cores are required, it answers every purpose.

For smaller cores of the same general shape, the box shown in Fig. 3 is the usual form. The two halves are cut from single pieces of wood and doweled together before the rectangle is laid out. Laying the rectangle out as shown makes it very easy to draw the sides of the box away from the core.

A core box made from a single piece of wood is shown in Fig. 4. It is cut out with a band saw. The irregular joint does away with the dowels. The joint line and rectangle are laid out before any cutting is done, and in drawing the lines for the rectangle, or square, as the case may be, allowance

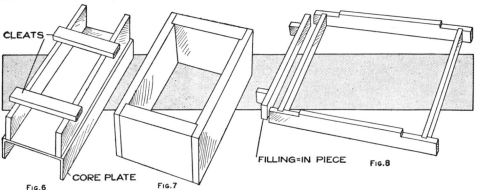

FIG.6      FIG.7      FIG.8

Where It Is Necessary to Make a Long Core for a Column, or a Similar Piece, It is Shaped on a Channel Iron with Straightedges, and Cores for Large Work are Made Up of Separate Pieces into Box Form

must be made for the stock removed by the band saw in cutting on the joint line.

Another standard form that is in general use is shown in Fig. 5. This is used where a thin core is desired and when the thickness of the box will not permit dowels. The box is only used for small, light cores.

The device shown in Fig. 6 is extremely simple, and gives excellent results on long cores for columns, and similar work. Two parallel straightedges, placed as far apart as the depth or thickness of the core, constitute the core box. These straightedges are kept to the proper width, or distance apart, with battens, or cleats, fastened across the face with screws. These battens are spaced about 28 or 30 in. apart. Channel iron is used for the core plate, and it is only necessary to remove the battens to free the core.

It happens sometimes that a very large core is required, and to save lumber and the necessity of handling a large and heavy body of sand, the core is made in four pieces and set up in place in the mold, as shown in Fig. 7. The sketch, Fig. 8, shows the box for making the sides with both ends cut down to receive the end cores. A filling-in end piece is used in each end of this box, to form the short end cores.

### Safety Dog for Small Lathe Work

A great many methods are used and tried for the protection of workmen from the danger of being caught in 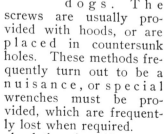 revolving set-screws of lathe dogs. The screws are usually provided with hoods, or are placed in countersunk holes. These methods frequently turn out to be a nuisance, or special wrenches must be provided, which are frequently lost when required. The simple lathe dog illustrated combines the necessary factors of safety and convenience. It consists of a plain metal ring, drilled and tapped for a left-hand thread. A steel rod, threaded at one end to fit the washer, is bent with its ends at right angles to each other, forming the tail for the dog and the wrench for the setscrew. No sharp corners, or dangerous projections, are presented, and the thread being left-handed, the dog tends to grip the work more firmly as it is being driven by the lathe.

### Testing Small Motors with a Magnetic Brake

In testing small motors by means of a prony brake the results are far from satisfactory, and other methods must be employed which are capable of giving more accurate and consistent tests. A method used with excellent results in testing very small motors of about $\frac{1}{20}$ hp. is shown in the illustration. The principal parts that constitute the testing device are a copper disk, A, mounted on the armature shaft; two electromagnets, B, connected by a yoke, C, the combination being mounted on a shaft, D, which is pivoted on the knife edges E and F, and a spring G, one end of which is fastened to the shaft D and the other end attached to a piece, H, mounted on the support J, as shown. The pointer K is attached to one end of the piece H, and so arranged that it may be moved over a graduated circular scale, laid out on the surface of the support J.

The operation of the device is as follows: When the disk A is revolved opposite to the poles of the electromagnets there are electric currents produced in the disk which react upon the magnets and tend to carry them around with the disk. Any movement of the electromagnets is prevented by turning the pointer K in the opposite direction to that in which the disk is turning, thus producing a torque in the spring until the pointer L is at its zero position. The position of the pointer should be noted and also the input to the motor together with its speed. If the torque produced in the spring G were known, the output of the motor could be easily calculated.

To determine this torque, proceed as follows: Attach two lever arms to the yoke C so that they extend out on opposite sides perpendicular to the axis of the yoke. Suspend from these two lever arms two scale pans of exactly the same weight. The points of suspension of the two pans should be exactly the same distance from the center of the shaft. Turn the pointer K to the position it occupied when a balance was obtained during the test, and then place in the proper scale pan sufficient weights to bring the pointer L back to the zero mark. The product of the weight in pounds, required to produce a balance, and the distance in feet the point of suspension is from the center of the shaft, gives the torque in pound-feet. This value of the torque may then be substituted in the following equation and the horsepower calculated.

$$Hp. = \frac{Torque \times 6.2832 \times R. P. M.}{33,000}$$

The accuracy of the device will depend upon the care exercised in constructing and operating it. The deflections of the pointer K for the various outputs may be changed by varying the strength of the electromagnets or the size of the spring. The supports E

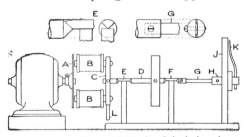

A Torque is Used as Basis for Calculations in Finding the Horsepower of a Small Motor

and F are so constructed that any movement of the shaft amounts to its turning on its own axis.

---

❡When brushing chips and dirt from a machine, be careful to keep them from falling into journals or parts where they will cause injury.

## Recoating Worn Plated Parts on Automobiles

An outfit that will recoat worn nickel parts on automobiles without removing them, is shown in the illus-

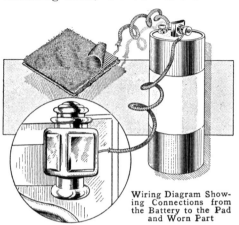

Wiring Diagram Showing Connections from the Battery to the Pad and Worn Part

tration. While this device will not put on the regular plate, it will refinish places where the nickel is worn off so they look like new and will last for some time.

Procure two pieces of good flannel, each about 6 in. square, also a piece of brass screen of the same size, and sew them together, with the screen between the flannel pieces. At one corner of the screen, solder a piece of copper wire for a connection. Make the electrical connection from the pad to the battery and to the article to be plated, as shown.

Prepare a solution as follows: Place in a 2-qt. bottle 6 oz. of nitric acid, and 4 oz. of mercury. This mixing should be done in the open air, and when doing it, one should be very careful not to inhale the fumes, or vapor, as it is a deadly poison. Allow the mixture to stand until it stops boiling, then add nickel, about the weight of two five-cent pieces, and let the solution stand for half an hour. Fill the bottle with distilled, or rain, water.

Apply the solution to the pad and rub it over the part to be coated. The result will be a fine lustrous color that will wear for a considerable length of time.

## Sockets for Broken-Shank Drills

When a drill shank is twisted off it is usually thrown away and a new one milled, or else some special socket

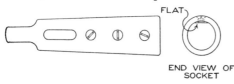

FLAT

END VIEW OF SOCKET

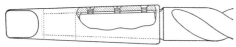

VIEW SHOWING DRILL IN SOCKET
A Socket for Holding a Drill That Has Its Shank Twisted or Broken Off

must be provided to drive it. With but very little change, a regular socket can be used to drive such drills without spoiling its service for drills regularly provided with shanks. For this purpose, several holes are drilled and tapped in the socket to fit slotted, headless or flat-head setscrews. The twisted-off drill is ground to provide a flat bearing for the setscrews. When inserted in the regular socket, it can be securely held in place by the setscrews provided with flat bottoms, which are screwed against the flat place on the drill.—Contributed by J. V. Romig.

## Simple Flexible Coupling for Transmitting Small Power

In connecting shafts that transmit small power, the simple flexible coupling illustrated can be made to serve the purpose as well as a complicated and expensive connection. The shafts are

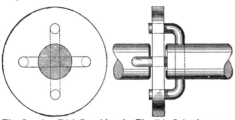

The Leather Disk Provides the Flexible Joint between the Revolving Shaft Ends

drilled for suitable-sized pins. These are bent at one end and then pressed or driven in place, after which the other end is also bent, thereby forming a letter C with the parallel ends equally distant from the shaft. A driving disk is required to complete the coupling. The disk is a circular piece of thick leather, provided with four holes to match the projecting ends of the coupling pins, but sufficiently large to give ample clearance for flexibility and free end movement of the shafts.

## Electric-Bell Alarm for Passenger Elevator

Speed governors, or brakes, are usually provided on passenger elevators to prevent them from dropping or traveling too fast. Hardly any attention is paid to the actual load carried, except to judge it approximately by the number of persons in the cage, which can only be a rough guess as regards actual conditions. In order to indicate when a limit load is being carried, an arrangement, as shown in the illustration, can be used by which

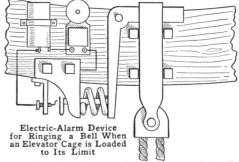

Electric-Alarm Device for Ringing a Bell When an Elevator Cage is Loaded to Its Limit

an electric alarm bell is rung. A bell-crank lever, attached to the cage frame, is supported at one end by a clevis fastened to the elevator cables; the other end fits up against a compression spring which rests against a bracket fastened to the elevator frame. One contact of the electric-circuit switch is rigidly fastened to the cage frame, and the other to a rod connected with the spring end of the bell crank. During an overload, the spring will be compressed sufficiently to allow the switch contacts to come together, thereby closing the circuit and ringing the bell.—Contributed by T. B. Lambert, Chicago, Ill.

# Inexpensive Wood Pulleys

### By PAUL A. BAUMEISTER

A T one time I had occasion to use some wood pulleys in connection with a small gasoline engine. The cost of manufactured pulleys was prohibitive, so it became necessary to devise some simple, cheap way to make them with the tools available. There were just three things to be considered, the material, how to turn them, and how to key them to the shafting.

The first was easy. A block of pine boards was built up in layers, as shown in Fig. 1. The joints between the boards of one layer were set at an angle to the joints of another layer. Enough layers were added in this way to make a block of sufficient thickness for a pulley of the desired width.

The boards were then screwed, or nailed, together, care being taken to leave no nails or screws projecting on the surface to be turned. A rough circle was then drawn on the boards, and the block was roughed out with a hand saw, to make the turning easier.

This latter operation was performed on an improvised lathe, made from a circular-saw mandrel and driven by a gasoline engine. A faceplate, as shown in Fig. 2, was made of wood. The pulley block was fastened to it with wood screws, and the whole mounted on the saw mandrel. An ordinary carpenter's chisel with a very slight bevel was used to do the cutting. Care must be taken to do all the turning from the face of the block, or the chisel will catch in the end grain of the wood and cause considerable trouble. Frequent grinding of the tool will help a great deal, as a sharp edge is the secret of smooth work. A slight crown is turned on the pulley to keep the belts from running off.

The pulley is bored to fit the shaft by using a narrow chisel. If the pulley is very wide, it may be easier to bore a few layers, then remove them, and finish the remainder. After the turning is finished, the pulley may be polished with some coarse sandpaper.

A very simple, as well as an effective, way of keying the pulley to the shaft is shown in Fig. 3. Assuming that the pulley is to be at least four layers thick, although this is not absolutely necessary, the two inner layers are notched, as shown in Figs. 1 and 3,

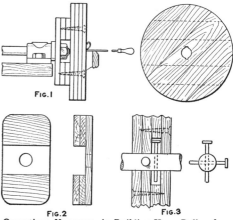

FIG.1

FIG.2            FIG.3

Operations Necessary in Building Up a Pulley from Pieces of Board, and Method of Keying It

the notches in one being at right angles to the notches in the other. Two holes are drilled in the shaft, at right angles to each other and at a distance apart equal to one layer of boards. The keys are parts of large nails, the size of which will depend on the construction of the wheel. The pulley is then assembled by slipping the layers over the shaft so that the nails fit in the notched layers, as shown in Fig. 3. The end layers are put on, and all four screwed together. The outer layers will prevent the pulley from slipping on the shaft. If there is one joint in each layer which comes on a diameter, the pulley can be assembled without slipping it over the shaft. This would allow its being put on a shaft upon which there were already other pulleys.

More than likely the pulley will need some turning after assembling, as it is nearly impossible to bore the pulley absolutely true. This can be done by driving in wood wedges between the pulley and the shaft. If the face is not smooth, a light cut can be taken while the pulley is in place, or coarse sandpaper can be used. If just ordinary care is taken, good serviceable pulleys can be made, even though they may look a bit more clumsy than those purchased of a regular manufacturer.

### Automobile-Radiator Cover for Winter

The owner of an automobile, having almost constant use for his car, desired to have some arrangement for a

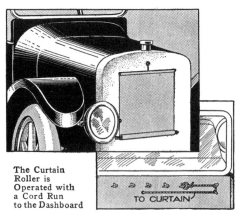

The Curtain Roller is Operated with a Cord Run to the Dashboard

TO CURTAIN

radiator cover that could be regulated from the driver's seat so that, in going against the wind, very little air should be admitted to the radiator, and when turning with the wind, it could be changed without stopping and getting out of the car. A short curtain roller, with its attachments, was procured and fastened over the open space in the radiator covering. A piece of the same material as used for the covering was attached to the curtain roller as a curtain, and a cord was fastened to the stick at the bottom.

The cord was passed through eyelets set to run it through the dashboard, where a ring was tied to its end. Hooks were screwed into the dashboard at various points over which the ring is slipped in making the curtain adjustments. It is only necessary to give attention to the cord end, when turning toward or with a brisk cold

wind, to regulate the proper amount of air for cooling the radiator.

### Lifting Microscopic Cover Glasses

To lift the very thin microscopic cover glasses in research work one person employs a device as follows: The device consists of a small brass tube about the size of a lead pencil, with a brass plate on one end, having a hole in its center, and a rubber bulb on the other—one taken from a medicine dropper. To lift one of these delicate glasses it is only necessary to moisten the surface of the brass plate, press the rubber bulb and then press the brass plate upon the glass. The suction holds it in place until released by pressing the bulb.

### Storing Sulphuric Acid

Sulphuric acid that is kept for any length of time in bottles not having a glass stopper, will become blackened by particles of carbon and organic matter resulting from contact of the acid with the cork, which will be quickly destroyed. The acid should be kept in glass-stoppered bottles. However, the blackened acid need not be thrown away, as it will do very well for charging batteries, and for many other purposes where extreme purity is not essential.

### Repairing a Broken Spirit-Level Bulb

A carpenter accidentally broke his spirit level and not being able to purchase a new glass and being sorely in need of a level, he repaired it in the following manner: The glass being broken on one end, the tube was filled with alcohol and then the opening sealed with sealing wax. The glass was put back in the frame and adjusted, and it worked as well as before.

⟪Keep all automobile electric globes screwed tightly in their sockets to prevent the breaking of the filaments by sudden jars.

## Sawhorse Attachment for Short Sticks

When it is necessary to saw a few short pieces, the ordinary sawhorse is an unhandy place to hold the wood.

Sawhorse Attachment That Provides a Way of Holding Any Short Length of Wood

As I had a great many short pieces to cut for a small round stove, I made an attachment, as shown in the illustration, that would hold a stick regardless of its length.

The attachment consists of four pieces of board, two of which are joined together in the same manner as the crossed pieces for the sawhorse ends, but in such a position that they will hang over the center crossbar and make the depth of the yoke the same as that of the sawhorse. The end of one piece bears against a board that is fastened to the front pieces of the sawhorse.

Another piece, hinged to the lower end of the opposite center-yoke piece, is provided with notches, or a rack made of nails, to engage the upper edge of the board, as shown. The manner of using the device is obvious.—Contributed by A. S. Thomas, Amherstburg, Can.

❡Worn ball bearings can be repaired by truing up the ball races and using larger balls.

## Disposing of Fumes from a Gas Stove

Where natural or artificial gas is used, the cost of building a chimney can be saved in the following manner: A 3-in. vent pipe is run from the vent of any gas stove, or heater, through the walls and up into the hood used over the kitchen range, about 6 in. from the bottom of the hood. Where the pipe passes through a wall, use asbestos wrapping as a precaution against fires. This will carry off the disagreeable odors of the burnt gases from the heater. The application of the heat in the hood creates a draft and will make the hood twice as effective.—Contributed by D. B. Koenig, Los Angeles, California.

## Tool Holder for Round Shanks

In most tool holders using round stock, difficulty is frequently experienced in fastening or unfastening the tools, due to the short grip usually made on the nut or lower part of the holder. This trouble can be overcome by making an equal length of grip on both parts, as shown in the illustration, thereby increasing the force with which the parts may be screwed together, or separated, and the tool gripped in place, or unloosened, as the case may be. This holder calls for $\frac{5}{16}$-in. stock. The grip jaws are provided with a slot, into which can

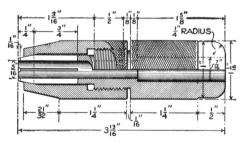

The Knurled Part on the Chuck and Handle are the Same Length to Provide an Equal Grip

be placed a pin fastened to the shank of the tool, thus preventing its slipping when under strain, as when using a screwdriver.—Contributed by J. R. Jarvis, New Haven, Conn.

## Easily Adjusted Automobile-Top Holder

In the usual method of fastening automobile tops when down, leather straps are used to bind the ribs in

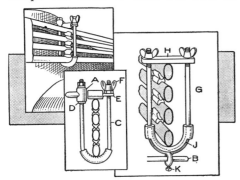

Automobile-Top Holder with Thumbscrew Adjustment, and Special Arrangement for Use with a Horizontal Bar

place. If the straps are not bound tight, the top will rattle. In order to prevent this noise, a strain must be put on the leather so as to reach a place where the strap will be tight. To avoid the tugging nuisance, and breaking of straps, an attachment may be made as illustrated, for automobiles having brackets similar to A, or a holder can be fitted to automobiles having a horizontal bar, as B, to support the top. In the former case, a rod, C, is selected which will enter the hole of the bracket A. This rod is upset, or a collar welded to it, at D, so that sufficient length will be allowed on the short end for the bracket A and a standard nut. The rod is then bent U-shaped to accommodate the several top ribs, sufficient length being allowed for a crosspiece, E, and thumb nut, F. The piece E is drilled to fit the rod C. It is covered with a piece of hose and the rod C is similarly covered at the bend to prevent marring of the ribs. In putting the top down, it is only necessary to swing the piece E out of the way, and drop the top into the U-shaped bracket, where it may be securely held by bringing E to bear on it, and screwing down the thumb nut F.

In the second case, the U-bracket may be formed of a suitable rod, forged so as to fit the rod B, and with the ends G extended to accommodate the top ribs and the crosspiece H, thumb nuts being provided at the extreme ends. Protective covering can be placed around H, as before. For the lower part, one half of the hose should be removed at the center, as shown at J, so each of the ends can slip over one of the sides G; the half section will still provide the necessary protection. The setscrew K locks the bracket in position on the bar B.—Contributed by Chester S. Ricker, Indianapolis, Indiana.

---

## Recoil on a Gun Stock

In order to lessen the kick of a gun, a recoil attachment can be used, as shown in the illustration. For this purpose, a special loose shoulder piece must be provided, or can be obtained by sawing the regular stock in two near the end. To keep the parts in line two 3/8-in. steel pins are necessary, being provided with heads at one end only. The loose shoulder end of the gunstock should be drilled through, to fit the 3/8-in. pins, and countersunk to about 1/2 in. on the inner edge, to fit suitable recoil springs. Two 5/8-in. bushings should be provided to serve as guides for the pins.

In assembling the attachment, the bushings are first placed on the pins so that they will bear against the heads, whereupon the springs are inserted. The pins can then be put through the holes in the special shoulder piece, and their outer ends riveted

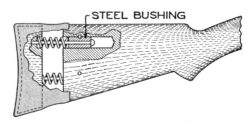

STEEL BUSHING

Recoil Device on a Gunstock to Take Up the Shock from the Firing

over to prevent them from pulling out with the recoil of the spring. In the main part of the gunstock, two holes are drilled to fit the guide bushings, and counterbored for about ½ in., if necessary, to fit the springs. These holes must extend sufficiently beyond the inner ends of the bushings so that the heads of the pins will not strike the stock when the springs are compressed to their limit. To fasten the bushings, holes are drilled for ⅛-in. pins, so that half of the pin is held by the gunstock and the remainder by the bushing. The opening in the gunstock may be covered with a strip of canvas, one edge being fastened to each piece of the stock; or, if preferred, a rubber casing can be used to cover the gap.—Contributed by L. Hamm, Moline, Ill.

### Perforator for Postage Stamps

Where return envelopes are sent out with a stamp attached many of them are detached for personal use. This could be guarded against by the use of a stamp perforated with a device having a series of needles or prongs, as shown. These could be arranged to suit the fancy of the user. A stamp perforated with the needles is almost impossible to remove without being torn.

### A Show-Window Attraction

One of the best methods of attracting the attention to a show window is to place in it some device which apparently operates of its own accord. Such an arrangement is shown in the illustration. It consists of an improvised paddle wheel driven by a concealed fan. The rotating device consists of a ball of cork, or other light material, to which are symmetrically hung razors, knives, toothbrushes, or similar articles, which will serve as paddles for the wheel. This ball is balanced on the point of a screw or

nail driven through a cork, which in turn fits in the neck of a bottle, thereby clearly indicating the absence of any

The Air Coming from the Slit Strikes the Projections on One Side Only

source of power through the base. On one side of the device a wall, or screen, must be provided, having slits, or holes, in it, and on the opposite side is placed a fan, carefully concealed from the observers. To rotate the ball, the fan is operated, which sends the air through the openings in the wall, causing it to strike the paddles and turn the ball.—Contributed by F. Armstrong, Pittsburgh, Pa.

### An Adjustable Precision Square

A machinist's, or toolmaker's, square, of novel, yet practical design, is shown in the illustration. Instead of the blade being solidly attached to the base of the square, it is pivoted on a pin. The plungers exert pressure against the blade on opposite sides of the pin. These plungers in turn are actuated by two blind setscrews. All that is necessary to adjust the square is to turn the setscrews. This square is easily con-

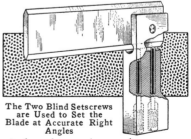

The Two Blind Setscrews are Used to Set the Blade at Accurate Right Angles

structed and may be made as accurate as it is possible to make any square.— Contributed by S. V. Brook, Hartford, Connecticut.

## A Bench Soldering-Iron Heater

The handy man at home can provide himself with a soldering-iron holder and heater that will serve the purpose of an

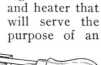

expensive one at the outlay of a little time and the cost of a 2-in. piece of pipe, 10 in. long, and a pipe tee. The pipe is threaded on both ends and cut to make two pieces, one 7 in., and the other, 3 in. long. The unthreaded end of the long piece is split, or sawed, to make it quartering; the pieces are turned out to form feet and holes are drilled in them. This pipe is screwed to the bench over a Bunsen burner. The tee is turned on the top of the pipe and the other short piece is screwed into one end of the tee. The short piece is then filed to the shape shown, to receive the soldering iron.—Contributed by O. F. Germaine, Mansfield, Ohio.

## Bushing Valve Cap to Raise Spark Plug

Poorly designed valve caps on an automobile engine placed the spark plugs so low that it was difficult to

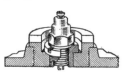

get a socket wrench on them when it became necessary to remove a plug. This also made the lower portion of the plugs extend into the combustion chamber, resulting in clogged platinum points and causing ignition trouble.

The difficulty was overcome by making a shoulder bushing to receive the plug, and enlarging the hole in the cap to receive the bushing. The shoulder of the bushing was slotted to provide a means of turning it in place. The work of fitting four such bushings was quite a job, but it was well worth the time.—Contributed by Adolph Kline, New York City.

## Muffler Cut-Out Made from Pipe Fitting

A simple and cheap muffler cut-out can be made for a gasoline engine from a pipe tee, a piece of sheet iron, and an iron rod. The tee should have a large side opening—unthreaded would be best. The valve consists of a thin sheet of stiff sheet metal, cut to a circular form, to fit the side outlet of the tee. The axis about which the valve turns consists of a round rod with one end bent at right angles. The other end should be sufficiently long to pass clear through the large part of the tee; the bent end simply forms the handle

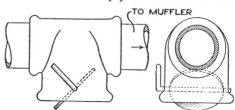

Cut-Out Made of a Tee Fitting Having a Large Side Outlet for the Disk Valve

for operating the valve. The axis end of the rod should be slotted to receive the valve disk. The side outlet of the tee is suitably drilled for the rod. In assembling the parts, the disk is put in place, and the slotted end of the rod put through the tee straddling the disk.

When carefully adjusted for proper operation, the disk and rod may be soldered together, or holes drilled through them, for rivets. The cut-out is then ready to be connected between the engine and muffler.—Contributed by D. C. Goff, Knoxville, Tenn.

⁋A machinist must remember that the warmth of the hand will change the size of a caliper or gauge of any kind.

## Rocking Base for Shaking Down Contents of Barrels and Boxes

When it becomes necessary to ship nuts, washers, or other small articles of a similar nature, a saving can be effected in the number of barrels or boxes used for shipment, if these articles are thoroughly shaken down by rocking the containers back and forth. To decrease the labor and time required in this operation, a simple arrangement can be made as illustrated. A cover of wood or iron, larger than the barrel bottom, should be obtained and fastened to a piece of pipe, or round rod. This should be secured to the floor with staples, or nails, driven on each side, permitting the device to rock back and forth. In use the barrel or box is placed on the platform

A Tipping Base for Use in Jostling Down Small Parts in Barrels and Boxes for Shipment

and its contents are shaken down by a rocking motion simplified by the roller bearing.—Contributed by John J. Kolar, Maywood, Ill.

## Spring to Hold Work against Lathe Center

It frequently is necessary to turn work in a lathe where one end is held to the faceplate center and the other supported in a center rest. To keep the work in place, it usually is tied to the faceplate with a cord, or wire, wound around the lathe dog. With this method it is necessary to have the work drawn tightly to the lathe center, and to do so, the faceplate must be unscrewed several turns when binding the work to the dog, after which the faceplate is turned to its usual position, thereby tightening the connection. To avoid this difficulty, a flat spring can be substituted for the cord. This is bent to clamp against the back side of the faceplate, at one end, while the

other end is fork-shaped, to straddle the work, and is clamped against the dog, forcing it and the work against the

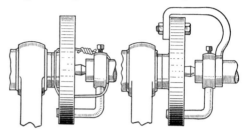

The Old Method of Wiring Work to a Lathe Center and Spring That Takes Its Place

center. The spring is held in place on the faceplate with a bolt and nut.

## Sharpening a Sickle

Where a grindstone is not convenient, a good cutting edge can be put on the ordinary sickle with the aid of a file. The sickle is clamped securely to a piece of board—old wringer clamps will answer the purpose—and shifted around in the various positions shown, so that a new surface is presented to the file. The arrows show the directions in which to file.

A tin disk, with a thick piece of leather as a face, makes a good guard for the hand. The leather will not spoil the edge of the sickle, should the file slip, and the tin prevents the sickle from cutting the hand, if filing is done with more vigor than care. A vise is

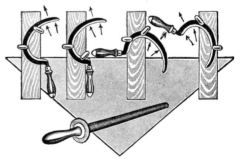

Various Positions for Clamping a Sickle to a Board for Filing Its Edge Sharp

not essential, as the board holding the sickle can be nailed to any convenient wood surface.—Contributed by James M. Kane, Doylestown, Pa.

## Homemade Safety Valve

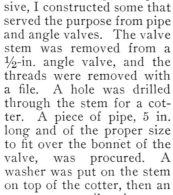

On my oxyacetylene-welding outfit there were needed several relief and safety valves. As these are quite expensive, I constructed some that served the purpose from pipe and angle valves. The valve stem was removed from a ½-in. angle valve, and the threads were removed with a file. A hole was drilled through the stem for a cotter. A piece of pipe, 5 in. long and of the proper size to fit over the bonnet of the valve, was procured. A washer was put on the stem on top of the cotter, then an open coil spring. The upper end of the pipe was fitted with a cap, drilled centrally and tapped for a ¼-in. rod. A rod, ¼ in. in diameter and about 2½ in. long, was threaded for its entire length, and a disk fastened to its lower end. The upper end was fitted with a knurled head. The pressure can be set at any number of pounds desired by this adjustment.—Contributed by A. H. Waychoff, Koenig, Col.

## Berry-Bush Trimmers

The essential parts necessary to make the illustrated berry-bush trimmer are two mower-sickle sections, a spiral spring, some wire, screws, and a wooden frame. The frame is made T-shaped with a handle, about 3 ft. long, and a crosspiece, about 6 in. in length, securely fastened at the top. Should this work loose, it can be strongly braced with triangular blocks fitted in the junction of the two pieces, and fastened to each. One of the sickle sections is rigidly connected to the frame. The other is drilled for a center hole in line with the regular rivet holes at opposite corners. The corners are bent up slightly, to provide an easier rocking motion. The section can then be fastened to the crosspiece with a round-head screw, a washer being placed next to the wood to line up the two sections. One end of the spiral spring is connected at the outer end of the sickle blade, and the other end to the handle, as shown. An operating wire connects with the opposite corner of the blade, and leads to a hand lever conveniently hinged near the end of the handle. When the hand lever is pulled down, the rocking section swings across the stationary piece, thereby cutting off the dead limbs, twigs, etc., caught between them. When the handle is released, the spring returns the rocking section to its original position, preparatory for another cut.—Chas. J. Donahue, Crete, Indiana.

## Procuring Clean Water from a River or Lake

To obtain clean water from a stream, or lake, for a camp, it must be taken from below the surface. This can be done with a large bottle by covering the hole in the neck and dipping it in the water deeply, then removing the covering and allowing the bottle to fill. The trouble of this method is that campers never have a large bottle at hand.

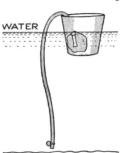

Cool, clear water can be taken from a depth of 15 ft. with the use of a small rubber tube. The illustration clearly shows how this may be accomplished. Place the tube in the water and in the bucket as a siphon, then push the bucket into the water as far as possible without letting any of the surface scum run in. Start the water flowing into the bucket as in starting a siphon.—Contributed by Geo. Goodwin, Ottawa, Ont.

## Improved Type of Automobile Sod Pan

The usual type of sod pan used in automobile construction is fastened to the frame side members of the car, and

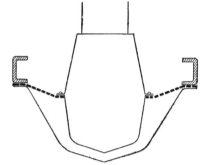

Sod-Pan Construction That Makes the Lower Part of the Crank Case Easily Accessible

passes under the engine crank case, as shown by the full line in the sketch. This is not only a very heavy and expensive construction, but the pan often jars loose, and must be removed from the chassis when being cleaned. The sod pan substituted is shown by the dotted lines, and simply consists of metal sheets, fastened on one side to the flange of the lower crank case, and on the other to the frame side members of the chassis. This construction is cheap, very light, and can easily be cleaned. The lower part of the crank case is exposed, but the dirt collected on it can be easily removed without disturbing the sod pan.—Contributed by Adolph Kline, Newark, N. J.

## Jig to Thread Pipes in a Bolt-Cutting Machine

Machine shops are frequently equipped with bolt threaders but have no provision for threading pipe in any

The Jig as It is Attached in the Chuck of the Bolt-Cutting Machine to Thread Pipes

other way than by hand. The simple jig shown can be easily made and will do the work with but little special preparation. It consists of a metal

block provided with a square opening at one end, to fit the pipe dies, and countersunk so that the pipe can enter far enough for the standard length of thread. The back end of the block is turned to fit the inside of the regular bolt-cutter chuck, and slotted to match the dies, any size answering the purpose.

In using the jig, it is put into the chuck with the slots slipped over the dies. It is best to protect these with strips of copper placed in the slots. The required pipe die is put in place in the square opening at the front end. The pipe is held with the vise, and threaded in the same way as a bolt. In backing off, either the machine may be reversed or the die withdrawn and unscrewed with a wrench.—Contributed by F. W. Bentley, Milwaukee, Wisconsin.

## Universal Joint on Drills and Taps

Castings are frequently designed for holes under overhanging portions,

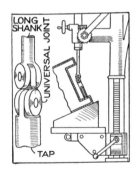

which makes it impossible to do direct machine drilling in a drill press unless some special arrangement is provided. If the cutting tools are constructed with universal joints, as shown in the illustration, the drilling and tapping can be easily accomplished. One end of the joint is fastened to the tool and the other to an arbor. The arbor end is gripped in the chuck of a drill press. In drilling such a hole, it is best to provide a special guide block which can be clamped in position on the casting.

Iridium is used principally for the hard points on gold pens, for making platinum hard and springy, and for making a black glaze on glass or porcelain.

## An Iceless Refrigerator

In order to build the iceless refrigerator shown in the illustration, a shaft of suitable dimensions must be provided, having its bottom several feet

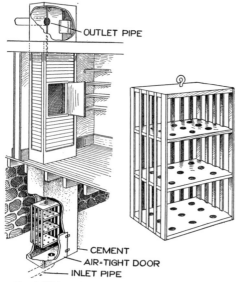

Dumb-Waiter Used to Lower Edibles in a Shaft Where They will be Kept Cool

below the surface of the ground, and the upper end extended above the receiving floor up to the ceiling or, better still, up into the attic. The lower part of the shaft, for a distance of several feet—or up to the receiving floor if possible—should be built of cement, the walls being several inches thick; the remaining portion, up to the top of the shaft, can be made of matched lumber. At a convenient distance above the floor, a door should be provided in order to give access to the lift. This door may be attached with hinges or made to slide in grooves, as preferred.

To conveniently get into the shaft at the bottom, an opening can be made which should be provided with a heavy air-tight cover, to be closed when using the refrigerator. An air-circulating pipe, leading from the outside, should be connected to the shaft at the bottom; another pipe should connect the upper end of the shaft with the chimney, thereby forming a complete and continuous air circulation which, to-

gether with the heat insulation provided by the cement walls, produces a temperature sufficiently low to keep almost any food.

A lift, or dumb-waiter, must be made, with its shelves perforated, as shown. One of its vertical sides is left open for placing the food; the other three consist of strips with spaces between. The air in its upward course is thus enabled to freely circulate through the lift.

The lift is suspended by a rope, which is passed over a pulley attached to the top of the shaft. A weight attached to the rope is used to counterbalance the lift. Provision for an outside suspension of the counterweight must be made, if the shaft is so short that the weight and lift come together before the lift can be brought to its proper position before the shaft door. For this purpose, a second pulley should be provided and conveniently suspended on one of the outside walls of the shaft; a hole must be bored for the lift rope, and the counterweight fastened to the loose end.—Contributed by H. R. Goodwin, Marblehead, Mass.

## A Handy Towel Holder

Hand towels hung on a rail often drop to the floor for the reason that they are hastily hung up and no care

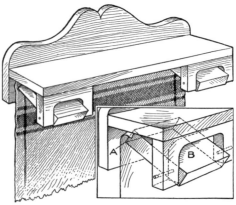

The Towel is Gripped at One End, Leaving Its Entire Length Hanging for Use

is taken to even the lengths of the ends. The hanger illustrated, the holding device being shown in the small sketch, grips one end of the towel, which cannot come out until the grips are released. Any person handy with tools can cut out the holder from any suitable wood. The edge A of the hinged block B holds the corner of the towel against the back piece.

## Penholder and Pencil Rack

A simple rack, made as illustrated and conveniently suspended on a wall or at a desk, will serve to keep penholders and pencils in a place where they may always be found. The parts necessary for its construction are a wooden frame and a coiled compression spring. The frame consists of two end blocks, fastened to a back piece which is drilled at one end for suspending it from a nail or hook. In selecting or making the spring, a No. 20 gauge brass spring wire, or one about $\frac{1}{32}$ in. in diam-

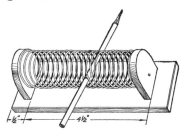

A Coil of Wire, Fastened between Two Supports on a Base, Makes a Good Pen and Pencil Rack

eter, should be used. The length of spring, when free, should be such that a pressure will be required to force it between the end pieces of the frame. In securing it in position holes should be provided in the frame so the ends of the spring may be passed through and bent down, to prevent them from pulling back. The completed holder should be stained and varnished to match the desk or wall it is fastened to.

## Emergency Steps

New fresh paint on steps compels the occupants of a house not to use them until the coating becomes dry. In some places it is almost impossible to discontinue the use of the steps for any length of time. To provide a means of using an entrance where steps are freshly coated with paint, I made the arrangement shown in the illustration.

Temporary Steps Made of a Few Boards, to Provide a Way for Entering over Fresh Paint

It is constructed of a few boards in step form, and is bolted together so that it can be adjusted to different heights, or taken apart and stored.—F. Ibbotson, Toronto, Can.

## Holding a Self-Closing Faucet Open

When a large quantity of boiling water is drawn from a self-closing faucet, the handle becomes too hot to be held unless it is covered with a cloth, or kept open in some other manner. A simple way to overcome the difficulty is to use an iron band, bent, at one end, to form a loose loop around the faucet which is held together with a rivet, or bolt and nut. The other end is made to fit the handle when it is in its open position. When not in use, the hook may be swung out of the way, as indicated by its dotted position.—Contributed by G. Jaques, Chicago, Ill.

❧Warm high-speed tools, especially the lubricant, before using them.

## Replacing Oval-Shaped Automobile-Wheel Rims

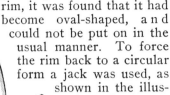

In trying to replace a demountable rim, it was found that it had become oval-shaped, a n d could not be put on in the usual manner. To force the rim back to a circular form a jack was used, as shown in the illustration. It was set with the base on the rim and the head under the hub, and sufficient pressure was exerted to force the rim to its original form, after which it was easily driven into place; the entire operation requiring less than two minutes.

## An Electric-Light Socket Hook

A hook by the aid of which an electric light can be attached to any particular place, is made as shown in the sketch. A band of sheet-spring stock is formed so that it will act as a clip on the lamp socket. The clip and hook can be made of one piece. The clip is slipped on and off the socket very easily, a n d proves a handy device for holding a light in a certain place temporarily.

## Round-Nose Attachment for Pliers

An attachment consisting of two tapered rods threaded at one end, by 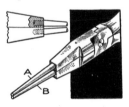 means of which ordinary pliers can be quickly transformed into the round-nose type, is h e r e shown. T w o pins, A and B, of suitable size, are tapered and the larger ends, which are turned down slightly to form a shoulder, are threaded. The ends of the plier jaws are ground on a slight angle, so that when they are drilled and tapped for the rods A and B, they will take the same angle, allowing them to close flush. Other attachments suited to special work can be made to fit threaded jaws, and prove of value to the mechanic without in any way interfering with the pliers being used in their original form.

## A Pencil-Point Protector

To avoid breaking the pencil point every time the pencil is dropped, make  a n attachment as follows: Cut a piece of rubber, that is about ⅛ in. thick, into a square, a little wider each way than the diameter of the pencil. Make a hole exactly in the center and force it on the pencil point, as shown.

The rubber can be used as an eraser and it will also prevent the pencil from rolling off the desk. If the pencil is dropped the rubber will prevent the point from striking the floor.

## Inexpensive Weather Strips

In cold climates weather strips on the door casings of houses are a necessity. The house owner who is also an automobilist can make for himself weather strips of the very best kind at very l i t t l e expense. Such a one is illustr a t e d. It  consists of a flat strip of rubber, fastened under a molding strip so that the yielding edge of the rubber will effectively seal the joint.

An old inner tube is cut into strips, 1 in. wide, which are fastened beneath strips of molding, about ¼ by ¾ in. in size. The strips are screwed to the door casing in such a position that the edge of the rubber will strike the door just before it strikes the door stop.